МАШИНЫ

MAKING **PROGRESS POSSIBLE**

Caterpillar

誇り

236

SUP

D330B

DOS

PORTE AO PRODUTO 9629

TECHNOLOGIE

VÅR HISTORIE

GETTING THE JOB DON

CUSTOMERS

All in a Day's Work

Seventy-five years of CATERPILLAR

EDITOR: GILBERT C. NOLDE

Published by Forbes Custom Publishing

Listed with the Library of Congress

ISBN: 0-8281-1422-6

First Edition
10 9 8 7 6 5 4 3 2 1
2000

Printed in Hong Kong

CATERPILLAR®

Forbes
CUSTOM PUBLISHING

right. **Cat® Fifty Diesel Tractor
carving Treasure Island
approach to the San
Francisco Bay Bridge, 1938.**

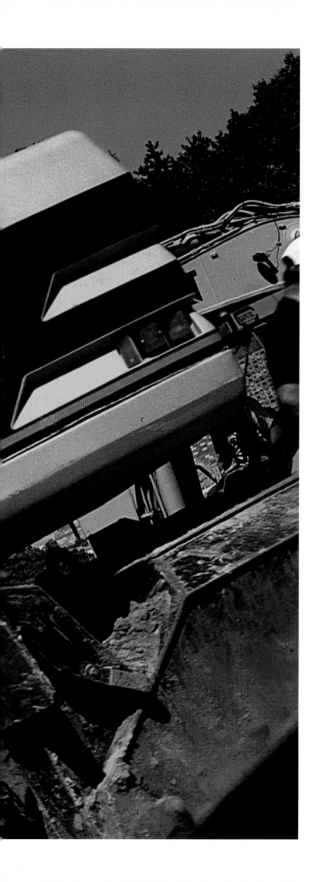

Proud of what we make. Proud of what we make possible.

History can be tricky.

Spend too much time reflecting on the past and you could jeopardize your future. Ignore the past and you could lose your sense of direction.

The trick is to find the proper balance—to celebrate your heritage while focusing on the future.

At Caterpillar, our focus has always been on the future. What will customers' needs be five years from now? How will we meet expectations of shareholders and employees? What resources will be needed to carry out growth plans?

But we also know it's important to have a firm understanding of our past. What principles have guided us? What risks did we take and how did we assess that risk? What kind of company were we then? What kind of company are we now? How has our relationship with our customers, dealers and suppliers changed over the years?

I hope that, as you read this book, you will gain a better understanding of what has made Caterpillar a great global company. I hope you will get a sense of the pride that Caterpillar people have in the products they make. And a sense of how Caterpillar products have helped change the world … literally.

Yes, we're certainly proud of what we make at Caterpillar. But we're even more proud of what we make possible.

Glen Barton, Chairman and Chief Executive Officer

Caterpillar Inc.

Contents

April 1925.
C. L. Best Tractor Co.

In 19th-century California, land was plentiful, but the means to work it were costly. Large-scale farming was possible if farmers could find a way to get the job done faster and more productively than by hand. To meet that customer need, two proud companies were launched, companies that would eventually merge to become the world's premier builder of earthmoving equipment.

In 1863, Charles Holt headed for California from his New England home. He started his own business, C. H. Holt & Company, "Importers of hardwood lumber," handling products of the Holt family lumber mill in New Hampshire. Charles' brothers William, Frank and Benjamin became partners in the enterprise, which soon adopted the name Holt Brothers.

Chapter 75 1

and The Holt
Manufacturing Company
merge to form
Caterpillar Tractor Co.

Introduced in 1913, the Holt 75 quickly found application on the heaviest jobs. It became the most popular of all tiller wheel crawlers. Thousands were built before the model was discontinued in 1924. This machine is hauling freight in the tropics.

Holt Brothers built a factory near Concord, New Hampshire, to serve the San Francisco trade. Benjamin, the youngest, stayed to manage it.

Lumber was cut principally in Ohio, shipped east for curing and fashioning into axles, wheels, poles and other items—then sent "around the Horn" to San Francisco.

But it soon became apparent that wagon wheels and other wooden items seasoned back East shrank, warped and fell apart in California's hot, dry climate. San Francisco, with its cool, foggy weather, wasn't any better as a manufacturing site.

So in 1883, Holt Brothers established the Stockton Wheel Company, with young Ben Holt as its president. The climate in Stockton, California, was perfect for seasoning wood. By the following year the company employed 40 people and produced 6,000 wheels and 5,000 carriage bodies.

In 1859, Daniel Best, barely 21, left his family's Iowa farm to seek gold in the West. He tried mining and lumbering, but success eluded him. Then, while working on his brother's California ranch, he noticed that farmers had to transport their grain long distances and pay hefty fees to prepare it for market. Why not clean grain in

BEGIN

the field with a machine most farmers could afford to own?

The first Best grain cleaners, patented in 1871, were successes. Best began to manufacture them in Oregon. Then the California wheat lands beckoned; and in the early 1880s a manufacturing branch was established in Oakland. Business was so good that Best took to stacking inventory in the streets. When Oakland police objected, Best bought a factory in nearby San Leandro, California.

right. **Daniel Best.**

far right. **Holt combines used "link belt" chains to send power from ground wheel (center of photo) to the combine's working parts. Combines like this one were operated by a four-man team: a "header tender" to raise and lower the cutting bar; a driver to control the horses; a machineman to level the machine, apply brakes when necessary and administer to mechanical needs; and a sack sewer to guide the grain into bags, sew them shut and drop them into the field for retrieval.**

left. **Benjamin Holt.**

far left. **All hands took a break when the photographer came to shoot this Best "sidehill" combine. Sidehill models were adjustable to harvest along hilly slopes.**

Enter the Combine

Of all the tremors that shook agriculture in the last half of the 19th century, few did so much to change farm life as the combined harvester. These huge wooden assemblages—some over 60 feet (18 meters) wide—"combined" operations of cutting, threshing, cleaning and sacking grain.

Combines increased the productivity of farm workers by as much as two-thirds over stationary reaping and threshing methods.

Neither Holt nor Best invented the combine. But between them, they were responsible for much of its early development. Daniel Best had begun experimenting with combines in the early 1880s in Oregon. The first Best combine, incorporating his popular grain cleaner, was sold in 1885.

The first Holt Brothers "Link Belt Combined Harvester," sold in 1886, represented major improvements over previous designs.

Most models used cast-iron gears to transmit power from ground wheels to the combine's working parts. Because early combines were drawn by as many as 40 horses or mules, a slight provocation—even a bee sting—could cause a stampede, stripping the machine's gears.

Holt solved the problem by transmitting power through chain belts.

N I N G S

HOW HOLT & BEST EACH MADE A TRACTOR, AND CREATED A COMPANY.

Both Best and Holt were pioneers in supporting their machinery once it went into the field. Dan Best would write each customer to see if he was satisfied; repairs were quickly made by Dan himself or a mechanic dispatched from the factory.

This concept of field service was unusual at the time. It appealed to customers then just as it does today. Best's wife, Meta, wrote in 1887, "Dan had a good many ups and downs this summer getting his harvesters running, but beat all of them that run against him. Sold all but one, and it is out cutting by the acres ... "

right. **Originally developed for farming, steam traction engines quickly found use in logging. This Best machine is hauling logs for the McCloud River Lumber Co. of northern California in 1894.**

lower left. **Even before Daniel Best's steam traction engine was marketed, he could see that the days of steam power were numbered. In 1888, Best began experimenting with internal combustion engines. By 1895, he offered engines from two to 200 horsepower (149 kW) for use in irrigation, sawmills, dairies and boats.**

center. **Holt steam traction engines played an important role in mechanizing agriculture. But the high cost of steam power—$4,500 to $5,500 for a Holt steamer, a vast sum at the time—meant that most 19th-century farmers still relied on horses, mules and oxen.**

far right. **Restored Best Steamer**

Steam

Daniel Best brought out his first steam traction engine in 1889. Almost immediately, he conceived of pairing his machine with a combine. Best's "steam harvester," patented in 1889, was a milestone in mechanized agriculture. But high costs kept it out of the hands of all but the most prosperous farmers.

Within two years, however, more than 25 Best steam traction engines had been sold. Models were offered under names like "Pathfinder" and "Native Son." Best now employed about 100 people, building combines, traction engines and a wide variety of other items.

Holt's first experimental steam tractor engine was built in 1890. At first, most Holt steamers were used for farming.

But freighting quickly became a major market for traction engines, especially for transporting lumber, ores and supplies where roads were marginal and the costs of animal hauling were high. Holt claimed his standard road engine could haul 40 to 50 tons (36 to 45 metric tons) at an average speed of three miles an hour, depending on road conditions, and do

it at half the cost of horse or mule teams. Even so, a fully equipped Holt freighting outfit cost upwards of $10,000.

Export markets proved lucrative for both Holt and Best steamers. By the turn of the century, Holt steam traction engines had found their way to Australia, Kenya, southern Africa, Mexico and Europe. By 1902, Best steamers were working in Siberia and elsewhere in Russia.

Stockton Wheel Company was incorporated as The Holt Manufacturing Co. in 1892, reflecting the diversification and

Early Holt Brothers catalog.

growth of the firm's product line. Benjamin Holt became the new company's president.

Holt now employed more than 300 people who turned out upwards of 200 combines, five steam harvesters and 10 steam traction engines annually. The payroll approached $20,000 a month.

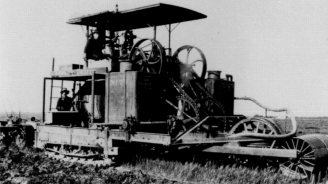

far left. **To support their enormous weight when working on soft soils, Best and Holt steam traction engines were fitted with extension wheels. This Best steamer was built for the Middle River Farming Co. of central California. Even with extension wheels, it could bog down. Freeing a mired steam engine was an engineering feat in itself.**

above left. **In 1904, No. 77's wheels were successfully replaced with tracks. Here it is in 1905 with its second, improved set of tracks.**

left. **Holt's wheel-type No. 77 steamer built in 1903.**

right. **Harsh conditions couldn't stop Holt crawlers hauling supplies for the Los Angeles Aqueduct. Blistering temperatures proved the dependability of Holt's new gasoline engine. And although sand attacked tractor undercarriages, Holt engineers used the experience to develop more wear-resistant track designs and materials.**

"Caterpillar" Name Born

In the Stockton area, soil was a deep, rich peat. When this soil was dry, a spark could ignite a smoldering underground blaze; when wet, it became heavy, boggy, treacherous.

Horses were shod with special fan-like "tule" shoes. When the huge steam traction engines went in, they too were equipped with special "shoes"—extension wheels at the rear and often an extra drum up front.

These extension wheels were only partially successful in improving flotation. They added greatly to the weight and made it difficult to steer and turn. A low spot could easily mire the machine—and freeing it from a bog could take days.

To increase the traction engine's area of contact with the ground, Benjamin Holt hit upon the idea of replacing wheels with tracks. Tracks were not a new idea—in fact, by the turn of the century, well over 100 patents had been granted in the United States, Great Britain and France for track-type mechanisms.

Most early attempts were failures; those that did work failed to attain any commercial success.

On November 24, 1904, the first Holt track-type tractor was tested. It soon went to work plowing soft ground near Stockton. The machine was pronounced "a decided success."

After more tests, the first crawler—with a new and improved set of tracks—was sent to the Holt family ranch for an entire winter of plowing.

Soon after the test of this first tracked machine, the "Caterpillar" trademark was coined by Holt. The trademark came to be applied to many products in the Holt line.

By 1906, a production-model steam crawler was ready. Golden Meadow Development Co. of Lockport, Louisiana, had earlier bought a wheel-type steamer. In the field, it sank to its frame and couldn't be budged. But Holt's new track-type model, purchased by Golden Meadow late in 1906 for $5,500, worked the marshy Louisiana lands for many years.

Even as steam crawlers were being placed on the market, Holt was experimenting with a new power source. Gasoline automobiles were appearing in increasing numbers. To Ben Holt, the advantages of the gas engine were obvious.

In 1908, engineers of the Los Angeles Aqueduct bought the first Holt 40-horsepower (29-kW) gas crawler. In November, 1908, three more gasoline tractors were purchased at $3,500 each. Then, in 1909, an order of 25 crawlers and 80 specially designed wagons, for a total of $141,000, consolidated the commercial success of Holt's new product.

above. **In 1906, Holt introduced the first production model of its steam-powered crawler. The No. 122 demonstrated the merits of track-type traction to contractors building the Los Angeles, California, Aqueduct.**

Move to Peoria—"Earthmoving Capital of the World"

The growing success of the track-type tractor, along with Holt's desire to expand its application outside the West, caused the company to seek a new manufacturing site. Benjamin Holt's nephew, Pliny Holt, led the search.

At first he settled on Minneapolis, Minnesota. A small staff was hired, plans were drawn up and parts ordered from Stockton. Employees began assembling a new model crawler.

About the same time, a Peoria, Illinois, agricultural implement dealer named Murray M. Baker heard about Holt's need for a new plant. Baker, who had successfully operated Peoria's first automobile agency and had sold tractors as well, thought he had just the proposition for Holt.

The Colean Manufacturing Company of East Peoria was one of many U.S. tractor manufacturers that failed to make the transition

Murray Baker and the bridge named after him. The Murray M. Baker Bridge, completed in 1959, spans the Illinois River between Peoria and East Peoria, Illinois.

from steam to gasoline in the first decade of the century. Colean employees lost their jobs. The relatively new, well-equipped plant stood idle.

Murray Baker got the word about Colean to Pliny Holt. Holt visited Peoria, liked what he saw and began negotiations to purchase the plant. The sale was finalized October 25, 1909.

left. **The first facility in the Peoria area. It was previously the Colean Manufacturing Company.**

Pliny Holt wrote to Baker: "I am sure that this… marks the beginning of one of the largest enterprises in the Middle West, and assures the City of Peoria of an industry that they will be proud of in the future."

Baker threw in his lot with the new company, becoming vice president and general manager. Employment, which at first consisted of Baker and three or four engineers brought from Minneapolis, slowly began to grow.

The first Peoria-built tractor—a 45-horsepower (33-kW), two-speed model—was completed and demonstrated to Julius Funk of Bloomington, Illinois. Funk was skeptical of the new product and demanded that it prove itself in the field before he would pay for it. The tractor performed, Funk paid and he continued to buy Caterpillar track-type tractors for decades afterward.

photo courtesy of CILCO

Exports

The year 1909 saw Holt's first export of a crawler tractor—to the Huasteca Petroleum Co. of Tampico, Mexico. In 1910, a Holt crawler was shipped to Argentina for demonstration. Within two months, orders were received for two machines worth $4,000 each.

Export orders grew rapidly. By mid-1911, Stockton's capacity for building crawlers was strained to the breaking point; facilities were expanded, a night shift added. Still, demand couldn't be met. It was decided that the East Peoria plant would handle exports and all U.S. business east of the Rocky Mountains, while Stockton would concentrate on the Pacific Coast, combines, wagons and other agricultural goods.

By the end of 1911, Stockton employed 625 people at an average wage of $70 a month. Holt had facilities in Stockton, San Francisco and Los Angeles, California; Spokane and Walla Walla, Washington; East Peoria, Illinois; Salt Lake City, Utah; and Winnipeg, Canada. Most of these were sales outlets and parts depots; Stockton and East Peoria were the only manufacturing locations of significance. A sales representative was permanently stationed in Argentina. Holt agencies were being established across Europe and even in North Africa.

above. **The Holt 30, or "Baby," was built long and low especially for farm and orchard work. Introduced in 1912, the 30 incorporated several important advances in design, including use of multiple-disk clutches and track links with open sides (so dirt wouldn't build up and clog the track).**

center. **1915 Wilkins Toy Caterpillar Tractor.**

right. **Holt's earliest crawlers were tested on ground next to the plant. Tests proved that more of the crawler's power was available for doing useful work—at the time, primarily pulling agricultural implements—than was the case with wheel tractors.**

bottom right. **The Holt 60 (shown in Pontiac, Michigan) was the company's largest crawler from 1911 to 1913. At this time, Holt tractor models were named after the brake horsepower of their engines.**

C. L. Best Forms Tractor Company

In 1908, Daniel Best, nearing 70 years of age, decided to sell out to Holt. Holt manufactured and sold a line of products under the Best name until 1913.

At first, Daniel's son, C. L. Best, was retained as superintendent. Then in 1910, he formed his own company in Elmhurst, California. A steel castings plant was established nearby, and the C. L. Best Gas Traction Company began building wheel-type gas-powered tractors from 20 to 80 horsepower (14 to 59 kW).

Almost immediately, young Best set to work on an experimental track-type tractor. After extensive development and testing, announcements of a new "C.L.B." 75-horsepower (55 kW) crawler began to appear in early 1913. The 75 was the first tractor to bear Best's "Tracklayer" trademark.

The 75 Tracklayer incorporated a number of significant advancements in design and construction. Among them were improved oscillation of the tracks to reduce shock loads on the frame and engine and improved metallurgy throughout the tractor.

Behind the strength of its new product line, Best's business grew steadily. By 1916, the company's monthly payroll was $25,000 and climbing. More manufacturing space was badly needed.

So in mid-1916, Best repurchased his father's former plant at San Leandro and began moving operations back in. By November, track-type tractors were being shipped out at the rate of five per week.

By 1925, the company was known as C. L. Best Tractor Co. When it merged with Holt, Best's plant became the first headquarters of Caterpillar Tractor Co.—and C. L. Best the first chairman of the new company.

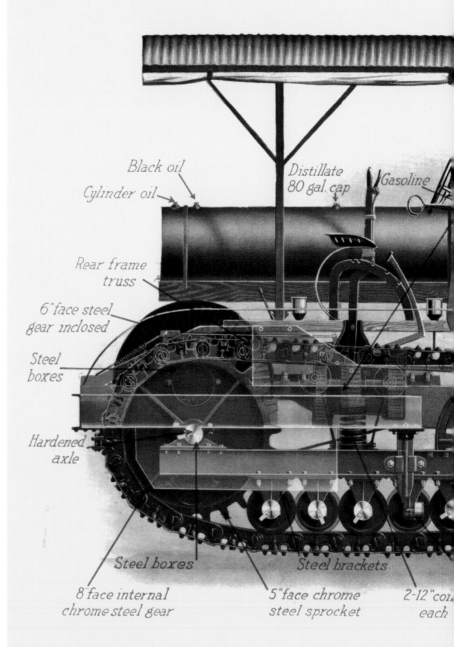

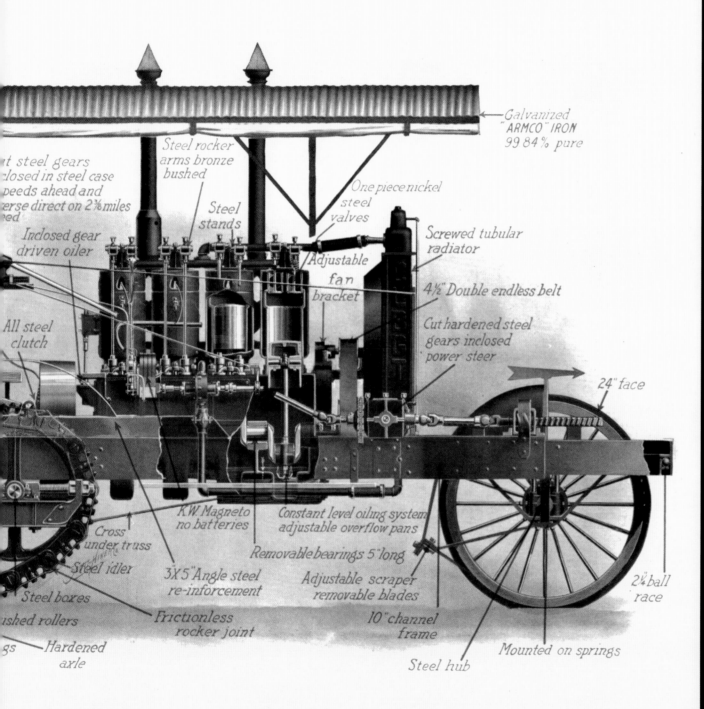

Galvanized "ARMCO" IRON 99.84% pure

Steel rocker arms bronze bushed

t steel gears closed in steel case peeds ahead and erse direct on 2⅜ miles ed

One piece nickel steel valves

Steel stands

Inclosed gear driven oiler

Adjustable fan bracket

Screwed tubular radiator

All steel clutch

4½" Double endless belt

Cut hardened steel gears inclosed power steer

24" face

K.W. Magneto no batteries

Constant level oiling system adjustable overflow pans

Cross under truss

Removable bearings 5" long

Steel idler

3 X 5" Angle steel re-inforcement

Adjustable scraper removable blades

Steel boxes

shed rollers

gs Hardened axle

Frictionless rocker joint

10" channel frame

Mounted on springs

2¼ ball race

Steel hub

above. **Starting in 1910 in Elmhurst, California, C. L. Best Gas Traction Company produced wheel-type tractors designed for farm work. This 80-horsepower (59-kW) model, like other Best wheel tractors and early crawlers, employed a differential in its drive train instead of dual steering clutches typically used by Holt.**

left. **In 1913, the 75 was the first track-type tractor marketed by Best bearing the "Tracklayer" trademark.**

below. **Beginning about 1915, Best dropped the tiller wheel and produced all-track crawlers like this 18-horsepower (13 kW) "pony Tracklayer." Customers referred to all-track machines as "muleys."**

Dealers

below. **Joseph A. Quinn and C. C. Budd founded Budd and Quinn, Inc., in 1919 in Fresno, California. They were a Holt Dealer, then became a dealer for Caterpillar in 1925. In 1958, the dealership was renamed Quinn Company.**

Independently owned dealers came on the scene early. Among the earliest was the Tunisian dealer Parenin. It was known as Ets. P. Parrenin in 1912, when its first Holt "Caterpillar" machine arrived in North Africa. The predecessor of the Hawaiian dealer, Pacific Machinery, took on the C. L. Best account in 1914. Yancey Brothers, headquartered in Atlanta, Georgia, became a Holt dealer in 1918.

Even before Caterpillar Tractor Co. was formed, we recognized that a strong, independently owned dealer organization was key to long-term success.

above. **British officer Ernest Swinton, often credited as the father of the tank, visited Benjamin Holt in April, 1918. Swinton said it was the "Caterpillar" track-type tractor which inspired his idea of the tank and helped change the course of the war.**

far right. **Wartime manpower shortages brought significant numbers of women into the industrial environment. These female employees are shown at work in Holt's Stockton machine shop in 1918.**

right. **Holt engineers developed many prototype and special purpose track-type vehicles for the U.S. military. This version of the Holt model 45 featured a "stretched" track for high speed and climbing ability.**

World War I

The contributions of track-type tractors as a means of hauling artillery and supplies were momentous. Of all the crawler tractors used in the war, the overwhelming majority were built by Holt—especially at East Peoria—or by other manufacturers working under Holt license. Nearly 10,000 Holt tractors went into action for the Allies. Holt's "Caterpillar" trademark became internationally known.

Growing Uses for Products

Born in the West as an agricultural tool, the crawler tractor quickly found more uses. Freighting ores. Hauling timber. Clearing land. And, importantly for the growth of both the Holt and Best companies, building roads.

In 1897, the first of a series of "Object Lesson" or model roads was built in New Jersey. In 1902, the American Road Builders and American Automobile associations were formed, both of which championed a national "Good Roads" movement. The Holt Manufacturing Company was an early and vigorous supporter, stating in its May, 1908, bulletin: "We want better highway laws, better highway administration, better roads, better methods of maintaining them and better spirit to back them."

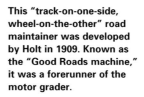

Benjamin Holt was among the first to realize that track-type machines had applications beyond farming and freighting. Even as the first Holt crawlers were proving themselves on the Los Angeles Aqueduct, Holt built and operated a single-track machine with an adjustable blade suspended beneath it. By spring of 1909, this self-propelled grader, one of the world's first, was maintaining San Joaquin County roads at a charge of $2 an hour.

This "track-on-one-side, wheel-on-the-other" road maintainer was developed by Holt in 1909. Known as the "Good Roads machine," it was a forerunner of the motor grader.

left. **For two decades, the conventional means of maintaining roads was with a track-type tractor and pulled grader. This Holt 75 with blade graders, shown near Peoria, Illinois, helped build a road which became known as "Caterpillar Trail."**

below far left. **Restored Caterpillar tractor at the Antique Caterpillar Machinery Owners Club convention.**

center. **The crawler was regarded almost from the first as a versatile earthmoving tool. Holt built side-dump wagons and other attachments for use with its machines.**

Another earthmoving tool, the land level, was manufactured by Holt for use with its tractors.

left. **At the Good Roads School in 1914, this Holt 75 leveled two miles of roads in 50 minutes. Because demonstration roads were wet, only the Holt crawler could work.**

Collecting and Restoring Old Products

Today, thousands of people around the world collect and restore old Holt, Best and Caterpillar machines.

above. **Members of the Antique Caterpillar Machinery Owners Club meeting at the demonstration area at Edwards, Illinois, with former Caterpillar Chairman Don Fites on November 9, 1993.** The 1200-member Antique Caterpillar Machinery Owners Club is the largest of the formally organized groups. The club puts on exhibitions, holds regular meetings and even has a quarterly publication. Their website address is www.acmoc.org.

left. **After 1919, the largest Best model was the highly successful 60. The "convertible" top identifies this tractor as a "Logging Cruiser" model.**

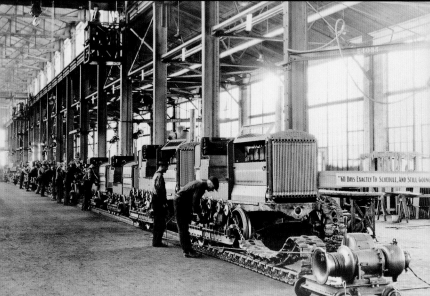

"60 DAYS EXACTLY TO SCHEDULE, AND STILL GOING"

above. **Sweeping changes brought Holt's East Peoria plant back to health in the difficult postwar period. Tractor designs created for military use were converted—like the 10-Ton. New methods of work yielded notable improvements.**

left. **Best brought out highly advanced tractor models in the postwar years. Introduced in 1921, the Best 30 became a benchmark for crawler tractors of its size.**

A New Company Begins

In 1925, newly formed Caterpillar Tractor Co. began with three manufacturing facilities: San Leandro, California, a plant occupying 12 acres, of which 5 1/2 acres were under roof; Stockton, California, a plant occupying 21 acres, of which 12 acres were under roof; and East Peoria, Illinois, a plant occupying 40 acres with 12 acres under roof.

Directors of the new company, headquartered in San Leandro, California, were:

C. L. Best, Chairman of the Board

R. C. Force, President

M. M. Baker, Vice President

P. E. Holt, Vice President

B. C. Heacock, Vice President and Secretary

O. L. Starr, General Factory Manager

A. L. Chickering

H. H. Fair

J. A. McGregor

Sales for the first year of operation were $13.8 million. The average number of employees for the year was 2,537. There were 1,919 shareholders of common stock.

These were the tangibles. But the newly formed company started with intangible assets of even higher value, assets that would continue to serve the company into the 21st century:

A brand name that would become a worldwide household word.

Engineering know-how, with a penchant for finding practical applications of new technology.

An emphasis on meeting customer needs.

A recognition of the importance of global markets.

Independent dealer representation both inside and outside the United States.

A focus on quality.

Product support as a high-priority corporate objective.

For the next 75 years, as Caterpillar grew to become one of the world's great companies, we never lost sight of these early principles.

It was the beginning.

TOOLS OF

The 1925 to 2000 story of Caterpillar has been largely the story of continuous product development—with more powerful, more rugged, more efficient and more versatile tools to do the world's work. We started as a new company in 1925 with five tractor models (the Thirty, the Sixty, the 2-Ton, 5-Ton and 10-Ton) and a few combines. Now, we build more than 300 different products, including engines and turbines from five horsepower (3.7 kW) to more than 22,000 horsepower (16 412 kW), and our financial and logistics products have become a significant part of our business.

Undergirding this product development is an ever-growing number of patents granted to Caterpillar inventors. Just since 1975, Caterpillar has been granted 10,090 patents worldwide. In 1998 alone, 912 patents were granted. More than 2,800 company inventors have been involved in creating new patent designs in the past 25 years. We're proud of this accomplishment. It says much about the creativity of Caterpillar people as they respond to customers' needs.

Chapter 2

75

THE TRADE

The D400E Series II
Articulated Truck and the
365B Excavator, both
introduced in 1999.

The tool that built a company

It started as a tool for farmers. Then it was used to haul freight, just as a locomotive would, but without the restriction of railroad tracks; the crawler tractor could go just about anywhere over land. For road builders, it was indispensable. As the decades rolled by, contractors, miners, loggers and site developers found more and more uses for the versatile machine. They asked for ever bigger and more powerful tractors, and Caterpillar responded. The track-type tractor ranks high among the 20th century innovations which changed the world.

Three Revolutionary Changes

"How did those early tractors become the powerful tools of today? Three revolutionary changes come to mind: the *diesel engine*, *Sealed and Lubricated Track* and the *elevated sprocket*. All three were technology breakthroughs. All three resulted from creative teamwork. All three involved enormous capital expenditures. And all three were high-risk. In fact, with each of these changes, we put the entire company on the line."

Bob Gilmore, president 1977-1985

Top row left to right:

This Sixty crawler tractor, nicknamed "Old Tusko," was one of the first Caterpillar machines to be diesel-powered. It weighed 19,000 pounds (8 626 kg) and produced 50 drawbar horsepower (37.3 kW).

The RD8, with 95 horsepower (70.9 kW), was introduced in 1935. Later the "R" was dropped and it became the famous D8. It reigned as power leader in the product family for 20 years.

Newest of the D8 models: the D8R. It has more than three times the power of the original D8 and continues as a standard for earthmoving machines around the world.

The team that developed and built the D9. When introduced in 1955, the D9 had 230 horsepower (171.6 kW). Today's D9R produces 405 flywheel horsepower (302.1 kW).

The Diesel Engine, 1931

In 1931, we introduced something to our track-type tractor line that was to change the industry—the diesel engine. This breakthrough gave our machines more horsepower than ever before and made them less expensive to own and operate. It pioneered the way for an industry that today runs almost entirely on diesel power.

One of the first diesel-powered units (Cat Sixty, Serial No. 1C12—pictured upper left) was sent to work in the Pacific Northwest of the United States. It was so powerful it continually broke any hitch it was attached to. At that time, the Oregon zoo was having a similar problem with an elephant named "Tusko."

"They couldn't keep the elephant penned up. Everything they put him in, he walked out of and through," said Harold Hartfield of Hartfield Estate Ranches, owner of the tractor. "About the same time, we were having a hard time finding hitches that would hold the Sixty. So we named it 'Old Tusko.'"

Sealed and Lubricated Track, 1973

Over the years, undercarriage maintenance became a major expense for our customers. Since the undercarriage takes most of the beating on a track-type tractor, we had to figure out a way to reduce cost and prolong life. The answer: the revolutionary Sealed and Lubricated Track. The track pin is permanently coated with a sealed-in lubricant, which minimizes metal-to-metal contact and slows pin and bushing wear. Precision manufacturing to extremely close tolerances made the improvement possible, along with the ingenuity of research engineers.

The Elevated Sprocket, 1977

The elevated sprocket concept was debated for years, but serious design efforts didn't begin until we started looking at building a track-type tractor bigger than the D9. By separating the drive sprockets from the track roller frame and elevating them above the tracks, more track would remain on the ground for improved traction. The elevated sprocket design was better able to absorb ground shocks for longer life and greater operator comfort. The modular design also made servicing easier.

The new design was first incorporated in the D10 crawler. A single D10 could accomplish the work that previously required two Cat D9 Track-Type Tractors working in tandem. Over time, the elevated sprocket became standard on all tracked machines down through the D5M.

"I was picked to be on a team of Research and Engineering personnel, and we created the D10 elevated sprocket configuration. The development and product introduction involved every discipline in the company. It was highly successful because of the total team effort. Our team generated 93 patents involving all systems in the concept. The challenge of beating competition in our core product was a tremendous incentive."

Ron Krolak,
Track-Type Tractor Chief Engineer, retired

The D11R Carrydozer is the largest in the line of Caterpillar track-type tractors, with flywheel horsepower of 850 (634 kW) and an operating weight of 239,550 pounds (108 660 kg). It is used in volume dozing applications such as prime stripping and reclamation.

Some Tough Tracks to Follow.

It would take another book to list all the improvements made in our track-type tractors over the years, changes that have been in response to customer needs. Cable to hydraulics. Computerized monitoring systems. Rippers. Torque dividers. Planetary power shift transmissions. Variable-pitch Power Angle Tilt blades. Improved metallurgy. Differential steering. The list goes on and on. But one thing hasn't changed: Caterpillar track-type tractors continually set the standard for the industry.

Cat Track-Type Tractors

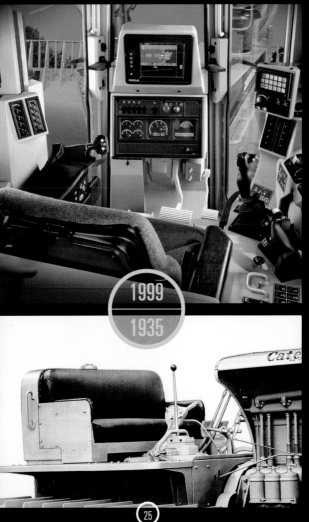

1999
1935

left. **Probably no other aspect of our track-type tractors has changed as much as the operator compartment. What started as a flat seat and some levers and pedals now includes computerized monitoring systems, fully adjustable contoured seats, air conditioning, sound proofing and panoramic viewing.**

Better Built Motorized Grader

RUSSELL
MOTOR PATROL
with TwoTon
CATERPILLAR POWER

The Two-Ton "Caterpillar" Tractor is well adapted to road work. It is economical, dependable and has plenty of power. Rubber faced tracks may be had for the "Caterpillar" when so ordered. Rubber tracks outwear steel tracks and do not mar surface of road.

Specifications

Weight Complete with Canopy—11,000 pounds.
Grader Unit only, 5800 pounds.
Blade—3 sizes, made of special carbon steel.
    8-Foot long.
    10-Foot blade, regular equipment.
    12-Foot maintenance blade.
    Angle reinforcement on back of blade.
Cutting Edge—Made of special carbon steel, $1/2$x6-inches.
Blade Beams—$3\frac{1}{2}$x$1\frac{1}{4}$-inches flat high carbon steel.
Blade Braces—$1\frac{1}{8}$-inches round.
Blade Pitch Adjustment—4 positions.
Blade Side Shift—12 inches.
Blade Lift Above Ground—12 inches.
Circle—52 inch diameter, 4x4x$1/2$-inch "T" steel.
Draw-Bars—5x3x$3/8$-inch angle.
Method of Blade Lift—Worm gear—cut gears completely enclosed—bronze bushings and collars for worm gear.
Lifting Links—$1\frac{3}{8}$ inch shafts, ball and socket connections.
    (2 inch steel ball.)
Lifting Arms—$1\frac{7}{8}$ inch shafts, special high carbon steel with take-up bearing in bracket to eliminate play.
Hand Wheels—30 inch diameter.
Frame—7 inch extra heavy channel, weight $19\frac{3}{4}$ pounds per foot.
Axle—Front, extra heavy, extra long—65 inches.
Wheel—Front, 32x5 inch rubber tires, Timken bearings.
Steering Control—Machined worm gears.
Tread—Front, 53 inches.
Wheel Base—14 feet, 4 inches.
Scarifier Attachment—Independently adjustable.
Weight of Scarifier—700 pounds.
Width of Block—48 inches.
Draw-Bars for Scarifier—$3\frac{1}{2}$x$1\frac{1}{4}$ inches, high carbon steel.
Size of Teeth—$2\frac{1}{2}$x$3/4$ inch.
Spacing of Teeth—4 inches apart.
Number of Teeth—12.
Lubrication—Alemite system—all principal parts.

RUSSELL MOTOR PATROL No 4

RUSSELL No. 4 MOTOR PATROL with CATERPILLAR Two Ton POWER

The cutting edge of road building

A familiar sight on road building projects around the world, Cat motor graders are also valuable in construction, mining and maintenance applications. Today, there are nine models, ranging from the 125-horsepower (93.25 kW) 120H to the 500-horsepower (373 kW) 24H.

When you look at the 1925 Russell Motor Patrol No. 4 (left) and the 1999 140H Motor Grader (right), you see a lot of similarities. Both have two wheels in front, a blade, an operator's station and a power unit. But they're as different as the Model A Ford is from today's automobiles.

The Russell Motor Patrol

The Russell Grader Manufacturing Co. of Minnesota had been producing pulled implements for ditching and road-contouring since 1903. The first Russell self-propelled motor grader was launched as the Motor Patrol No. 1 in 1920. In 1925, Russell introduced Motor Patrol No. 4, which incorporated a Holt 2-Ton.

In a late 1920s advertising piece, the Russell Motor Patrols were described as "Nerveless, fearless, tough, with the rugged stamina of wear-resistive steels—all rightly put together to make a hardy constitution. These things the engineers have given the Russell to make it master of its job—stamina, proper balance, large capacity, low cost of upkeep. Russells will do the tough work—the most work for the fewest taxpayers' dollars."

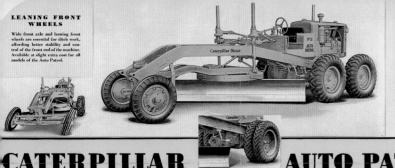

top left. **The No. 10 and No. 11 Caterpillar Auto Patrols from 1938 featured tandem wheels and diesel engines.**

center left. **This No. 20 Caterpillar Motor Patrol from 1931 featured a Caterpillar No. 20 Tractor under the grader unit canopy.**

bottom left. **The current 14H Motor Grader.**

Motor Graders

Introducing the First Motor Grader

In 1928, Caterpillar purchased Russell and, in 1931, produced the first true motor grader. Called auto patrols, the new machines were a milestone in the road maintenance industry. The engine was placed over the axle, giving the operator much better visibility and less dust to contend with. High-pressure pneumatic tires provided greater speed and higher productivity. These features offered so many advantages that they were soon adopted by the entire industry.

The introduction of tandem tires in 1934 was the next big breakthrough. The No. 11 Caterpillar Auto Patrol not only had tandem tires—an industry first—but also incorporated a Caterpillar diesel engine. The popular No. 12 Motor Grader appeared in 1938.

A Culture of Continuous Improvement

Through the years, Cat motor graders have been continuously improved with innovations like constant mesh transmission, in-seat starting, hydraulic steering boosters, direct electric starting, an accelerator-decelerator, self-adjusting brakes and four-speed reverse transmissions.

Today's H-series machines give operators even better comfort and control with a quieter cab, electronically controlled transmission, suspension seat and a new blade-positioning system. Technological advances like "priority-proportional, pressure-compensated" hydraulic control valves assure greater productivity.

The blend of design and function strengthens our leadership in motor graders.

The LEXION 465 Combine was introduced in 1997. It's the most advanced, most productive combine in the world.

Tools for Agriculture

Back to our roots

Our predecessors, Holt and Best, got their start producing what was then "cutting edge" farm machinery. But the world changed and so did we. Demand shifted to machinery for road construction, mining, paving and more. And we quickly established ourselves as the world leader in almost all those businesses.

"Leap" technology

What happened to agriculture? We continued selling track-type tractors, scrapers, track loaders and motor graders for use in land clearing, forming, terracing, leveling, preparing the soil and even cultivating. Cat engines powered pumps and machines. But few of our products played a central role in the planting and harvesting of major crops. In the grand scheme of what was Caterpillar, ag equipment sales played a minor role.

That all changed in 1987 with the introduction of the Challenger™ 65 tractor with the patented Mobil-trac™ system. An industry observer said at the time, the ag equipment business, characterized up to then by "creep" technology, had just experienced "leap" technology. Our new undercarriage had the potential to revolutionize farming much as Benjamin Holt had done with his innovations at the turn of the century.

The standard 40-inch (1016-mm) diameter drive wheel has a 60-degree chevron pattern molded of hardened rubber for superior debris rejection and maximum belt grip. It provides excellent performance in a wide range of underfoot conditions.

Belt tread bars are 2.5 inches (63.5 mm) high and placed at a 30-degree angle for a smooth ride and excellent debris rejection. The bars are shortened in the center to provide comfortable roading.

A beefy box-section frame adds strength and durability.

An optional 1000-pound (454 kg) slotted cast drive wheel provides exceptional performance in extremely wet or muddy conditions. This special-application drive wheel helps eliminate belt-to-driver slip sometimes experienced in extremely slippery or greasy conditions, or with certain vegetable residue.

Scissor-like movement of the suspension system allows for equal weight distribution between each midwheel and continuous belt contact with the ground. This results in maximum traction and floatation, and a smoother ride.

Four pairs of 14-inch- (4.2-cm) diameter midwheels are coated with molded rubber. This reduces dirt buildup and helps the rubber belts cushion the vibrations and the shock of uneven terrain.

Caterpillar blends its own rubber belt compound. Each belt contains multiple layers of steel cable for precise tracking: four layers on the 25- and 30-inch (635- and 763-mm) belts and five layers on the 30-inch (762-mm) reinforced and 35-inch (889-mm) belts. Other tracked tractor manufacturers rely on outside suppliers for belts and track components, while Cat designs and manufactures all its track components to tough Caterpillar standards.

Molded guideblocks maintain belt alignment and improve belt tracking in hilly terrain.

The two-inch/50.8-mm rubber coating on the idlers absorbs shocks and provides a comfortable ride for the operator.

The unique Caterpillar track tensioning system utilizes a nitrogen-boosted cylinder to generate 34,000 pounds/151.3 kN of force. A sophisticated recoil system safeguards belts from excessive tension caused by debris intake.

Tapered roller bearings and Cat heavy-duty Duo-Cone seals are durable and maintenance-free.

Air springs feature an air-pressure valve adjustable from 60-90 psi/ 413.4-620.1 kPa to fine-tune the tractor's ride and steering characteristics to match your conditions.

Holt's small, self-propelled harvesters were first mass-produced in 1921.

The first Challenger 65, introduced in 1987.

1968. Smaller crawler tractors were used in a variety of farming applications. This tractor in Washington is preparing land for fallow.

With the Challenger 65 tractors, we officially reentered the agricultural equipment market. Subsequently, six other models were introduced. Then, in 1997, we formed a joint venture with one of Europe's premier manufacturers—Claas KGaA—to produce and market state-of-the-art combines in the U.S. to serve customers in North America and Australia.

All of our agricultural tractors are configured to use Mobil-trac undercarriages. The advantages are greater traction and flotation, reduced soil compaction and more versatility. This results in reduced cost and more productivity on the farm. Several combine models offer a choice of wheels or Mobil-trac undercarriage.

Hoses to Belts

Rubber track was a natural outgrowth of Beadless Tire technology, which in turn had grown out of Caterpillar's industry-leading work in hydraulic hose.

XT-3 hose, developed in the 1960s, has alternating layers of high tensile wire and rubber. Caterpillar now has a factory in West Plains, Missouri, that makes a line of high-pressure hose and the new generation of XT-3 ES hose, as well as XT-5 and XT-6, used for a variety of applications. The breakthrough technology allows us to use extreme high-pressure hydraulic systems—a requirement for machines like the D11R and the 994G.

The Beadless Tire had wire cable within the tire carcass plus a rubber belt that held steel shoes. This rubber belt work helped lead to the belts for the Challenger machines. We stopped making the Beadless Tire in the late 1980s because tire companies had developed radial tires that could be used on our equipment.

To eliminate problems of ruptures, leaks and coupling failure on hose supplied by others, we developed our own hose. It's called XT-3 and features a special formulation of rubber and wire cable.

The need to solve common causes of earthmoving equipment tire failure (such as heat deterioration and cut-through from rocks) led to development of steel shoe Beadless Tires.

We used that technology background to develop the belted track that led to the Mobil-trac system. We had been working toward a four-wheel-drive agriculture tractor, but dropped that plan and developed the Challenger 65 tractor instead.

"Holt established a philosophy when he made combines: Build a more durable, reliable product for a premium, and provide the best possible product support. That philosophy started with agricultural products and has been true throughout Caterpillar's history."

Dennis Disberger, New Product Introduction Manager—Combines

Challenger Tractor and LEXION Combine

High Volume Production

Until the mid-'40s, Caterpillar depended on various outside suppliers for pull-type scrapers compatible with our crawler tractors. This practice of focusing on the base machine and purchasing attachments from other suppliers had dominated our way of thinking for many years. For example, we purchased bulldozing blades and controls. R.G. LeTourneau manufactured a large assortment of pull-type scrapers which were sold through Cat Dealers.

top. **Pull-type Caterpillar No. 80 Scraper from 1954.**

above. **The Cat Triple 657s were built in response to the LeTourneau triple and tandem machines that also worked on the San Luis Canal in California. Caterpillar and California dealer Peterson Tractor Co. worked together to develop the triple-scraper arrangement.**

left. **Today's 657E.**

His 1938 "Tournapull," powered by a Cat diesel engine, was a breakthrough for the industry. Our alliance with LeTourneau was terminated in 1944 with the announcement that Caterpillar was going to start production on a new line of scrapers.

The Second World War delayed our entry, but after the war we introduced our first tractor-towed scrapers—the No. 80 in 1946, the No. 60 in 1947 and No. 70 in 1951. Wheeled tractor scrapers got their start in 1947 with the DW10 Tractor and No. 10 Scraper. The four-wheel DW10 was first introduced in 1940 along with the W10 Wagon, but production stopped during WWII. By 1948, Caterpillar had designed a 15-cubic-yard (11-cubic-meter) struck capacity prototype model, the Cat DW21. It was introduced in 1950 and went into full production with the opening of the Joliet, Illinois, plant in 1951.

In 1962, we introduced the first of our twin-engine scrapers—657 and 666. Today's 657E in tandem-powered version can pick up 44 cubic yards (33 cubic meters) of dirt in one load. These machines can whittle down a mountain and fill a valley in short order.

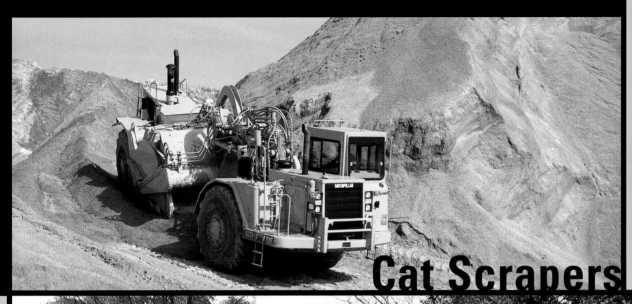

Cat Scrapers

left. **Today's 627F, introduced in 1993, is rated at 555 flywheel horsepower (414 kW) and has a heaped capacity of 20 cubic yards (15 cubic meters).**

below. **Officially released in 1951, the DW21 was the company's first two-wheel tractor-pulled scraper. The DW21G was the last version; its production ended in 1960.**

From attachment
into **integrated** machine

Pipelayers

above. **583R Pipelayer lays pipe for a new development in the midwestern United States.**

left. **During World War II, pipelaying became vital in the U.S. as oil imports became almost impossible. Oil tankers were prey to submarines.**

In the decades that followed World War II, Caterpillar created some new product lines by redesigning tractors and attachments into completely new machines. One such attachment was the pipelayer. Initially, Caterpillar purchased pipelaying attachments from the Trackson Company of Milwaukee, Wisconsin. The acquisition of this company in 1951 opened the door for integrated product design.

The big breakthrough was the No. 583 Pipelayer, introduced in 1955. A true "industry first" machine, the 583 had a lifting capacity of 130,000 pounds (59 020 kilograms). The 583 entered the market just as the demand for oil, gas and water pipelines around the world began to rise.

Today's pipelayer lift capacities range from 40,000 pounds (18 145 kg) to 230,000 pounds (104 330 kg). Along with track-type tractor features like the elevated sprocket and planetary shift transmission, these machines have specialized pipelayer features—boom and hook draw works driven by independent hydraulic winches, oil disc brakes and hydraulically actuated counterweights.

The breakthrough No. 583 Pipelayer, the first in the industry to feature this integrated design, was introduced in 1955. Since its introduction, the 583 has consistently been the number one choice for pipelaying jobs worldwide.

above. The trans-Alaska oil pipeline began construction on April 29, 1974. The three-year, $7.7 billion project employed as many as 14,000 workers. One of the biggest projects of this century, the pipeline was built by a seven-company consortium called Alyeska.

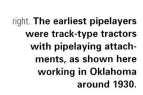

right. The earliest pipelayers were track-type tractors with pipelaying attachments, as shown here working in Oklahoma around 1930.

While Caterpillar introduced its first track loader in 1952, the actual thinking for this product can be traced as far back as 1937. At that time, the Trackson Company of Milwaukee, Wisconsin, first provided a shovel front-end option for the Cat Thirty. Subsequently, Trackson manufactured "Traxcavator" vertical-lift, cable-operated, front-loading shovel attachments for the D2, D4, D6 and D7 crawler tractors.

Innovative thinking
expands product line

In 1950, a hydraulic Traxcavator option was added to the Cat D4. It was around this time that someone began asking questions. "What if these shovels weren't attachments? How much better could we make this machine if we created—from the ground up—a new, totally integrated design?" In 1951, we acquired the Trackson Company.

top right. **A 953C clearing brush for a new road in Sterling, West Virginia.**

right. **Caterpillar Diesel No. 6 Shovel is used for feeding the hopper of a Cedarapids hot mix plant in 1954.**

below. **The No. 6 Shovel was an "industry first" upon its introduction in 1952. Cat engineers combined a front-end loader attachment with a track-type tractor to create the integrated-design track loader.**

bottom. **This 963C digs a new basement in a housing development.**

Just one year later, the No. 6 Shovel—the first integrated-design track loader in the industry—was introduced.

Track loaders have evolved into highly versatile construction machines with features like hydrostatic drive, advanced hydraulic controls and comfortable cabs. Today, the Caterpillar track loader line is the most complete in the industry and features special application versions for steel mills, waste handling and demolition.

Cat Track Loaders

left. **Rear-engine track loaders—for better stability—hit the market in 1980 when the 943 and 953 loaders started rolling off the assembly line.**

Cat 980G and 988F Series II Wheel Loaders work side-by-side in a coal pit.

Loaders

988F CAT

980G CAT

The 914G was Caterpillar's first hydrostatic-drive wheel loader. It was introduced in 1995.

Cat Wheel Loaders

The first Caterpillar Wheel Loader wasn't called a wheel loader—it was introduced as a "Wheel-type Traxcavator" in 1959. The No. 944 was soon followed by the 922 and the 966. All of these machines had rigid frames and steered with their rear wheels. While this design was functional, it was not optimal. The advent of the articulated steering design increased speed and maneuverability and propelled the introduction of the Cat 988 and a redesigned 966B in 1963.

And we still called them Traxcavators.

Ultimately, it was customer confusion that prompted us, in late 1965, to rename them wheel loaders.

In the late 1970s, we created a real stir by introducing the Z-bar linkage design on the 988B. The improved strength and force of this design solidified our leadership. And, this tradition of leadership has continued to grow. Advanced electronic engines and monitoring systems, completely new steering options and load-sensing hydraulics are just some of the advancements we have brought to these machines.

Productivity by any **other** name

With over a dozen different wheel loader models, Caterpillar has developed the most comprehensive line in the world. And, with the introduction of the Caterpillar G-Series Wheel Loader line, we have again raised the bar—not so much for the industry, but for ourselves.

The 992G, introduced in 1997, shook the industry with a one-piece lift-arm design that had three-times the strength of the previous models.

left upper. **The No. 944 was the first rubber-tired front-end loader built by Caterpillar. Released in 1959, it steered with the rear wheels.**

left lower. **Articulation added operational flexibility to wheel loaders. The company's first articulated wheel loader was the 966, shown in a French gravel operation.**

Invented in Europe in the 1950s, hydraulic excavators quickly became popular. This is not surprising. They offered more power, worked faster and were easier to operate at lower cost than cable excavators.

We saw the opportunity and began development. Not only would excavators change the face of construction, but the very process we used to enter this market would help change the way Caterpillar

Teamwork
pays off

developed new products. Caterpillar introduced its first hydraulic excavator, the Cat 225, in 1972. Prior to this, development typically happened in a very linear fashion—meaning design, manufacturing and marketing had little interaction.

Because the Cat 225 was on a fast track to market, it was decided that all groups working together would speed the process.

The Cat 225 was the first hydraulic excavator (100 percent) designed and built by Caterpillar.

The 245 was introduced in 1974 and was designed for heavy-duty lifting and trenching. At introduction, this workhorse was available in trenching, mass excavating and front shovel arrangements. Future updates would add heavy lift and deep trencher to these offerings.

The Total Project Description, authored in January, 1970, states: "It is the intent of this description to unify all groups concerned toward common objectives. If the functional planning is done within this framework, the tactical plans which evolve should guide the entire organization's thinking and actions ... "

Outlined in this same document is the New Product Introduction process—a process Caterpillar still uses today.

Teamwork proved prolific: the 235 was introduced in 1973, the 245 in 1974 and the 215 in 1976. New models and model updates in the 200 family abounded through the '70s and '80s.

As the world economy began to recover from the recession of the late 1970s and early 1980s, most U.S. and European manufacturers had ceded their leadership to the advances of Japanese firms. In Japan, excavators were more than 80 percent of the new construction machinery sales and represented potential sales of 10,000 units a year. This created an advantage to firms familiar with the Japanese market.

Caterpillar has one of the longest running successful joint ventures between a Japanese and an American firm. In 1963, Caterpillar developed an equal-ownership manufacturing and marketing company with Mitsubishi. This partnership was formed to offer Caterpillar product in Japan. However, this agreement did not cover hydraulic excavators and Mitsubishi had developed a successful line of its own.

Cat Excavators

left. **This Cat 320B L begins excavation for a new sub-division.**

Wheeled excavators work on jobs where speed and mobility are important. This M318 is removing railroad ties along a road in the Northwest United States.

In 1986, the joint venture was expanded to include hydraulic excavators and the company was renamed Shin Caterpillar Mitsubishi Ltd.—"shin" being the Japanese word for new. Design engineers were transferred from Aurora, Illinois, and Gosselies, Belgium, to the new Hydraulic Excavator Design Center in Akashi, Japan, to form a unique international design team.

In 1992, the 325, the first of the 300 family, was introduced. The product combined the individual strengths from each part of the world and offered a design which was highly reliable, productive, distinctively styled, and offered a wide variety of attachments. This philosophy was continued and expanded when the B series, the latest offered by Caterpillar, was introduced, improving operator comfort, controllability and serviceability. The joint venture put in place over 35 years ago continues to pay off.

In 1994, Caterpillar became the leading producer of hydraulic excavators in the world—a position we maintain today.

top. **The latest addition to the 300 family, the 365B, features the industry's most advanced hydraulic controls. This is the first excavator equipped with a Vital Information Display System—an electronic monitoring and control system for the operator.**

middle. **Introduced in 1992, the Cat 325 was the first in the 300 family excavator line.**

right. **The Cat 345B L Series II was the first excavator introduced in the year 2000.**

Excavators have evolved beyond their jobs on construction sites. They have come to be viewed as mobile hydraulic power units able to work almost anywhere. With advanced hydraulics and electronic control technologies, excavators can power a wide range of tools. In the past, we did not build tools for our machines, but purchased them from other manufacturers. Today, acquisitions and joint ventures combined with our manufacturing expertise have culminated in a complete line of Cat work tools not only for excavators, but for other machines as well.

Cat work tools for excavators include specialty buckets, hammers, scrap and demolition tools, shears, crushers, grapples and forestry tools. Here, a 322B with a hydraulic hammer breaks out concrete.

Cat Work Tools

Teamwork Pays Off—Again

The idea of mounting a loader bucket on the front of a tractor and a backhoe on the rear was actually born on the farm. But it wasn't until Case in the United States and JCB in the United Kingdom came out with their heavy-duty units in the 1950s that backhoe loaders gained recognition as a construction tool.

In the 1970s, small contractors emerged as a growing market segment. Caterpillar had already introduced the D3 Track-Type Tractor, the 931 Track Loader and the 910 Wheel Loader in response to those needs. Toward the end of the decade, it became clear that backhoe loaders held significant opportunity and we decided to add them to the product line.

The team concept which had originated with the Cat 225 Excavator was adopted and expanded. The development process for the Cat 416 Backhoe Loader from concept to customer was unlike any other ever undertaken at Caterpillar.

In a former warehouse (known as the "skunk works") in north Peoria, the development team of more than 50 people literally "took down the walls"—all shared one room with no offices. "That," says Jim Bockhaus, project manager, "created an atmosphere that promoted open communication and timely decisions." Open communication with the Leicester, England, plant, where the 416 would be assembled, was also critical to the team's success.

"The result of all this is the most cost-sensitive machine Caterpillar has ever built," says Bockhaus. "The 416 is a good example of what a small group of people can do by directing their efforts toward a common objective."

In 1999, we produced our 100,000th backhoe loader.

Smaller backhoe loaders, like this 426B, are often used for trenching water, sewer and utility lines to residential structures.

left. **A 428C moves backfill material on a small commercial construction site.**

above. **Officially introduced in 1996, the 436C Backhoe Loader features optional full hydrostatic all-wheel steering and a box-section backhoe boom designed for strength and balance.**

left. **The integrated toolcarrier linkage combined with the hydraulic quick coupler allows the backhoe loader to use a variety of Cat work tools.**

Cat Backhoe Loaders

In response to the economic constraints of the early 1980s, a group of Caterpillar managers developed long-term corporate strategies to achieve the company's goals for sales and profits through 1995. In order to carry out these strategies, the group had to look at customer needs and trends across a variety of industries. One of the key conclusions was that customers need to complete more tasks with fewer machines, to help increase efficiency and reduce cost.

This IT28G works on underground utility jobs as well as street cleaning and road maintenance for a large county in the south central United States.

As a result, Caterpillar integrated toolcarriers were one of the innovative products designed to deliver high levels of versatility with one machine.

Introduced in 1985, Cat integrated toolcarriers combine the performance of wheel loaders with hydraulic quick couplers and a wide range of Cat work tools.

Today, customers in construction, industrial, agriculture and many other markets can change work tools in minutes without leaving the cab.

above right. **Equipped with a bucket, this IT14G is ideal for loading or backfilling.**

right. **The parallel lift feature makes it easier to handle palletized material.**

Integrated Toolcarriers:
More with less

Telehandlers: The long reach

Work tools such as root crop buckets, grain pushers, bale spikes and manure forks boost machine productivity in agricultural applications. Here a TH62 moves feed from storage to livestock.

A TH63 with extension boom and pallet fork delivers palletized material to the second story level in a matter of minutes.

Telehandlers have been manufactured at Caterpillar's Leicester, England, factory since 1995. The five models have been designed to meet the material handling needs of the construction and agriculture industries worldwide.

Caterpillar telehandlers lift capacities range from 6,000 to 10,000 pounds (3000 to 5000 kilograms) with lift heights up to 44 feet (13.5 meters). With full-time four-wheel drive, tight turning radius and compact size, these machines maneuver well in tight spaces.

A wide range of work tools and a standard quick coupler make the machines versatile and productive, enhancing their value for the customer.

Telehandlers

In 1962, Caterpillar introduced its first off-highway truck—the 769. With the entry of the 769 into the off-highway truck market, Caterpillar quickly set the standard for the industry. Cat 769 features, which were also integral to the design of subsequent models, included non-fade braking with oil-cooled brakes, pneumatic oil independent wheel suspension for superior ride, automatic power shift transmission to optimize speed with minimal operator effort and rugged structures for long life.

For a brief time in the mid-1960s to early 1970s, Caterpillar entered the electric drive market with a two-axle 85-ton (77-metric ton) truck (779) and a twin engine 240-ton (217-metric ton) coal hauler—the largest hauler in the world when introduced in 1965. A limited number worked in the Midwest U.S. (southern Illinois).

New products developed relatively quickly. First was the 50-ton (45-metric-ton) 773, big brother to the upgraded 769B. The 777, an 85-ton (77-metric-ton) capacity truck, was introduced in 1975. Today, all three of these original mechanical drive trucks are still in production.

The next steps up in capacity came with the introduction of the 150-ton (136-metric-ton) 785 in 1984 and the 195-ton (176-metric-ton) 789 in 1986 and the 240-ton (217-metric-ton) 793 in 1991, all of which were aimed at the mining industry. Most recent were the introductions of the 793C in 1996 and the 797 in 1998.

QUARRY TRUCK

775D

775D CAT

CATERPILLAR

777D

Cat Trucks

far left. **The Cat 769 was the first off-road truck built by Caterpillar.**

center left. **The 240-ton (217-metric-ton) 786 Coal Hauler was the first experimental diesel-electric drive prototype. It is pictured here at its introduction in October 1965. It had dual cabs and engines at each end that allowed entering and exiting a loading/dumping site without turning around.**

above. **The 775D Quarry Truck was designed specifically for aggregates applications.**

above right. **The 777D was introduced in 1996 and has a capacity of 100 tons (90 metric tons).**

To complete the product line capacity-wise, the quarry trucks—44-ton (39-metric-ton) 771C and the 65-ton (58-metric-ton) 775B—were introduced in 1992. These trucks were designed specifically for the aggregates industry with larger-volume truck bodies.

In 1996, the D-series trucks were introduced with hydraulic electronic unit

injection engines which were more fuel-efficient and offered more environmental advantages such as reduced emissions, smoke and noise.

Since 1962, more than 30,000 Caterpillar off-highway trucks have been built in Decatur, Illinois. A large percentage of these trucks are still working around the world today.

3690 mm (12' 1") vazio
3590 mm (11' 9") carregado
500 mm (20")
3713 mm (12' 2")
8200 mm (26' 11")
12' E vazio
60°
F vazio
G carregado
A
C
B
H

The Biggest Truck Yet

The 360-ton (326-metric ton) 797 is the largest of the Caterpillar line of mechanical drive trucks, as well as the largest truck ever built. "Just how big is the biggest? It will easily haul: four blue whales, 217 taxicabs, 1,200 grand pianos or 23,490 Furbies," according to a *New York Times Magazine* article.

Caterpillar developed the 797 from the ground up in response to mining companies' need to reduce cost per ton in large-scale operations. During the truck's development, a customer advisory council—consisting of representatives from each major mining sector including coal, copper and oil sands—was formed to review ideas and make suggestions. The truck was designed and built within 18 months by using computer modeling and simulation implemented by a high-tech assembly line.

And, the 797 has brains as well as brawn. There are eight on-board computers that control everything from tire traction and transmission shifting to air suspension seating.

above. **This 797 article appeared in the December 20, 1998, issue of the *New York Times Magazine*.**

right. **Each 797 tire weighs 10,000 pounds (4540 kg). Twelve of these tires stacked tread to tread would rise higher than the Statue of Liberty from toes to torch.**

Articulated Haulers

Caterpillar's entry into the articulated truck market actually dates back to the mid-1950s when tractors from the scraper product were matched to Athey rear-dump trailers, often referred to as "rockers." Their appeal came from their ability to work in adverse ground conditions that were virtually impossible for rigid-frame trucks.

While the same in concept, current articulated truck design makes "rockers" look old and clumsy. The modern articulated truck line began in 1972 when DJB Engineering, Ltd., opened a factory in Peterlee, England, to build articulated trucks—using Cat drive trains.

In 1985, Caterpillar bought the product rights, and renamed the machines Caterpillar. In 1996, Caterpillar bought the manufacturing company, facilities and property in Peterlee, England, and made articulated trucks 100 percent Caterpillar. Current machines include two-axle, four-wheel-drive and three-axle, six-wheel-drive models ranging from 25-ton to 40-ton (22-metric-ton to 36-metric-ton) capacity.

They work as earthmoving systems with Cat excavators and wheel loaders, or as multipurpose hauling systems, such as waste container handlers and coal haulers.

top. **A "rocker"— predecessor to the articulated truck.**

middle. **D300E working on a new development.**

bottom. **D400E Series II in a sand and gravel operation.**

Traditions of **growth** and **strength**

From the beginning, Caterpillar products have been a part of the history of mining—track-type tractors clearing cover from coal mines, loaders and excavators loading on- and off-highway trucks, motor graders maintaining haul roads…in fact, just about every machine and engine we make is used in the mining industry.

In 1987, we formed the Mining Vehicle Center at the Decatur, Illinois, plant. This opening followed the 1985 introduction of the 785 and 789 trucks. When the center was formed, Cat began development of four new large mining machines—the 994 Wheel Loader, 793 Truck, 24H Motor Grader and the 844 Wheel Dozer. The center's most recent innovation is the 797 Truck.

In 1997, Caterpillar purchased the rights to the large wheel dozers produced by Tiger Engineering Pty., Ltd., of Australia. Tiger began producing large rubber-tired wheel dozers, primarily with Cat components, in 1981. The machines have always been sold and serviced through the Caterpillar dealer organization.

Caterpillar has also become more involved in underground mining. In 1997, we bought Elphinstone Pty., Ltd., located in Tasmania, Australia, a manufacturer of underground mining equipment.

Today, Caterpillar has the broadest line of mining systems in the industry—matching machines to specific mining conditions. And, we never stop looking for ways to increase the value of those machines. Often the best way to do that is through new technology. We have developed a variety of technologies including: Global Positioning System communications integrated with machine controls and business software; Computer Aided Earthmoving Systems that give operators a near real-time color display of the job as it progresses; a program called DOZSIM that creates virtual dozing applications and analyzes volume, time, cost and overall productivity; and Vital Information Management Systems that monitor machine systems for potential problems and transmit pertinent data back to the office.

right. **The illustration represents the breadth of our mining line.**

far right top to bottom. **Elphinstone R1700 Load Haul Dump Series II, 994 Wheel Loader/ 785B system, and an 824G Wheel Dozer.**

Mining and Aggregates

Aggregates Industry

The aggregates industry includes not only stone for structures and foundations but aggregate for concrete, road surfacing, bedding materials and riprap. Some of the first Caterpillar tractors and scrapers were put to work opening limestone quarries across North America. For hauling materials out of the pits, Caterpillar tractors with wagon attachments were the predecessors of the articulated and off-highway trucks used in the industry today.

With the introduction of larger wheel loaders like the 988 in 1963 and the 992 in 1968, the larger but more cumbersome shovels and draglines were replaced with these smaller, more agile machines. Matched to the 769B or the larger 773, these loaders and haulers provided the first systems for aggregates.

top left to right. **980G working in a gravel pit, D9R in crushed stone and a 992G at the face.**

left. **A 990 and a 988F tandem loading in a quarry.**

While there were many Caterpillar machines working in aggregates applications long before the 1990s, there were no machine configurations designed specifically for this industry until 1992. At that time, Caterpillar introduced two off-highway trucks as "Quarry Trucks"—the 44-ton (39-metric-ton) 771C and the 65-ton (58-metric-ton) 775B. What differentiated these trucks from other Cat off-highway trucks was the bodies. They could handle mild- to medium-hardness materials without liners and do so in greater volumes than the 769 or 773 models. Today, we offer a variety of body options for the entire truck line.

The 5130 Front Shovel, the first of Caterpillar's 5000 series, was also introduced in 1992 to meet the needs for high volume loading. Today, both the 5130B and the 992G are matched to the 777D Truck; the 990 Series II is matched to the 775D and the 988G is matched to the 771D. For sand and gravel applications, 300 family mass excavators are matched to our line of articulated trucks.

Introduced in 1992, the 5130 was the first of Caterpillar's 5000 series front shovels. It is shown loading a 777 Truck.

Forestry Products

Built for the woods

Until 1944, when we announced that we would begin making our own attachments, tractors were outfitted with specialized logging tools such as Hyster arches or winches, which were used to grasp or drag logs. Since the late 1940s, Caterpillar has introduced a large number of forestry machines specifically to meet the needs of the forestry industry. In the late 1970s, some Caterpillar excavators could be customized for forestry work with log-loading configurations.

In the 19th century, teams of oxen—like these in Salisbury, Maryland—did some of the toughest work, but logging was still a back-breaking job.

In 1926, this Sixty was used at the Davies Johnson Lumber Co., Calpine, California, to snake 32-foot (9.76-meter) logs 1,500 feet (457.5 meters) down the mountain.

The 227 was the first purpose-built excavator designed to satisfy a specific market segment outside of the traditional earthmoving market.

Today, Caterpillar has gone well beyond the modified excavator to designing machines specifically for work in the woods. Feller bunchers grip, cut and bunch small logs with a single front-end tool. Swing machines are multi-purpose machines used for road building, processing, loading and reforestation processes.

We introduced our first wheel skidder, the 518, in 1971. This veteran product stayed in production until 1996. Today, we make two models of wheel skidders, the 525, introduced in 1995, and the 545, in 1999.

Our first track skidders were the D4H and D5H skidders in 1989. The two current models are 527, introduced in 1996, and the 517, in 1999. They have two grapple options— swing-boom and fixed-boom—as well as a winch configuration.

Cat started designing and building machines especially for forestry work. The first was the 518 Skidder. This 525 Wheel Skidder features an Auto-Grab hydraulic grapple.

Cat has a complete line of log-handling machines for millyard operations. Swing machines sort and pile logs in high storage decks. Wheel loaders unload trucks or load and carry lumber around the yard. Wheel and track dozers with chip scoops or special blades move material after processing.

We manufacture a wide range of grapples, clamps and forks designed to handle logs efficiently, without damage. All Cat forestry tools work with Cat quick couplers and are precision-matched to the hydraulic systems on Cat forest machines. Forestry work tools specifically match machines and material.

Forestry

Millyard

above. **A 325 A Series swing-type Log Loader off-loads from truck to high storage decks in 1994.**

right. **966 Wheel Loader unloads logs using a fork.**

far right. **Track-type tractors offer excellent traction on steep woodchip piles. This D10N is equipped with a blade made for the purpose.**

far left. **The Cat 580 Harvester uses a computer-aided cutting and measuring system.**

left. **Cat 574 Forwarder loading logs for hauling.**

In 1997, Caterpillar acquired Skogsjan AB, a Swedish manufacturer of cut-to-length forestry machines.

We entered the cut-to-length market with the introduction of Cat forwarders and harvesters in October, 1999. Working these machines together as a system offers environmental and economic advantages because it reduces machine movement by eliminating repeated trips over the same ground. The harvester, with its computer-aided cutting and measuring system, fells the tree; then the forwarder carries the timber from the site.

At the Söderhamn, Sweden, plant, three models of harvesters, two models of forwarders and four models of harvesting heads are produced.

Currently sold in Northern Europe and North America, these machines show potential in Asia, Russia and South America as business methods change.

right. **A harvester (foreground) and forwarder work together to fell trees, process them at the stump and remove them with little impact on the terrain.**

Paving the way

The Caterpillar connection to the paving industry started during the era of the Better Roads Program in the 1920s when Caterpillar track-type tractors were used to pull Russell graders. That connection grew throughout the years as our earthmoving line diversified. It was strengthened even more in 1984 when Caterpillar entered into an agreement with CMI Corporation of Oklahoma to offer a complete line of branded paving products, which included models to produce and lay down asphalt and cement.

In 1987, the association between the two companies was discontinued. Caterpillar purchased CMI's subsidiary, RayGo, Inc., of Minneapolis, Minnesota, a leading manufacturer of soil and asphalt compactors, and other technology for the manufacture of asphalt paving and pavement maintenance equipment.

We once again increased the paving product offering in April, 1991, with the purchase of Barber-Greene, world-renowned producer of paving equipment. The Barber-Greene Company introduced the first practical asphalt paver in 1931, so its link to the paving industry rivals the longevity of Caterpillar.

Today, Caterpillar offers the most technologically advanced line of cold planers, reclaimers/stabilizers, asphalt pavers, and vibratory and pneumatic compactors. All of these products are marketed by the worldwide Caterpillar dealer organization.

above. **A double-drum vibratory compactor with machined steel drums for a smooth finish.**

below. **Cutaway diagram for an inside look at the vibratory drum system.**

right. **This Barber-Greene BG-245C Track Paver used on roads and highways has a paving width of twenty four feet two inches (7.4 meters).**

far right top. **This CP-563C padded drum vibratory compactor uses a hydraulic leveling blade for trench filling and back dragging.**

far right center. **This CB-534C vibratory double-drum compactor featuring a three amplitude vibratory system gives the operator the flexibility to match the centrifugal force to the job.**

bottom row, left to right. **Soil stabilizers, like this RM-350B, are used to stabilize base materials before paving. The RM-350B has the balance of power, weight and drive to work in demanding applications.**

Typical applications include landfill liner compaction, highway and street construction, industrial site preparation and large trenching. The CS-563C is used on granular soils when smooth surface is desired.

The static weight of a pneumatic roller like this PS-360B provides the compactive forces and the rubber tires concentrate this force onto small areas. Because the tires are flexible, high horizontal pressures develop, assisting with compaction.

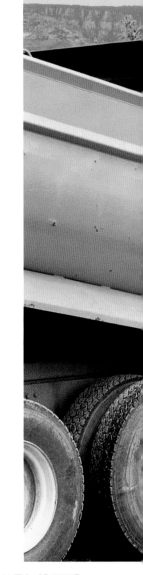

far right. **This AP-1050B asphalt paver features the exclusive Cat Mobil-trac system, the same system found on the Challenger tractors. In paving it offers the flotation and traction of a crawler suspension as well as the ride quality and mobility of wheels.**

BG-245C

Scrap & Demolition

In the 1980s, the scrap and demolition industries gained attention as opportunities to expand the use of Cat excavators as material handlers.

While many other Cat machines—wheel loaders, integrated toolcarriers, track-type tractors and trucks—work in this industry, the workhorses of the Caterpillar line are the material handlers. Scrap and demolition customers found excavators offered advantages over lattice-boom cranes in both speed and precision. The 235C Scrap Handler arrangement was introduced by Custom Machine Products Division in 1988, simultaneous to the introduction of the standard 235C. Auxiliary equipment manufacturers Young and Pierce provided material-handling fronts and tilt risers as well as a number of different tools such as clamshells, grapples and magnets.

With the introduction of the 300 series excavators, we provided specially designed machines, built and supported by Caterpillar.

above right. **A Cat 350 Material Handler with three-piece front and material handling grapple.**

right. **Cat 320 Material Handler uses a magnet to sort scrap metal.**

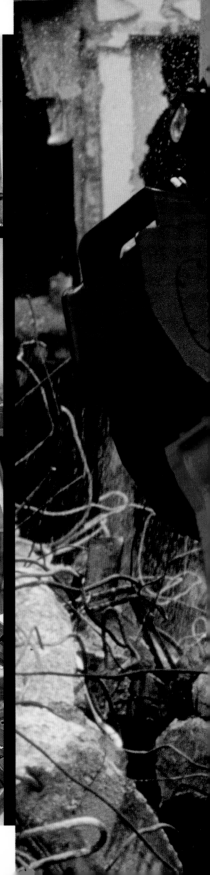

left. **A Cat MP20 Multiprocessor with pulverizer jaws crushes concrete at a demolition site.**

In 1998, we purchased Material Handling Crane Systems, Marion, Ohio, to handle the specialization work on material handlers. In that same year, we introduced the 330B L Demolition Machine. It's a specialized version of the forestry swing machine. Both the 330B L and the 345B L were also offered as ultra-high demolition machines. These had three-piece fronts which could reach heights up to 68 feet (20 meters).

As environmental regulations pressed scrap yards to better control runoff and ground water, the yards were paved. To protect the pavement from track damage, wheeled undercarriages for material handlers were introduced.

In 1999, we introduced a wheeled under-carriage for the 325B MH. Its design advantages included a two-axle carrier and increased overall lift capacity.

Today, Caterpillar offers a complete line of quick couplers and work tools designed specifically for the scrap and demolition industries.

top. **A 973 Demolition Special Track Loader moves torn-down debris.**

above. **This Cat multiprocessor is equipped with shear jaws used to cut through iron girders and rebar.**

Rugged machines for waste handling

Waste Handling

Since 1960, waste generation has been growing in the U.S. at a two-percent annual growth rate—double the population growth rate. As countries become more industrialized, world waste generation will increase at a similar rate. Sanitary landfills and transfer stations, where waste is compacted and loaded for transport to sanitary landfills, have become a global necessity.

As you can imagine, landfills and transfer stations are tough applications that take a real toll on machines. Because of their strength and durability, Caterpillar products have long been the equipment choice for dozing, spreading waste and cover materials. Since the space for landfills is limited, maximizing the available area by achieving the highest levels of compaction is a must.

Cat Sixty Tractor spreads residential trash at a municipal site in the 1930s.

Seeing this need, Caterpillar introduced its first landfill compactors in the early '70s. These steel-wheel machines, specifically designed for waste, offered better compaction rates than standard track-type tractors.

We have continued to develop these purpose-built machines and today offer the 816, 826 and 836 Compactors. In addition to track-type tractors and steel-wheel compactors, other Caterpillar machines help meet waste-handling challenges.

Articulated trucks and scrapers are used in landfills for construction of cells and handling of daily cover material. Articulated trucks are also used as special-container and refuse-handling trucks. Medium wheel loaders, small excavators, track loaders and integrated toolcarriers are used in transfer stations.

In 1996, strategic analysis identified the significant opportunity this industry offers Caterpillar and our dealers. In 1998, the Corporate Waste Group was formed to take full advantage of enterprise strengths and gain incremental sales in this industry.

above. **This 826G Compactor moves over a landfill cell, compacting trash before adding soil as cover. The extra catch-guard extending above the blade keeps trash from rolling over the top and piling up in front of the compactor.**

top right. **A Cat 966G uses a refuse bucket to move trash at a transfer station.**

center right. **This D8 gets ready for another pass across a cell at a landfill site.**

lower right. **This 973 Waste Handler has extra guarding and protection features specifically designed for work in landfills and transfer stations.**

Cat quality—Size doesn't matter

Not only does Caterpillar manufacture some of the largest equipment in the world, we also manufacture a variety of products designed specifically for independent contractors and smaller construction jobs.

Track-type tractors were one of the first product lines that offered Cat power and durability in machines sized to work in tight quarters or residential areas. Today, D3C, D4C and D5C Tractors are available with a variety of configurations to match specific job and ground conditions.

The Cat 300 family excavator line features several models designed specifically to meet the needs of building contractors. The Cat 307, 311, 312, 315 and 318 are easy to operate and transport.

Track loaders, because they can perform so many different tasks on a site, are often the first to arrive and the last to leave. The 933 Track Loader was introduced in 1955 and is still available. Both the 933C and 939C feature a hydrostatic drive system that allows independent power to each track for increased speed and maneuverability.

We've offered a variety of wheel loader sizes since the early 1960s. Backhoe loaders, integrated toolcarriers and telehandlers are newer additions to the Cat product line, entering the market over the past two decades.

Many contractors start their businesses with a single backhoe loader because of its versatility, maneuverability, transportability and low operating cost. This 426C excavates a basement in a residential neighborhood.

Although track-type tractors have become more sophisticated, their role on the job site has changed very little over the years. On many building construction sites, the small dozer is the primary machine. This D3C XL clears a lot for new construction in central California.

bottom left. A large part of track loader maintenance costs are in the undercarriage. Regular inspections of tension, lubrication and wear help reduce those costs.

bottom right. Wheel loaders are used for a wide variety of tasks and can be equipped with a variety of work tools. This 928G Wheel Loader loads trucks carrying bedding material.

One of the biggest advantages of the 300 family excavators is their transportability. With a truck and a low-boy trailer, this 315 can be moved from job to job quickly and easily.

The development of a complete line of building construction products has bolstered Cat dealers' rental fleets. Building contractors rent about 40 percent of the primary machines they use, making them the most prolific renters in the equipment-using community. Throughout the 1990s, building markets have sustained consistent growth, and the rentals of contractors' favorite tools—

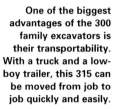

The 307B is available with an offset boom option for work in the tightest spaces. The boom can be offset left or right.

excavators, backhoe loaders and telehandlers—have grown in direct proportion. Caterpillar has been there to meet the needs not only for machines but for a variety of work tools as well.

Headquartered in Cary, North Carolina, Caterpillar Building Construction Products Division continues to drive new innovations for this market.

In 1998, the same year that Caterpillar introduced the largest machine it had ever built, it also introduced a line of compact equipment. The market for compact machinery was growing aggressively throughout the 1990s.

Previously, Caterpillar had chosen not to enter the compact market, leaving it to other companies to fill the need.

But the demand for compact products continued to increase at a rate higher than that of traditional construction equipment. Driving this trend: the production shift worldwide to more building construction and urban renovation.

All you expect from Cat…
only smaller

In addition, there is a trend toward rental as a substitute for ownership. The introduction of The Cat Rental Stores coincided with the introduction of the compact machine line.

The Cat compact machine line includes mini hydraulic excavators, compact wheel loaders and skid steer loaders. In addition to the machines, each model features a complete line of work tools for a variety of applications. Skid steer loaders alone have over 30 families of work tools available.

left. **Cat mini hydraulic excavators, like this 301.5 breaking ground for a new driveway, work efficiently in tight spaces.**

right. **Skid steer loaders are one of the fastest growing construction populations.**

This 216, equipped with a pallet fork, keeps brick layers supplied continuously.

far right top. **Compact wheel loaders are designed for power and control. This 902 moves foundation material out of the way.**

far right bottom. **Skid steer loaders are often used in agricultural applications. Here a 216 moves straw into storage.**

Caterpillar.
The name instantly brings to mind
yellow machines at work. Only a few companies
in the world are so closely identified
with the products they manufacture.
The quality, teamwork and value
every Caterpillar product represents
are a great source of pride for our employees,
dealers, suppliers and customers.

Not long after Caterpillar was formed, our engineers began work to develop a diesel engine for use in tractors. The problem was that diesel engines at that time were slow in speed, and they were big and heavy. They were used almost exclusively in stationary and marine applications.

Henry Kaiser, who in World War II became famous for building ships, was pressing Caterpillar to install diesel instead of gasoline engines in tractors. The only U.S. manufacturer of engines of a size suitable to put into tractors was Atlas of Oakland, California. "If you don't put Atlas diesels in your Cat chassis, I will," Kaiser reportedly told Cat President R. C. Force. He did just that. Purchasing two or three Sixties, he removed the gasoline engines and installed Atlas diesels. When the tractors went to work on a Mississippi River levee job, he soon discovered that these bulky engines were too heavy for the tractors and were poorly protected from dirt and dust. After that, several diesel engines, from both inside and outside the U.S., were bought and tested, but none filled the requirements for tractor use.

The tractor diesel had to operate at higher speeds. It posed new fuel and oil filtering problems because of working conditions. It needed stronger, lighter metals with better ability to conduct and resist heat.

The engineers went to work. They designed a four-stroke, water-cooled, pre-combustion chamber engine. We invested more than one million dollars in the project—a tremendous sum in those days. By 1931, the engine—called a D9900—was ready to power the Sixty tractor. Four engines, hand-built, were produced that year.

Power for the world.

The new diesel engine weighed 5,175 pounds (2352 kilograms) and developed 86.8 horsepower at 700 rpm. The first prototype of the D9900 (nicknamed "Old Betsy") today is on display in the Smithsonian Institution's National Museum of American History in Washington, D.C.

Full-scale production started in 1932. We were in the diesel engine business.

In that same year, we began manufacture of our own fuel system to achieve interchangeability of fuel system components. The focus on product support made this achievement an early goal, but the

Editor's note: To convert horsepower to kilowatt (kW), multiply horsepower rating by 0.746

below. **1934. Caterpillar D6600 engine pumping water for irrigation.**

above. **The busiest short line in the world: trains powered by Caterpillar D8800 engines haul concrete at the Grand Coulee Dam.**

left. **1954. D17000 diesel engine powering a cotton gin in Alabama.**

prevailing wisdom was that the extremely tight tolerances necessary were beyond the capability of manufacturing processes. Caterpillar refined the available machining technology of the day to become the first American diesel manufacturer to mass produce its own pre-calibrated fuel injection equipment.

The availability of a lightweight diesel with simplified maintenance requirements prompted a change in stationary power plants. Since many gasoline engines were removed from tractors and put to work pumping water, running a sawmill or generating electricity, it was only natural that the more efficient diesel engine became the preferred power source for these applications too.

In June, 1932, the first Caterpillar diesel for use by another manufacturer was sold to Thew Shovel Co. of Lorain, Ohio. This D9900 powered a 1.5-cubic-yard (1.2 cubic meter) power shovel. Other original equipment manufacturers soon saw the diesel's advantages and adapted it to their applications.

The company's diesel production in 1933 exceeded that of the entire United States in the preceding year. Four new diesels entered the line that year: the D6600, D7700, D8800, and D13000—5.25-inch bore, 8-inch stroke engines. Our 1933 annual report to stockholders stated, " ...considerable progress has been made in selling diesel engines, both as stationary power plants and in the products of other manufacturers."

above and left. **The tugboat CSG-240 carries in its hull a D13000 marine gen set, manufactured in 1937. The D13000 was identified as the oldest working Caterpillar product in Vietnam by the Cat dealer V-TRAC.**

Then, in 1935, the line was extended by the addition of the eight-cylinder D17000. This marked the first Caterpillar engine not offered in our earthmoving equipment; it was designed strictly for industrial and marine applications. It was so successful that it stayed in the line for 20 years. It developed 160 horsepower at 850 rpm from its 1,622 cubic inch (27.2 liter) displacement and weighed 7,600 pounds (3447 kilograms) ...a far cry from today's engines.

The 1935 shareholders' report reflected the rapid growth of models used in diverse applications: "Caterpillar diesel engines are available in five sizes, ranging from 47 to 130 horsepower. They are also used by a number of manufacturers of power shovels, hoists, rock crushers, locomotives, air compressors and other machinery. They are becoming popular as power units for cotton gins, flour mills, ice plants, pumps, standby generators and other uses."

From nine manufacturers offering Cat diesels in 1932, the list rose to 17 in 1933, doubled to 34 in 1934, and went over 100 in 1938.

The industrial diesel revolution was in full swing, with Caterpillar leading the way in the U.S. When the U.S. diesel production reached two million

horsepower in 1937, Caterpillar accounted for one-third of the total.

In 1939, we introduced the first complete generator set with matched engine and generator sold and serviced by a single manufacturer.

Throughout the '30s, there were problems along the way as the engine line grew. One problem was sticky piston rings caused by improper lubrication. We went to work with the major oil companies, beginning a relationship that has lasted up to this day, and solved the problem.

Another problem was parts interchangeability. We developed ways to interchange parts manufactured at any plant, worldwide, and to interchange parts from one engine to another of the same model.

Despite their weight and relatively slow speed, some early Cat engines found their way into trucks. Then, in 1939, we introduced a diesel engine designed specifically for truck use. The six-cylinder D468, rated 90 horsepower at 1,800 rpm, ran all day on $5 worth of fuel. Then, as today, primary benefits of diesel power were less maintenance, longer life and lower fuel consumption compared to gasoline engines. In 1940, our second truck engine, the D312, was introduced. Both truck engines were

top. **Before Cat truck diesels were available, owners mounted standard Cat diesels in their trucks, such as this Mack in the 1930s.**

above. **1939. This truck, used to haul heavy equipment, is powered by a Caterpillar D4600 engine.**

discontinued with the advent of World War II and were not built again.

After the war, we resumed expansion of the engine line. In 1948, the 12-cylinder, 500-horsepower D397 was announced. It was Caterpillar's largest engine at that time, eclipsing the D17000 that by then was rated at 200 horsepower. An eight-cylinder version, the 300-horsepower D375, was developed to fill lower power requirements.

These two engines were the first of that size and horsepower built in quantity on an assembly line, anywhere in the world. The line was located in the first Caterpillar plant designed solely to build diesel engines, Building KK in East Peoria. It opened in 1947.

By 1950, our industrial engines covered a range from 30 horsepower to 520 horsepower.

The 1950s were years of evolution. We created separate lines of marine engines and generator sets, and new attachments were developed. In 1953, a separate engine division replaced the engine sales group that had been established in 1931. Sales increased steadily as more special engine adaptations were offered to meet specific applications.

We first offered a turbocharger in 1955, followed in 1958 with a jacket water aftercooler. Both product innovations allowed the diesel to produce more horsepower while reducing exhaust emissions and noise.

6.25-inch Bore Family Introduced

In 1957, the in-line six-cylinder D353 was introduced, the first of a new 6.25-inch bore, 1,200 rpm family. The V8 D379, second member of the family, was offered in 1961. The V12 D398 was added in 1962, and the V16 D399 in 1967. The latter extended Caterpillar's horsepower offering to 1,425. This family of engines became the number one choice for oil field power and was produced for over 30 years.

We introduced a family of marine transmissions in 1958 to meet industry demand for off-shore supply and crew boats, fishing vessels, river push boats, oceangoing tugs, workboats and utility vessels.

In July, 1959, the industrial engine plant at Mossville, Illinois, started production and added 544,700 square feet (50 603 square meters) to our factory space for engine production.

Truck Engines

In 1959, we again turned our attention to the truck engine business, and, in 1960, we launched the first configuration of the 1673, a highly turbocharged, small-cubic-inch engine. At 220 horsepower it was lighter, smaller and with higher horsepower than most competitors, but not designed to package in a truck chassis. We shipped 49 that year. Twenty-four months after introduction, we had sold a total of 346 truck engines—compared to over 150,000 in 1999!

"Our early education in the truck engine business was not inexpensive. We soon found that the load factor in a truck was far higher than in a tractor.

"One of the most gratifying experiences in my career was being involved in our truck engine partnership with Ford when I was vice president of the engine business. The contract with Ford moved us into a high volume segment of the truck engine business for the first time. It wasn't without risk. Truck engine configurations were totally different from what we were used to. I remember talking to Rex Robinson in the Research Department. He said, 'We can do it.' Our dealers weren't used to this kind of business, and we had to find ways to educate and motivate them. It was a challenge and the outcome, for me, was very fulfilling."

Lee Morgan, chairman 1978-1985

As a result, our early engines tended to suffer mechanical failure rather than wear out. Our concepts in engine design would never again be the same. It was apparent that one model of truck engine was no more competitive than a two-man soccer team. We needed more players. Our next model to enter the lineup was the highly successful 1693, the largest, heaviest, most expensive, most durable truck engine yet seen in North America. Owner-operator Bill Liberty was among the first to be recognized in the press for joining the 'Century Club.' He was ticketed for driving a hundred miles an hour in a fully loaded five-axle combination. The legend was born." Ray Hartwell, Truck Engine Marketing Communications

In 1964, our fifth anniversary in the truck engine business, we sold a total of 2,730 units. In 1999, we shipped that many in five days of production!

A major breakthrough in the business came in the early 1960s when we reached a contractual agreement with Ford Motor Company to become the exclusive source for mid-range engines, thus assuring us a customer base justifying the development and tooling of the 1100 series.

It took the market by storm. Customer acceptance resulted in the sale of 163,000 of these engines in the 1968-1978 time frame. The 1100 series did more to establish our identity as a truck engine manufacturer than any other single factor.

Engines

Engine Expansion

In mid-1969, work started on one of the largest development programs ever undertaken for any product family at Caterpillar—the 3400 family of engines. Four years later—good turnaround time for new product in those days—the world's most modern engine manufacturing factory for that time was added to the Mossville, Illinois, complex to produce the 3400 family. Building BB, with 1.2 million square feet (111 500 square meters), opened in 1973. In 1977, Building DD, at 1.3 million square feet (120 800 square meters), was added to build the 3200 and 3300 families of engines, bringing total Mossville engine manufacturing space to 3.9 million square feet (362 000 square meters).

above left. **1940. A D3400 marine engine powers the *Josie Ortisi*, a 31-foot (9.3-meter) crab, shark and rock cod fishing boat.**

left. **The first people to work in Building BB on the 3406 engine in 1974.**

below left. **The current facility at Mossville, Illinois.**

The 3300 family of heavy-duty engines was introduced in 1973, the same year we began to remanufacture used truck engines on an exchange basis. This made Caterpillar the first U.S. producer of mid-range diesel truck engines to establish its own captive facility devoted exclusively to remanufacturing.

The success of Cat diesels paved the way for expansion in the 1980s. Traditionally, diesel engine manufacturers focused either on large engines (with comparatively small sales volume) or on smaller engines (with large sales volume). We decided to expand the product line in both directions, and launched the most aggressive new engine introduction campaign in our history.

The 3500 family, with engines ranging from 800 to 1,600 horsepower, went into production in 1981. The 3600 family went into production in 1985. These engines dwarfed even the 3500 engines. Ranging from 1,700 to 7,300 horsepower, they represented the largest engines designed in North America since the early '60s, and the largest engines ever produced by Caterpillar.

To build these new large engines, we opened the Lafayette, Indiana, facility in 1982.

Cat offers customers remanufactured engines and engine components through the Cat REMAN program. Engines are remanufactured to like-new specifications at our plant in Corinth, Mississippi.

below. **1999. These Peterbilt trucks are running 3406E truck engines.**

left. **The 1673 truck engine, released for sale in 1959, was a 525-cubic-inch (8.6 liter) engine with 225 horsepower.**

left. **The 1674 in-line, six-cylinder truck engine was introduced in 1967. It was a dual overhead cam, turbocharged and aftercooled at 270 horsepower.**

left. **The 3408 truck engine, from 1975, was a 1099-cubic-inch (18 liter) engine. It was available as a 400 horsepower direct injected or 450 horsepower with a pre-combustion chamber.**

Next we introduced the smallest engines we'd ever made. The four- and six-cylinder 1.1 liter (per cylinder) family was launched in 1987. General Motors selected the 3116 (six-cylinder member of the 1.1 liter family) as the only diesel option in a new line of medium-duty trucks. In October, 1988, the 3176 heavy-duty truck engine was unveiled.

Even as we continued with new product introductions, we refined and upgraded existing engines. A good example is improvements to the 3406 truck engine during the 1980s.

The popularity of the 3406 as a heavy-duty diesel truck engine had grown steadily since its introduction in 1974. The 3406B was introduced in 1983 with changes such as the "new scroll" type fuel system designed to optimize fuel economy.

In 1985, ATAAC (air-to-air after cooling) was introduced for the 3406B. ATAAC improved both economy and power by cooling the air which had been heated in the turbocharging process.

The 3406B PEEC (programmable electronic engine control) engine was unveiled in 1987. The PEEC system represented Caterpillar's first commercial use of sophisticated electronics in diesel operation. Solid-state electronics possessed the required durability and held the potential of pushing diesel engines to new levels of flexibility, economy and performance.

In 1989, the 3406B multi-torque engine was added to the truck engine line. In this case, PEEC electronics allowed engineers to tailor a torque and horsepower curve outside the capabilities of a traditional mechanically controlled diesel engine.

The End of an Era

The 3406 truck engine, first introduced in 1974, became one of the best-selling truck engines in the world with a production run of nearly 575,000 units.

In December, 1999, the last two 3406E truck engines were shipped. One of these two historic engines went to Peterbilt's Denton plant…the other to Peterbilt's Madison plant. Introduced in 1994, the 3406E was the first fully integrated Caterpillar high-horsepower engine.

Expansion into the '90s

New and improved products, joint ventures, acquisitions. By these means, we dramatically expanded engine opportunities throughout the 1990s. A joint venture with C. K. Birla Group in India has been producing engines on the Indian subcontinent since 1989. Named Hindustan Powerplus Limited, the joint venture offers eight models of Caterpillar engines with horsepowers ranging from 200 to 2,500.

In 1981, we acquired the Solar Turbines International Division of International Harvester Company, headquartered in San Diego, California. This gave us the ability to compete for sales in applications best served by turbines rather than diesel engines.

Solar is the world's leading manufacturer of industrial gas turbine engines in its size range. Solar gas turbine engines and turbomachinery systems are used on land and offshore for the production and pipelining of crude oil, petroleum products and natural gas; generating electricity and thermal energy for a wide variety of industrial applications; and for a growing marine propulsion market.

Solar Turbines' products are often used on offshore rigs for the production or pipelining of crude oil, petroleum products and natural gas.

top. **An FG Wilson quality inspector examines this generator before it's shipped.**

above. **MaK Motoren GmbH builds engines as large as 22,000 horsepower.**

In January, 1995, we announced a joint venture with Empresa Nacional Bazan Motores to develop, produce and sell a new higher power, lightweight 3618 engine for use in naval vessels and other fast sea craft.

Later that same year, we announced a planned joint venture with Emerson Electric Company to develop and manufacture diesel generator sets through FG Wilson, an Emerson subsidiary. In 1999, we acquired 100-percent ownership of FG Wilson. In turn, Emerson Electric acquired Kato Engineering, a company that Caterpillar had bought in 1998. FG Wilson is a leading packager of diesel-powered generator sets and is headquartered in Larne, Northern Ireland.

A major acquisition in late 1996 gave us the opportunity to expand into even larger engine sizes. We acquired MaK Maschinenbau GmbH from Fried. Krupp AG of Kiel, Germany. The Krupp's diesel engine subsidiary, renamed MaK Motoren GmbH, had sales of $355 million in 1995 and 1,500 employees.

A joint venture in China in 1997 gave us the means to produce engine-related castings for medium- and heavy-duty diesel engines. This joint venture is with Asian Strategic Investments Corporation and CITIC Machinery Manufacturing, Inc.

Perkins Engines Company Limited, acquired by Caterpillar in 1998, is recognized globally as a world leader in diesel and gas engines. Since the company was established in 1932, more than 15 million Perkins engines have entered service. Ranging from five to 2,600 horsepower, Perkins engines power more than 5,000 different applications from 1,000 equipment manufacturers.

The main plant is in Peterborough, England, with other operations in the U.K. and associated companies around the world.

Natural Gas Engines

In addition to its diesel-powered engines, Caterpillar began building natural gas engines in the late 1940s. Today, the Lafayette Engine Center in Indiana has responsibility for the entire gas engine line. The first 3500 series gas engine was assembled and tested at Lafayette in 1986, and the first 3600 series gas engine was assembled and tested in 1991.

The final assembly and testing of 3300 and 3400 series gas engines began in 1992. Caterpillar has become the world's leading producer of natural gas engines.

Power Systems

In 1987, the Lafayette Engine Center formed a Power Systems group to customize engine systems including generator sets, power modules, petroleum pumping units, well-servicing units, gas engine- and electric-driven chillers, controls and switchgear. In 1999, assembly and testing of these products moved to a new facility in Griffin, Georgia.

New and Improved Products

In 1996, we introduced the Hydraulic Electronic Unit Injector, a first-of-its-kind fuel system that improves engine performance through a new means of fuel injection. Powered by engine oil rather than diesel fuel, the injector burns less fuel, lowers gaseous and "white smoke" emissions and greatly enhances "startability"—the injector can start an engine at 20 degrees Fahrenheit (-7 degrees Celsius) in less than one second.

The C-16 engine.

Fleet Engines Put Technology to Work

The C-15 and C-16 heavy-duty truck engines, introduced in November, 1999, are built on the successful design platform of the 3406E. Along with the C-10, introduced in 1995, and the C-12 of 1996, these low-weight engines deliver high horsepower for fleet operations.

Our mid-range offering, the 3126B, features a hydraulically actuated, electronically controlled unit injector fuel system and is best suited for medium-duty truck fleet and bus owners.

right. **This gen set powers drying systems inside a Midwestern U.S. grain elevator.**

below. **Hoffer Plastics Corporation, South Elgin, Illinois, uses eight G3516 gaseous fuel engine/generator sets, a high-tech computer system and utility-grade switchgear to cut its yearly electricity bills in half.**

Cat Engines

Engines

Dealer Support

By the end of the century, more than 2,800 truck engine parts and service outlets (called TEPS dealers) provided nearby service for the growing truck engine population. Our rapid growth would not have been possible without these additional parts and service locations. In addition, a growing number of Caterpillar dealers have established separate engine centers and separate businesses to handle the growing engine volume.

We enter the new century with a full line of engines from five horsepower to over 22,000 horsepower. We provide power for medium- and heavy-duty on-highway trucks, electrical power generation, marine propulsion and auxiliaries, construction and mining and agricultural equipment, petroleum drilling and pumping, stationary and mobile industrial applications, locomotives and more.

above. **Five Cat 3608 engines drive the auxiliary ship-board electrical power on U.S. Navy ships which distribute supplies during battle. The engines had to pass rigorous shock tests to prove their reliability under battle conditions.**

right. **Employees (left to right) Nate Austin, Elaine Latia, Joseph Lim, Tracie Flagg and Gary Jones from Lafayette Engine Center, Indiana, in front of a 3500 engine.**

In marine engines alone, we offer 20 propulsion systems in 216 different ratings and 15 generator sets in a total of 70 different ratings. Twelve years ago, Caterpillar produced one basic engine for marine pleasure craft. Today, there are 10 models.

right. **In 1994, Cat Rental Power was contracted for all the temporary power supplied to the Olympic Games in Lillehammer because the Olympic Committee had deemed it "the most reliable rental power equipment and service in the world."**

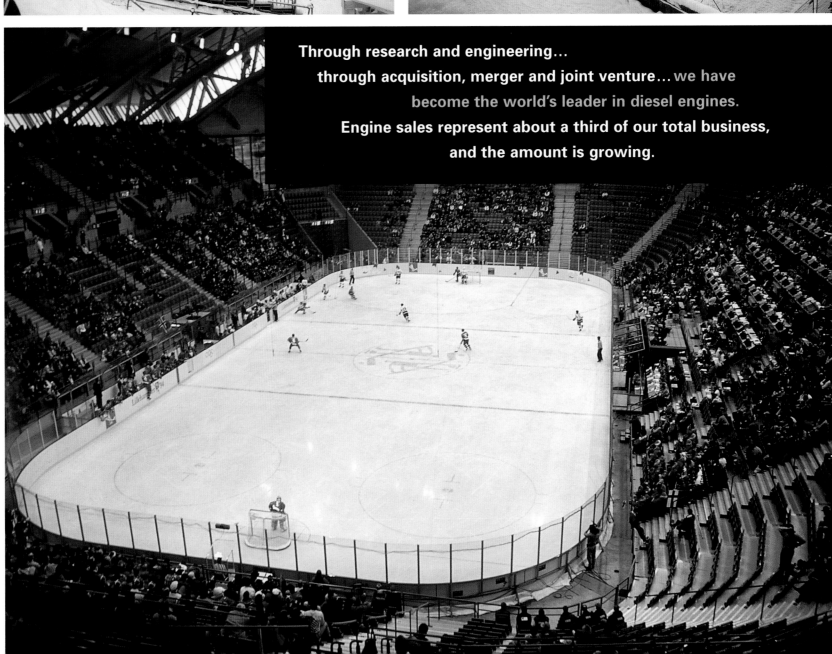

Through research and engineering…
through acquisition, merger and joint venture… we have become the world's leader in diesel engines.
Engine sales represent about a third of our total business, and the amount is growing.

Financial Products

Yeng Tong Construction Pte., Ltd., works primarily on marine construction projects throughout Singapore and southeast Asia. The company decided in 1997 to make the switch to Caterpillar equipment and Cat dealer Tractors Singapore Limited. Financing was their only obstacle. They didn't want to commit too many of Yeng Tong Construction's cash resources to equipment—but they also didn't want to pay the high interest rates charged by local financing companies. With the help of Cat Financial, the company acquired 14 Cat 330B Excavators, two Cat 966F Wheel Loaders and a Cat 345B Excavator.

With the new fleet, Yeng Tong Construction is landing construction projects throughout Asia. Currently, they are working on the biggest project yet—building sea walls to help add to the size of the island of Singapore.

left. **Using several excavators, Yeng Tong Construction builds sea walls to help expand the island of Singapore.**

below. **Goh Hoon Leong (right) and Goh Hong Soon (in left photo, on the left) have been partners in Yeng Tong Construction Pte., Ltd., of Singapore since 1984.**

Caterpillar Financial Services, Inc.

Helping
customers succeed

åIn 1981, Caterpillar formed a small subsidiary to lease Caterpillar lift trucks. Just two years later, the renamed Caterpillar Financial Services Corporation expanded its focus to offer a wide range of financing alternatives for the entire product line. In the past decade, Caterpillar Financial has expanded across the globe to better serve Cat customers worldwide. By 1999, it was financing over half of the Caterpillar machines delivered worldwide.

The Financial Products Division includes over 40 subsidiaries, mostly involved in financing or leasing Cat products. It also includes Caterpillar Insurance Services Corporation, which offers extended warranty, physical damage and transit coverage to Cat subsidiaries, dealers and customers. Established in 1983, the company was providing insurance coverage to more than 70,000 machines and 28,000 engines by 1998.

right. **Cat Financial and CGT, the Cat dealer in Milan, Italy, helped Dr. Lucchetti buy a Cat 988F II Wheel Loader to work in the Carrara quarries.**

Caterpillar Power Ventures Corporation supports the corporate growth objective in power generation through developing, owning and operating electrical power generation projects powered by Caterpillar engines or turbines.

Caterpillar Redistribution Services, Inc., (CRSI) has the goal of strengthening the dealer organization by enhancing the availability of late-model/low-hour Cat products to dealers either for direct purchase from CRSI or for purchase from other dealers.

For more than five generations, Dr. Erich Franco Lucchetti's family has worked in the Carrara quarries, extracting some of the world's most recognized marble.

Guglielmo Vennai S.p.A. was formed in 1924 and is one of the largest companies working in the Carrara quarries. Dr. Lucchetti, managing director, owns several Cat wheel loaders and excavators, which he uses to load and haul blocks of marble. When he decided to purchase a Cat 988F II, he turned to his Cat dealer and Cat Financial. They put together a package with the best interest rate and fast approvals—all from a single source.

The new Cat wheel loader will be moving some of the largest blocks of marble in the world.

right. **Marble from this quarry was used in two of Michelangelo's most famous works—the *Pietà* in the Vatican and *David* in Florence, Italy. Today, this quarry's marble adorns the faces of buildings along Fifth Avenue, New York City and Michigan Avenue, Chicago, Illinois.**

By contracting with Cat Logistics, companies gain excellent distribution while minimizing their investment in systems, facilities and personnel.

Logistics

Caterpillar Logistics Services, Inc.

Helping companies grow

The early 1980s was a time of corporate self-evaluation and review. We wanted to find new ways to use our strengths to open new avenues of growth.

As a result of that process, Caterpillar Logistics Services, Inc., was founded in 1987. This wholly owned subsidiary was formed to share Caterpillar's worldwide distribution expertise with other companies. Cat Logistics provides customized solutions that help companies transform distribution from a cost of doing business to a competitive advantage. Cat Logistics manages client transportation, inventories, information systems and distribution centers. It also provides forecasting, information management and networking services.

Cat Logistics began with six employees and one client. Today, it delivers services to dozens of companies and employs more than 3,400 people worldwide. Cat Logistics has achieved double-digit sales growth in each year of its existence, and plans are in place to continue growing at that pace.

Cat Logistics has 44 distribution centers around the world and a total of 6.9 million square feet (641 010 square meters) of warehouse space. Commercial offices for Cat Logistics are located in the United States, Belgium, Britain, Singapore and Germany.

The total value of products shipped by Cat Logistics annually exceeds $8 billion.

Cat Logistics received Sun Microsystems' Supplier Performance Award three years in a row.

Cat workwear and footwear on display at a trade show in Germany.

Scale models, like this one of a Cat 5130 Front Shovel, are available for many current and historical machines.

In-store display at Irish Menswear, Leicester, England.

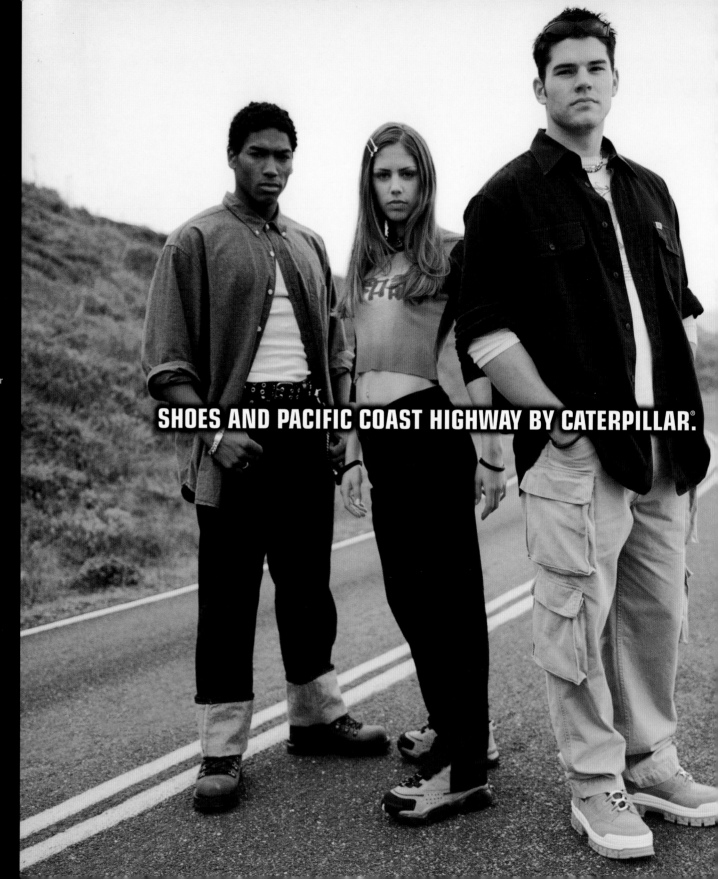

SHOES AND PACIFIC COAST HIGHWAY BY CATERPILLAR.®

Photo from the year 2000 advertising campaign for Cat footwear.

Trademark Merchandise Licensing

Even in the company's earliest years, we put the name Caterpillar on various specialty items and company handouts. It wasn't until the late 1980s and early 1990s, however, that we started seriously working with licensees to enhance the company's image through consumer-oriented branded products. By tying the licensed merchandise to our core products, Caterpillar has built a strong image of the Caterpillar brand as a lifestyle.

Sales of Caterpillar-branded merchandise, including footwear, apparel, watches, scale models and toys, are now in excess of $900 million. Recognition of this presence was reflected when *License Magazine* listed Caterpillar as number three in corporate licensing sales after Coca-Cola and Harley Davidson.

"You must have a strong brand to be successful in licensing, and what you do in licensing must enhance brand equity. We want, in particular, to increase awareness of Caterpillar and what it stands for among the youth. They'll be our future machinery and engine customers, employees and stockholders."

Lois Boaz, manager of Corporate Brand Equity

CATERPILLAR®

By listening to customers, applying technologies and focusing on quality, we've built one of the world's strongest brand names.

Building roads and dams, levees and airports…working farmlands and orchards, stretching pipelines across continents …generating power for trucks, locomotives, ships or entire villages.

The work we do at Caterpillar is about progress, and progress is what our products do to make people's lives better.

It's delivering back-up power to a hospital in Chile.

It's plowing fields in Nebraska or mining ore in Ghana.

It's building better housing in Poland. It's digging a deeper well in Australia.

At Caterpillar, it's all in a day's work.

Chapter 3

Making progress

possible

Cat 777 Mining Trucks
waiting to begin work
on the Three Gorges Dam
in China.
Dealer: The China Engineers, Ltd.,
Construction Equipment Division

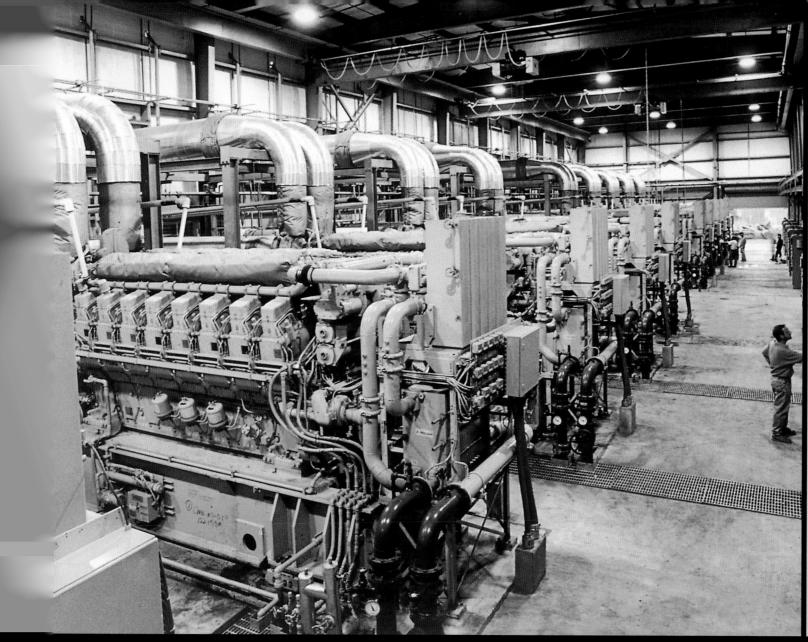

left. **1997. Cat gen sets at the Esquintla steel mill in Guatemala not only power the mill, but also put additional energy back into the country's power grid.**
Dealer: Corporacion General de Tractores, S.A.

below left. **Challenger tractors, specially equipped for the extreme temperatures, pull sleds across Antarctica.**
Dealer: William Adams Tractors Pty., Limited, Australia

left. **M318 Wheeled Excavator preparing area on the edge of a village near Ahlfeld, Germany, for building construction.**
Dealer: Zeppelin Baumaschinen GmbH

left. **In midtown Manhattan, New York, this Lorain 57 Shovel, powered by a Cat D11000 diesel engine, works on the approach to the Queens/Midtown Tunnel in 1938.**
Dealer: H.O. Penn Machinery Company, Inc.

1949. A Caterpillar D4600 engine powers a Bucyrus Erie crane to build a sea wall in Rio de Janeiro, Brazil.
Dealer: Sotreq S.A., Brazil

left. **1997. Cat tractors and excavators move the 70-year-old, 2,700-ton Gem Theatre building 1,850 feet (564.3 meters) to preserve its historic value for Detroit, Michigan.**
Dealer: Michigan CAT

world trade center

above. **Logging in the northwestern United States.**

left. **When construction began on New York City's 110-story World Trade Center in 1966, a wide range of Cat equipment helped excavate 16 acres of earth and rock. Material was hauled to the Hudson River where it was used to create 23 acres of new land.**
Dealer: H.O. Penn Machinery Company, Inc.

left. **Nearly a hundred pieces of Cat equipment constructed a 69-kilometer (42.8-mile) section of Highway 407, a toll road just north of Toronto, Ontario, Canada.**
Dealer: Toromont

Miloslav Ptácek (second from left), owner of Ptácek Construction, Prague, Czech Republic, talks with his Cat dealer about his new Cat excavator, shown at work in Prague.
Dealer: Phoenix-Zeppelin S.S.R.O.

left. **Stockpiling salt for road maintenance in Illinois.**

far left. **1966. A woman looks across the Sahara desert of Mauritania in Africa to the arrival of a Caterpillar machine—part of a $66-million-dollar project to mine and haul iron ore from Fort Gouraud to Port Etienne.**
Dealer: J. A. Delmas Export

top. **A No. 12 Motor Grader working on the Santa Ana Parkway project in Los Angeles, California.**
Dealer: Shepherd Machinery Co.

above. **1987. A Cat 627E Auger Scraper at work reclaiming mined sand dunes near Richards Bay, South Africa.**
Dealer: Barlows Equipment Co.

below. **A 110,000-seat stadium at Homebush Bay, Australia, is the focal point of the 2000 Summer Olympic Games in Sydney. More than 35 Cat machines completed over 500 000 cubic meters (650,000 cubic yards) of cut and fill work for the foundation of the structure.**
Dealer: Gough & Gilmour Holdings Pty., Ltd.

left and right.
594H Pipelayers building a pipeline in Tamaulipas, Mexico, were just a fraction of the equipment working to develop Mexico's petroleum industry in the late 1970s.

below. **Gas line development in Minnesota.**
Dealer: Ziegler Inc.

left. **Caterpillar equipment not only works to mine coal and ore, but also works to reclaim the land—such as this golf course over a strip mine in West Virginia.**
Dealer: Cecil I. Walker Machinery Co.

below. **1930s. Snapshots from a land-clearing demonstration in East Peoria, Illinois.**

left. **1938. The Seventy-Five Tractor with a LeTourneau rooter (later called a ripper) ripped up hard material so it could be dozed or loaded.**

below. **The Nicewonder Group mine in Virginia started working with Caterpillar Financial Services in 1987. By 1997, when this photo was taken, the company owned 125 Cat machines.**

above. **1930. Caterpillar Fifteen with the two-row "New Idea" corn picker harvesting corn in Bourbonnais, Illinois.**

right. **1990s. D11N.**

From 1969 to 1971, a fleet of Caterpillar equipment worked on construction of the Dallas-Fort Worth International Airport in Irving, Texas.
Dealer: Darr Equipment Company

right. **California housing development.**
Dealer: Hawthorne Machinery Co.

left. **Bound for an oil rig in the Gulf of Mexico, this 490-ton Solar turbine is being loaded onto an ocean-going barge at the Solar TurboFab facility in Houston, Texas.**

below. **Caterpillar equipment dominates this construction site in central England where a new three-lane highway was completed in 1999.**
Dealer: Finning (U.K.) Limited

left. **1942. D7 Tractor clears the streets of London after an air raid.**

above. **1938. Powered by D13000 engines, these two cranes are backfilling sewer trenches for the New York World's Fair in 1939. In the background are the Perisphere and the Trylon, famous trademarks of the fair.**
Dealer: H.O. Penn Machinery Company, Inc.

right. **1932. In a letter to Caterpillar, Mr. Elmer Haag, Oswego, Illinois, wrote that he used his Caterpillar Fifteen "52 weeks a year, and seldom hitches up the team anymore."**

below. **The Raúl Leoni Dam in Guri, Bolívar, Venezuela, set the world record at the time for earthmoving. On November 11, 1982, 540 Cat machines moved** over 162 000 cubic meters (210,600 cubic yards) of earth. The dam was completed in 1984.
Dealer: Maquinarias Venequip S.A.

left. **Two 773D Off-Highway Trucks, a 990 Series II Wheel Loader and a D9R Tractor were delivered to the Sonichar Mining Company in Niger, West Africa, in February, 1999.**
Dealer: Manutention Africaine Niger

below. **Logging in southeastern U.S.**

below. **1941. Drilling for oil in Santa Fe Springs, California, this Wilson rig, powered by a Cat Diesel D17000, was in operation 24 hours a day.**

alaskan pipeline

right. **In 1993, Russia bought more than 300 Cat track-type tractors—the first group of which shipped from the Port of Milwaukee.**

below. **In 1997, Caterpillar dealer Zahid Tractor & Heavy Machinery Company, Ltd., sold 99 Cat backhoe loaders, 22 excavators and 10 wheel loaders to the Nesma Group for laying fiber optic cables in Saudi Arabia's largest cities.**

below. **1931. Using a Killefer disk attachment, this Fifteen works a California orange grove after irrigation.** Dealer: Shepherd Machinery Company

left. **Officially released in 1951, the DW21 was the company's first two-wheel tractor-pulled scraper and was often used in road construction.**

above. **1947. The *M.V. Irene W*, powered by a Cat D13000, hauls a load of fresh salmon off the shores of Vancouver, British Columbia, Canada.**
Dealer: Finning Power Systems

right. **The backhoe loader is a common sight on construction projects around the world—like this school addition in North Carolina.**

below. **1999. Scenes from the Mongol Gazar gold mine in central Mongolia. 769D Trucks haul more than payload; they also haul lumber for new mining camps.**
Dealer: Wagner Asia Equipment

left. **1997. The Dalaman Akköprü Dam project in southwestern Turkey will provide hydroelectric generation, irrigation and flood control for the region.**
Dealer: Borusan Makina Servis ve Ticaret A.S.

above. **Before wheel loaders and off-highway trucks became popular, shovels and tractor-pulled wagons were often used in load-and-haul applications.**

below. **In 1946, this No. 12 Motor Grader maintains roads on a banana plantation in the Dominican Republic.** Dealer: Implementos y Maquinarias C. por A.

right. **1934. Clearing an area in Deer Creek Meadows National Park in California, this Seventy-Five featured a LeTourneau Angledozer attachment.**

above. **An early model No. 12 Motor Grader spreads gravel on a new road near the Pacific Ocean.** Dealer: Peterson Tractor Co.

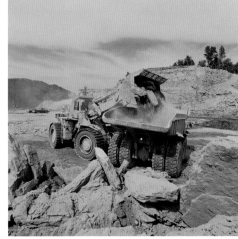

right. **1980s. Wheel loader with Beadless Tire in rock work.**

right. **1949. A D8 is preparing the surface for more track in a copper mine in Antofagasta, Chile.** Current dealer: Finning Chile S.A.A.

black & white photos courtesy of U.S. Bureau of Reclamation

left. **Hoover Dam, on the Colorado River in Nevada, was the highest dam in the world when it was built in the 1930s. Lake Mead behind it has a shoreline of over 822 miles (1323 kilometers) when full.**
Dealer: Cashman Equipment Company

far left top. **Many Cat machines worked to build the dam. This is a view of the down-stream end during foundation excavation in April, 1933.**

above. **An early 944 Wheel Loader works at Cape Canaveral, Florida, in August, 1960.**
Dealer: Ringhaver Equipment Co.

right. **From clearing and excavation, to sewer and water and site finishing, there are Cat machines involved in all phases of housing construction.**

above. **1990. Cat equipment builds part of a new highway system in Kuala Lumpur, Malaysia.** Dealer: Tractors Malaysia (1982) Snd. Bhd.

right. **Brazilian iron mine, 1970s.**

left. **1985.
A D9L
compacts a
coal pile at
a strip mine
in southern
Illinois.**
Dealer: John
Fabick Tractor
Company

We work with a common purpose—
to encourage progress,
to improve quality of life,
and to make a positive difference
in our world.

The Joliet, Illinois, plant opened in 1951. It was a milestone in our post World War II expansion. The new plant would help avoid overconcentration at East Peoria. Alongside the line of tools and attachments made at Joliet in the 1950s is Plant Manager Bill Naumann, later Caterpillar chairman.

The story of manufacturing & facilities

Where and How

We've come a long way. From three manufacturing locations in 1925 to 88 in 2000. From sweat-of-the-brow manual labor to high-tech, computerized processes.

The original three locations were San Leandro and Stockton, California, and Peoria, Illinois. After the Stockton plant closed in the 1930s, we operated in only two locations until the 1950s.

But by the end of the century, there were 41 manufacturing facilities in the United States and 47 outside the country, plus remanufacturing plants, marketing headquarters, Cat Financial locations, Caterpillar Logistics operations, parts distribution centers, training centers, technical centers and proving grounds.

Chapter
75 74

1990s: Final assembly
at a Shin Caterpillar
Mitsubishi plant in Japan.

From design to finished product

Changes in manufacturing have been just as dramatic as the growth in facilities. The drawing board has gone the way of the slide rule. The traditional design, build, test and rework approach is obsolete and has been replaced by a paperless, seamless, computerized process.

New programs have cut time for some projects from 36 months to two months and have reduced the chance of error. Mathematical functions such as simulation and analysis are easier and more efficient. Computerized motion studies make it possible to understand how a component will perform before it's actually built.

When we first started building Caterpillar products, draftsmen would create a line drawing of the product. They would then build a test model to make sure the design was correct. Often, after testing, the draftsmen would have to go back to the drawing board. Models were built, tested, redesigned, rebuilt, retested over and over until the product met Caterpillar's standards. Needless to say, the work was tedious, slow and costly.

But now, computer-aided design has dramatically reduced the time it takes to create a new product. By "building" the project in a virtual environment, engineers can test components before building prototypes to reveal any design flaws.

In addition, the design is instantly available to all other engineers. Changes made to one component or part design are quickly reflected throughout the entire system. Then, when a prototype is made, there is a much greater chance of success the first time.

The 1944 tool design room in the East Peoria plant.

Today, no models have to be designed or built by hand. They can be created electronically in three dimensions by computer.

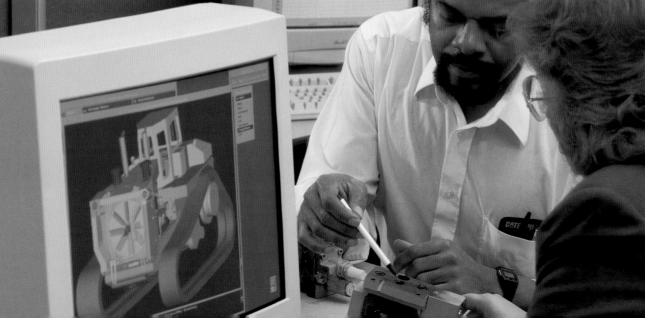

In the 1920s, making components was a laborious, time-consuming function.

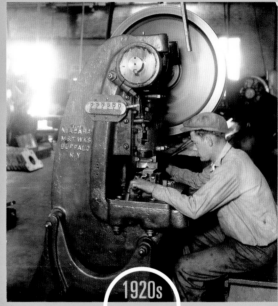

1920s

1990s

In the 1990s and into 2000, computer-controlled manufacturing systems mean high productivity with minimum effort. This planet-gear, flexible-manufacturing system operates in the Transmission Business Unit in East Peoria, Illinois.

The East Peoria, Illinois, plant expanded in 1947 when a new diesel engine factory, known as Building KK, opened. Today, it's the home of the Transmission Business Unit.

top left. **First overseas Caterpillar subsidiary in Newcastle, England.**

center left. **Gosselies facility in Belgium.**

bottom left. **The sprawling East Peoria plant in 1930.**

U.S.-based, global reach

By 1930, the East Peoria, Illinois, plant had become one of America's major industrial complexes with more than 25 acres of manufacturing space under roof. But after World War II, capacity couldn't keep up with demand. New Building KK (925,000 square feet) (85 932 square meters) was opened in 1947 to manufacture diesel engines and Building LL (850,000 square feet) (78 965 square meters) was added to the complex in 1949. By 1950, East Peoria facilities had more than six million square feet (557 400 square meters) under roof. Still, more capacity was needed.

The company foresaw major logistical problems caused by overconcentration in one location. The decision was made to expand beyond the Peoria area, and that led to the creation of the Joliet, Illinois, plant in 1951. That same year, we started a manufacturing facility in Great Britain—moving outside the U.S. borders for the first time.

Sales potential in the United Kingdom and its Commonwealth trading partners was enormous. But

there was a shortage of U.S. dollars to pay for Cat products. In addition, import restrictions required that certain parts be manufactured locally.

We formed our first overseas subsidiary, Caterpillar Tractor Co. Ltd., to produce parts that could be paid for in British pounds. In 1951, the new subsidiary moved into facilities that had been built in 1881 as railroad car shops. About 125 people were employed at first. It was the beginning of our expansion around the globe. Within a decade, subsidiaries were formed in Brazil, Australia, France, Canada and Switzerland. In addition, new plants were built in Decatur, Aurora and Mossville, Illinois, and Glasgow, Scotland. And a new Technical Center opened in Mossville, Illinois. It was a period of dramatic growth.

Today, 75 percent of our products are made in the U.S., while 50 percent of our sales are outside. That makes us one of the major positive contributors to the U.S. balance of trade. We're U.S.-based with a global reach.

Brazil in the early 1950s had a rapidly growing economy. However, shortages of U.S. dollars and fierce parts competition made it difficult for Cat dealers. So, in response, a Brazilian subsidiary, Cat Brasil, was formed in October, 1954, to procure and sell parts. Restrictions required that Cat Brasil also manufacture selected machines to ensure continued imports of U.S.-built Caterpillar products.

"All five of our families lived in the Hotel Jaraguá awaiting clearance of our household goods. Many of our initial employees were interviewed in our hotel rooms. I remember answering the phone one evening and the caller saying, 'Is standing here Geraldo Farias Rodrigues applying for job with Caterpillar.' Geraldo was hired and four years later became the parts manager. He replaced me when I returned to the U.S.

additional items to Caterpillar specifications. By the end of the year, we were providing our Brazilian dealers with many parts which previously had to be imported."

Paulus Gerardus Dona, Piracicaba plant industrial director (retired 1990), added:

"The first facility of 10 000 square meters (108,000 square feet) built one kind of motor grader, two kinds of cable-operated scrapers, and parts—mainly undercarriage parts. The first No. 12E Motor Grader was shipped in October, 1960.

"In the early 1970s, we started looking for land to build another facility outside the city of São Paulo. There was no room for expansion to build bigger products in São Paulo. After a wide search, we settled on the Piracicaba site. By May, 1976, the Piracicaba plant shipped its first product, a 769 Off-Highway Truck. Later, a nine-month study with a consultant indicated one plant would be more efficient, and, by 1993, all production was centered in Piracicaba. In the process, I spent 600,000 kilometers (372,000 miles) in four company cars between the two plants."

The story of a subsidiary:
Caterpillar Brasil Ltda.

In 1955, the subsidiary began construction of a new factory in São Paulo. Bill Oedewaldt, first parts manager of the facility, provided this report:

"In early January of 1955, the five of us (Bob Loskill, managing director; Jack Smith, chief engineer; Ed Sluetz, purchasing manager; Bill Van Order, treasurer; and I) set up shop in three small, sparsely furnished offices in the financial district of São Paulo. Our managing director, Bob Loskill, commented that we were starting at 'scratch minus 10,' the 10 being the language barrier.

"Our first warehouse facility and offices were in the District of Lapa, in the city of São Paulo. Phone service was not available at the beginning. When we needed to make phone calls, locally or to the U.S., we had to wait in line at a nearby grocery store to use their phone.

"By mid-1955, we had several locally produced items for sale. Our first item was the 9F6700P oil filter. This was a memorable time for all of us. Working with local companies, our purchasing and engineering personnel developed sources to produce

131

left. **Building D fabrication area in Piracicaba, 1999.**

below. **Current view of Piracicaba facility.**

above. **The painting area in the Piracicaba facility, 1999.**

left. **1955. Bob Loskill, first managing director, had no telephone when the Brazilian operation began. He had to stand in line at a nearby grocery store. Here he waits at the end of the line.**

Cat Brasil Today

Today, Cat Brasil Ltda. has a diversified product line, producing 21 models of six product families that are exported to more than 120 countries. In 1994, Cat Brasil was certified by ISO 9002 and in April, 1999, it received the certificate MRPII Class A (Manufacturing Resource Planning)—both awards for quality achievement. In October, 1999, Cat Brasil received word that it had earned the National Prize of Quality, equivalent to the Malcolm Baldrige National Quality Award in the U.S.

Subsidiary Expansion

By the end of 1999, Caterpillar had almost 400 subsidiaries, affiliates and joint ventures, many the result of acquisitions. Some are very small, like a single building making work tools in the Netherlands, and some are very large, like Caterpillar of Australia Ltd., Caterpillar Mexico, S.A. de C.V., Shin Caterpillar Mitsubishi Ltd., Perkins Engines Company Ltd., Solar Turbines Incorporated and MaK Motoren GmbH & Co. KG. The company has grown into an enormously complex entity with a true global presence.

Factory Modernization Program

In 1987, we set in motion a $1.8 billion plant modernization program to speed production and lower costs. The program was completed in 1993. We called it the "Plant with a Future" program, which was symbolic of the importance of this major effort to the company's future.

This program has rearranged equipment into production cells, linked by automated material handling. The cells are set up to process families of similar parts from start to

above left. **Motor grader assembly line at Decatur, Illinois, facility prior to "Plant with a Future" program.**

above right. **Decatur assembly line after the modernization program. An automated guided vehicle (far right photo) moves the product down an assembly highway. The plant is organized so that various products can move on the assembly highway in random order.**

Plant with a Future

finish, in any order and in any quantity needed by the assembly line. Work is now in a continuous flow. Material handling is automated and computer-controlled. "Just-in-time" inventory control is standard. Suppliers deliver material just in time, at the point of use, dramatically reducing work-in-process inventory.

Factories operate with integrated information systems. Computers communicate with each other from the top level (plant host computer) to the lowest level—controlling machine, rotor or material-handling equipment—using common language. This enables us to coordinate movement of material or tooling and to activate machines and equipment as needed and in harmony.

The investment is paying huge dividends for the company. In-process inventories have been cut by 60 percent, and manufacturing process time has been reduced to six days from 25 days. The return on investment is more than 20 percent.

Computers have taken testing to amazing levels. On the left, hundreds of sensors record drive train data. On the right, robotic laser welding proves an efficient manufacturing technique.

Testing and monitoring of components and their performance are the cornerstone of Cat durability. Before computerization, all testing was conducted and recorded manually.

Technical Center and Proving Grounds

In 1957, many of the company's research, development and test activities were consolidated into a new facility north of Peoria. The first building to be completed was the Engine Lab, and the last of six major buildings was opened in 1971. In total, the facility covers 204 acres with 19 acres under roof.

Patent for real-time monitoring of multiple machines on a work site.

To provide additional testing facilities, the Arizona Proving Ground opened in 1945, followed by the Peoria Proving Ground in 1947. The Arizona Proving Ground moved from Phoenix to Tucson in 1989. The high temperatures and rock composition are ideal for testing large mining machines.

These facilities, plus an operation in Leicester, England, are part of the Technical Services Division. About 2,000 engineers, scientists and technical support personnel make sure that Caterpillar continues to offer innovative and technologically advanced equipment. These employees generate more than 200 patents each year.

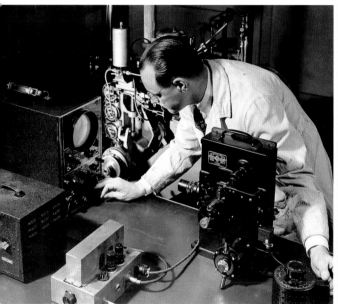

To deliver the most reliable components, we test them under a variety of conditions.

above. **Electrical relays are actuated and monitored.**

below. **Components are subjected to extreme temperatures.**

The Arizona Proving Ground actively tests many types of equipment, but focuses primarily on mining and aggregates machines.

top, left and right. **Production tests that simulate working conditions. The trucks are 797s—our largest mining truck.**

bottom. **Testing of scrapers about 1950.**

Focused Facilities

The '90s have seen a new kind of manufacturing facility emerge at Caterpillar. We call them "focused facilities"—small plants that concentrate on a single product or component. The Morganton, North Carolina, facility is a good example. Opened in 1998, it employs 120 people who produce engine components: oil coolers, piston pins and burner tubes. These facilities supplement and support our larger manufacturing and assembly factories.

Heat treatment area in the Morganton, North Carolina, facility.

We've found that people in these smaller, modern, clean facilities quickly develop a "passion for quality," a term frequently heard around Caterpillar. Former Chairman Louis Neumiller said in 1951, "Let's not get lost in our bigness. Let's retain the advantages of a small company—the congeniality, the flexibility, the respect for people." The focused facilities help us do just that.

Global network

Corporate Headquarters
Peoria, Illinois

Marketing Headquarters

INSIDE THE UNITED STATES
San Diego, California
Miami, Florida
Mossville, Illinois
Peoria, Illinois
Cary, North Carolina

OUTSIDE THE UNITED STATES
Melbourne, Australia
Gosselies, Belgium
Piracicaba, Brazil
Peterborough, England
Kiel, Germany
Hong Kong
Tokyo, Japan[1]
Singapore
Geneva, Switzerland

Financial Products Locations

HEADQUARTERS
Nashville, Tennessee

INSIDE THE UNITED STATES
Phoenix, Arizona
Atlanta, Georgia
Chicago, Illinois
Baltimore, Maryland
Las Vegas, Nevada
Dallas, Texas

OUTSIDE THE UNITED STATES
Melbourne, Australia
São Paulo, Brazil
Calgary, Canada
Toronto, Canada
Santiago, Chile
Prague, Czech Republic
Copenhagen, Denmark
London, England
Paris, France
Munich, Germany
Dublin, Ireland
Milan, Italy
Seoul, South Korea
Kuala Lumpur, Malaysia
Mexico City, Mexico
Manila, Philippines

Warsaw, Poland
Lisbon, Portugal
Singapore
Madrid, Spain
Stockholm, Sweden
Bangkok, Thailand

Manufacturing Locations

INSIDE THE UNITED STATES
Gardena, California
San Diego, California
Jacksonville, Florida
Griffin, Georgia
Jefferson, Georgia
LaGrange, Georgia
Thomasville, Georgia
Aurora, Illinois
Champaign, Illinois[1]
Decatur, Illinois
DeKalb, Illinois
Dixon, Illinois
East Peoria, Illinois
Joliet, Illinois
Mapleton, Illinois
Mossville, Illinois
Peoria, Illinois
Pontiac, Illinois
Sterling, Illinois
Lafayette, Indiana
Emporia, Kansas
Wamego, Kansas
Danville, Kentucky
Menominee, Michigan
Minneapolis, Minnesota
New Ulm, Minnesota
Oxford, Mississippi
Boonville, Missouri
West Plains, Missouri
Omaha, Nebraska
Clayton, North Carolina
Franklin, North Carolina
Leland, North Carolina
Morganton, North Carolina
Sanford, North Carolina
Marion, Ohio
Greenville, South Carolina
Sumter, South Carolina
Dyersburg, Tennessee
Rockwood, Tennessee
Houston, Texas

OUTSIDE THE UNITED STATES
Burnie, Australia[1]
Melbourne, Australia
Perth, Australia
Gosselies, Belgium
Piracicaba, Brazil
Montreal, Canada
Leicester, England
Peterborough, England
Peterlee, England
Shrewsbury, England
Skinningrove, England
Slough, England[2]
Stafford, England
Stockton, England
Wolverhampton, England
Arras, France
Grenoble, France
Rantigny, France
Kiel, Germany

Wackersdorf, Germany
Zweibrücken, Germany
Gödölö, Hungary[2]
Bangalore, India[1]
Mumbai, India[1]
Jakarta, Indonesia[2]
Anagni, Italy[1]
Bazzano, Italy
Frosinone, Italy[1]
Jesi, Italy
Milan, Italy[1]
Akashi, Japan[1]
Sagamihara, Japan[1]
Monterrey, Mexico
Saltillo, Mexico
Tijuana, Mexico
Torreon, Mexico
's - Hertogenbosch, The
　Netherlands

Belfast, Northern Ireland[1]
Larne, Northern Ireland[1]
Erliban, People's Republic
　of China[1]
Shunde, People's Republic
　of China[1]
Tianjin, People's Republic
　of China[2]
Xuzhou, People's Republic
　of China[2]
Janow Lubelski, Poland[2]
St. Petersburg, Russia
Johannesburg, South Africa
Söderhamn, Sweden

**Remanufacturing
and Overhaul
Facilities: Caterpillar**

INSIDE THE UNITED STATES
Corinth, Mississippi

Prentiss County, Mississippi
De Soto, Texas
Mabank, Texas

OUTSIDE THE UNITED STATES
Melbourne, Australia
Gosselies, Belgium
Edmonton, Canada
Bandung, Indonesia
Dublin, Ireland
Kuala Lumpur, Malaysia
Nuevo Laredo, Mexico
Tijuana, Mexico
Veracruz, Mexico
Port Harcourt, Nigeria

**Remanufacturing and
Overhaul Facility: Solar**

OUTSIDE THE UNITED STATES
Villa Hermosa, Mexico

**Parts and Service
Support Center**
　Morton, Illinois

**Parts Distribution
Centers: Caterpillar**

INSIDE THE UNITED STATES
Hayward, California
Los Angeles, California
Denver, Colorado
Miami, Florida
Atlanta, Georgia
Morton, Illinois
Indianapolis, Indiana
St. Paul, Minnesota
Kansas City, Missouri
York, Pennsylvania
Memphis, Tennessee
Dallas, Texas
Spokane, Washington

OUTSIDE THE UNITED STATES
Melbourne, Australia
Grimbergen, Belgium
Piracicaba, Brazil
Toronto, Canada
Sagamihara, Japan[1]
Monterrey, Mexico
Beijing, People's Republic of China
Moscow, Russia
Singapore
Johannesburg, South Africa

**Parts Distribution
Centers: Solar**

INSIDE THE UNITED STATES
New Orleans, Louisiana
Dallas, Texas

OUTSIDE THE UNITED STATES
Melbourne, Australia
Gosselies, Belgium
Edmonton, Canada
Singapore

**Parts Distribution
Center: Perkins**

OUTSIDE THE UNITED STATES
Manchester, England

**Cat Logistics
Distribution Centers**

INSIDE THE UNITED STATES
Hayward, California
Los Angeles, California
Union City, California
Atlanta, Georgia
Champaign, Illinois[1]
Joliet, Illinois
Morton, Illinois
Mossville, Illinois
Greenfield, Indiana
Indianapolis, Indiana
Lafayette, Indiana
Plainfield, Indiana
Omaha, Nebraska
Reno, Nevada
Columbus, Ohio
Sharonville, Ohio
Allentown, Pennsylvania
York, Pennsylvania
Nashville, Tennessee
Edgerton, Wisconsin

OUTSIDE THE UNITED STATES
Buenos Aires, Argentina
Melbourne, Australia
Bornem, Belgium
Gosselies, Belgium
Lummen, Belgium
Puurs, Belgium
Nova Odessa, Brazil
Piracicaba, Brazil
Guelph, Canada
Saskatoon, Canada
Toronto, Canada
Fradley, England
Hemel Hempstead, England
Leicester, England
Manchester, England
Metz, France
Bologna, Italy
Sagamihara, Japan[1]
Seoul, South Korea
Almere, The Netherlands
Singapore
Guadalajara, Spain
Huddinge, Sweden
Taipei, Taiwan

**Training Centers and
Demonstration Areas**

INSIDE THE UNITED STATES
Opelika, Alabama
Tucson, Arizona
San Diego, California
Miami, Florida
East Peoria, Illinois
Edwards, Illinois
Clayton, North Carolina

OUTSIDE THE UNITED STATES
Melbourne, Australia
Piracicaba, Brazil
Chichibu, Japan[1]
Sagamihara, Japan[1]
Erliban, People's Republic
　of China[1]
Kunshan, People's Republic
　of China
Singapore
Málaga, Spain

Technical Center
　Mossville, Illinois

Proving Grounds

INSIDE THE UNITED STATES
Tucson, Arizona
Peoria, Illinois

OUTSIDE THE UNITED STATES
Ono, Japan[1]

This list current as of
November 15, 1999.

[1] Facilities of affiliated companies
　(50%-or-less owned)

[2] Partially owned subsidiaries (more
　than 50%, less than 100%)

Steel, bearings, paper clips, tires, hydraulics, computers ... and thousands more. Our 1999 purchases from suppliers amounted to more than $12 billion.

All the suppliers in this chapter are certified suppliers, meaning they have met stringent and exacting requirements following continuous improvement plans over a period of time.

Working Together

Chapter 5

We shop for value.

Value, we believe, results from relationships with suppliers who understand our *passion for quality* and who can help us meet our customers' needs for long-lasting, hard-working products. Suppliers make proprietary products to our specifications because we insist that *all* Caterpillar products be "Caterpillar to the core."

The Certified Supplier Program began in 1978 with three suppliers. Today, there are more than 1,100 worldwide and they account for 80 percent of our purchases. We wish we could tell you about all our quality suppliers, but that would be a monumental task. The few examples in this chapter will have to suffice.

right. **We are one of the world's largest users of steel. Some oldtimers at Cat even refer to the company as "steel cutters." In 1999, we bought more than two billion pounds of steel from steelmakers around the world, in addition to the gray iron from our own foundries.**

left. **Each certified supplier receives a plaque that must be re-earned each year.**

CATERPILLAR
CERTIFIED SUPPLIER
KOMET OF AMERICA, INC.
Schaumburg, Illinois
is recognized as a
supplier of quality material
CUTTING TOOLS

The Story of Caterpillar and Suppliers

left. **Molds ready for pouring.**

right. **Tapping the furnace for 25 tons of steel.**

below right. **Red hot casting of an axle spindle for an off-highway truck comes out of the heat treat oven ready to be quenched.**

below center. **D8R Tractor frames with steel cast final drive cases await the assembly line in East Peoria.**

below far right. **The cast steel front suspension strut is installed on an off-highway truck at Decatur, Illinois, facility.**

far right. **Track roller frames which use several steel castings line up to wait for their tractors.**

Harrison Steel Castings Company

Located in the small town of Attica, Indiana, Harrison Steel Castings Company is a family-owned business that started supplying The Holt Manufacturing Company in 1914. Today, the third generation of the Harrison family manages the business, which has grown to 700 employees.

Harrison Steel Castings supplies Cat with a variety of steel and ductile iron castings ranging from small adapters to large spindle axles for the largest off-highway trucks. Easily recognizable items are the cast steel final drive cases or track roller frames for the D7 and larger tractors, or the tilt linkages and cross tubes on the lift arms of medium-size wheel loaders.

Caterpillar consumes almost all of Harrison Steel's production. As Scot Swift, sales manager, explains, "As Caterpillar goes, so goes Harrison Steel."

The relationship between Caterpillar and Harrison Steel has changed dramatically over the years, driven by new product introduction schedules and the Concurrent Process and Product Development Program. Explains Tim Hays, superintendent of Casting Engineering at Harrison, "Ten years ago we would get a blueprint after a part was designed, figure out if we could make it and what changes to request. Sending prints back and forth and producing sample castings to get a production pattern could take months. Now we work with Caterpillar as the product is being designed. Prints are shared electronically, and it is not unusual to have a production casting after the first sample."

Modine
Manufacturing Co.

Located in Racine, Wisconsin, Modine was founded in 1916. Modine became a supplier to Holt's Peoria plant in 1917. The Modine "SPIREX" core radiator was developed by founder A. B. Modine as a rugged, heavy-duty radiator for non-automotive use. It was the best available for Holt's track-type tractors because it could handle the heat generated in slow-speed, off-highway applications, and it would stay together despite the vibration.

When Holt began supplying track-type tractors to the U.S. Army in World War I, Modine SPIREX radiators were specified for both the 2-ton and 5-ton models. Modine has been working with Caterpillar from its very beginnings, developing heat exchange products.

"The most significant factors about our relationship with Caterpillar are the spirit of partnering we enjoy and the early involvement in new product development," says Ron Lodes, spokesman for Modine.

Today Modine supplies radiators, oil coolers, aftercoolers and air conditioning condensers for many earthmoving and engine products.

right. **Heat exchange module being assembled for a Caterpillar earthmoving product includes the radiator, shroud, aftercooler and oil cooler all packaged into one module for easy installation into the machine. Modules are rubber mounted in the machine for vibration protection.**

bottom left. **Advanced Modular Cooling System being assembled for a D8R Tractor by Ben Tanner in Caterpillar's Building SS in East Peoria, Illinois. AMOCS was a significant cooling system design improvement for high capacity cooling and durability.**

bottom right. **Radiator core sections being assembled for an 800-horsepower Caterpillar power generation set.**

TC Industries

The TC stands for Terra Cotta. The company started in 1870 as a manufacturer of terra cotta drain tile and brick. But in 1941, the company's kilns were taken over to heat-treat metal for war supplies.

At the end of World War II, George Berry was able to buy the newly installed heat-treat equipment and start commercial heat treating of metals.

TC did its first job for Caterpillar in 1948 with the heat treat of cutting edges and end bits for dozer blades.

Today, from factories in the U.S., Canada and Britain, TC Industries supplies Caterpillar with more than 3,000 part numbers of cutting edges, wear plates, end bits, bucket edges and track shoes.

As supplier of a very competitive product, TC Industries has been able to find cost-cutting solutions and deliver high quality heat treated products. Innovations such as DH-2 and DH-3 edges have improved value to the end user.

TC Industries participates in the program of direct shipment to Caterpillar dealers in North America to reduce transport costs and rehandling of the heavy steel edges.

Said George Berry IV, president and third generation in the family-owned business, "Supplying Caterpillar has been a challenge of continued improvement in quality, delivery and pricing. Trust, communication and openness have been the key to the relationship over the years."

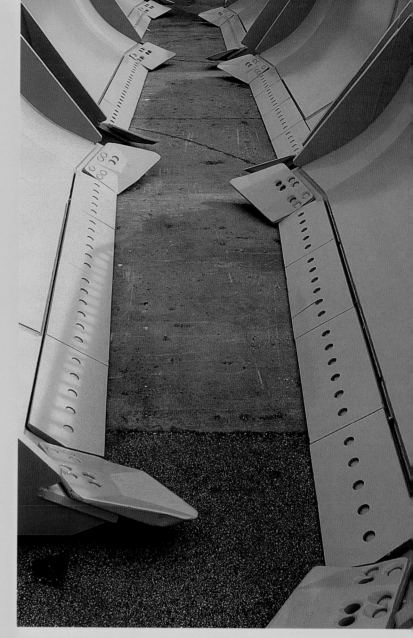

Michelin

In the 1960s, when Caterpillar introduced the 600 family wheel tractor scrapers, it became apparent that tire technology was limiting the ability to build bigger machines. Existing tires could not carry the weight with any speed.

Then the Michelin radial steel-belted tire became available in sizes to fit Caterpillar machines. The radial tire could carry heavier loads faster than bias tires and last longer.

In a 1970 field report, Bill Miles, Caterpillar sales representative for Spain and Portugal, wrote, "Twenty-eight 769 trucks running at Rio Tinto mine in southern Spain were getting only 2,400 hours on bias ply tires. After converting to Michelin radials, they got over 4,000 hours per tire."

As Caterpillar's rubber-tired product line grew in size and models, Michelin's tire development kept pace to provide the tires of all sizes Caterpillar needed for its expanding product lines. These included new design tires for the largest off-highway trucks as well as tires for small compact products.

Michelin's development of the 55/80R63 tire made possible our development of the 797 mining truck.

Right. **Caterpillar's largest truck, the 797, was developed in cooperation with Michelin's development of the tire for it. François Michelin made an early commitment to develop radial tires to fit Caterpillar machines. Now retired, here he is shown (third from right in gray sweater) in 1999 at the Arizona Proving Ground with the Michelin earthmover tire management team led by President René Fontes (fourth from left).**

bottom right. **The 55/80R63 tire for the 797 truck is tested at Michelin's proving ground in Almería, Spain. A 793 truck was modified to test the new larger tire on the rear axle.**

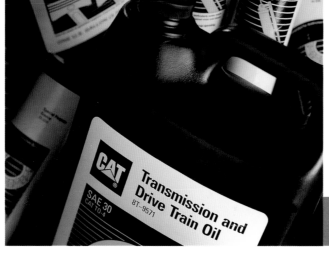

ExxonMobil

ExxonMobil Corporation

Since the development of the first diesel engine in 1931, Caterpillar has been involved in the research and development of improved fuels and lubricants. Products such as Series II oil and CH-4 oil were results of this work.

But, in many places in the world, customers did not have access to superior lubricants.

In 1987, Caterpillar signed an agreement with Mobil Oil Corporation for Mobil to blend and distribute worldwide a range of Caterpillar-branded lubricants so that customers would have access to superior lubricants for their machines and engines.

ExxonMobil blends the lubricants to our specifications at 32 locations throughout the world and uses its distribution system to deliver Caterpillar lubricants to dealers and customers in 72 countries.

Over the years, cooperation between Mobil and Caterpillar has brought major improvement in transmission oils that give longer life to gears and bearings. Today that research is focused on developing improved oils for low-emission hydraulic systems and higher horsepower engines.

above. **Lubricating oils are available in various grades to fit the machine or engine operating environment. They are packaged in several size containers including bulk quantities.**

right. **Special trucks equipped for preventive maintenance service deliver Caterpillar lubricants directly to customers' machines in the field.**

Keen
Transport Co.

above. **A Keen Transport truck loaded with five of Caterpillar's new skid steer loaders leaves the Sanford, North Carolina, plant headed for a dealer.**

above right. **A Keen-developed I-beam trailer carries a complete D9R Tractor with a total load height of only 13 1/2 feet (4 meters).**

OVER SIZE LOAD

Keen Transport Co's. association with Caterpillar started in the 1950s as a hauler of machines from Caterpillar factories to dealers in the Northeast U.S. Soon, more and more dealers started using Keen to transport their machines.

When the Aurora, Illinois, plant introduced the 992 Wheel Loader in 1969, Harold Keen developed an I-beam detachable gooseneck trailer for transporting the big wheel loader. This trailer allowed the wheels to be mounted and the machine driven off at the delivery site without using cranes. Today, Keen operates more than 85 I-beam trailers, nearly half of this type operating in North America. They are used extensively for hauling large Caterpillar machines.

In 1972, Keen opened a yard next to the Aurora facility to handle outbound truck shipments. Today, Keen handles all truck and rail loadings from Aurora. Similar operations were added at Morton and Decatur, Illinois; Clayton, North Carolina; and more recently at LaGrange, Georgia; DeKalb, Illinois; and

Waco, Texas, to consolidate shipments and store machines and engines for dealers.

Facilities have been built at Baltimore, Maryland; Savannah, Georgia; Miami, Florida; Houston, Texas; and Los Angeles, California, to receive products shipped into the United States from overseas factories. Storage, assembly and distribution to North American dealers are managed from these centers.

Most recently, Keen became the outbound transportation supplier for the skid steer loader factory in Sanford, North Carolina. To economize, skid steer loaders are shipped to dealers in truckload lots of five or six loaders per truck.

above. **Track-type tractors unload at port of Málaga, Spain, for Caterpillar demonstration area. AEI-LustCom arranges shipments of U.S.-sourced products to destinations throughout the world.**

below. **A 992D Wheel Loader weighing 70 tons is off-loaded by ship's crane directly onto a waiting trailer. Advance organization by AEI-LuskCom ensures fast off loading with no heavy lift cranes needed.**

AEI-LuskCom

below. **Emergency parts orders are loaded at Morton Parts Distribution Center for AEI to ship out of Chicago's O'Hare Airport.**

In 1925, the Holt brothers traveled to New Orleans and made arrangements with P. Brad Lusk to handle ocean traffic and customs clearance for the export of Caterpillar products. That relationship established 75 years ago continues today.

In 1957, Caterpillar signed on with an emerging air freight forwarder, AEI, to handle all of Caterpillar's worldwide air shipments, which, at that time, were mostly the shipment of emergency parts orders. Since then, the export and import business has grown tremendously.

In 1996, AEI and Lusk merged their operations to handle all of Caterpillar's overseas transportation and customs activities. Combined, they have established systems that have become the standard for international trade.

In 1969, Caterpillar was the model Lusk used for establishing with the U.S. government the use of automated tapes to file export declarations.

The next year, Caterpillar was also the model for a system called Luskcom® which electronically tracked the flow of material orders. It was an early example of electronic commerce.

LeRoi Somer

1939 Century develops its
first alternator.

1955 Caterpillar becomes customer.

1972 SR4 brushless alternator introduced.

1975 Century bought by Gould Inc.

1976 20-year product development agreement
signed with Caterpillar.

1980 First 1000-kilowatt alternator built.

1982 First form wound alternator.

1986 First solid state automatic
voltage regulator.

1995 SR-4B alternator introduced with digital
voltage regulator. MagneTek Inc. acquires
Gould. First alternator shipped to
FG Wilson for Olympia line of gen sets.

1998 Emerson Electric Co. buys MagneTek
alternator business. LeRoi Somer becomes
power alternator division.

1999 Caterpillar and Emerson jointly buy
FG Wilson and Kato. Caterpillar gets
FG Wilson and LeRoi Somer gets Kato.

1999 New agreement signed for future
product development.

In 1955, Century Electric Co. started supplying Caterpillar with alternators for assembly into power generation sets. The management and the factory have stayed the same, but, today, Century Electric has become part of LeRoi Somer, the power generation division of Emerson Electric Co.

LeRoi Somer supplies Caterpillar with alternators. These range in capacity from 65 kilowatts to 5,000 kilowatts for diesel and gas engine gen sets. For gas turbine applications, units up to 18 megawatts are built. More than 250,000 alternators have gone into Caterpillar gen sets during the past 44 years.

The years between have seen many milestones of cooperation to develop the Caterpillar family of power generation products.

below left. **Caterpillar 3516 power generator set with Kato alternator.**

below. **Stator for a large alternator is assembled at LeRoi Somer's Lexington, Tennessee, plant.**

below left. **An assortment of the many fasteners manufactured by Fontana.**

left. **Loris Fontana. In 1996, Fontana was awarded Engine Division's Annual Quality Improvement award for the development of improved cylinder head bolts for on-highway truck engines.**

far left. **Bolts being installed on track-type tractor.**

Fontana Luigi S.p.A.

Headquartered in northern Italy, Fontana Luigi S.p.A. is a manufacturer of bolts, nuts and many types of fasteners. Fontana became a Caterpillar supplier in 1963 when the Grenoble, France, facility opened.

Guided by owner Loris Fontana, the company became the first supplier in Europe and the sixth worldwide to achieve

"Caterpillar Certified Supplier" status. 1999 marked 20 years as a certified supplier. In 1996, Fontana was awarded Engine Division's Annual Quality Improvement award for the development of improved cylinder head bolts for on-highway truck engines.

The C-12 engine in the Caterpillar European Racing Truck with its very high horsepower uses a special cylinder head bolt supplied by Fontana.

Today, Fontana manufactures many of the bolts and fasteners that hold Caterpillar machines and engines together. Its products are shipped to Caterpillar plants throughout the world.

The quality of the bolt has come to symbolize the quality that goes into Caterpillar products.

Over the years, Fontana has participated with Caterpillar to develop new boron steels for use in bolts and other fasteners. Individual products have been designed for critical applications. And, working together, we and Fontana have developed a better network of distribution for just-in-time delivery to Caterpillar plants.

left. **Wiring harnesses are hand built using a harness board to ensure correct make-up. Each complicated harness has its own board.**

American Cable

American Cable Company was founded in 1976 in Philadelphia, Pennsylvania, by Carlos Gonzalez, Sr., to manufacture heavy-duty and customized battery cable assemblies. Gonzalez had emigrated to the United States in 1967 from his native Cuba.

American Cable grew, and in 1989 began supplying Caterpillar with replacement battery cables for parts service. Today, American Cable supplies battery cables to Caterpillar factories and parts operations throughout the world, producing more than 1,500 part numbers of battery cables.

In 1998, the company expanded its product line and began to supply Caterpillar with wiring harnesses for various products. Over 400 different wiring harnesses are now in production.

Said Carlos Gonzalez, Jr., company president: "Our success in modernizing our manufacturing and operating systems and to integrate our production schedules electronically with our customers is largely attributed to Caterpillar's help and coaching. This has enabled us to be recognized for the consistent quality of our product and provide just-in-time delivery at competitive prices."

right. **Diesel engine starter motors require heavy-duty battery cables to carry the high current loads. This worker at East Penn uses battery cable color-coding to ensure proper hookup.**

EAST PENN

East Penn Manufacturing became the supplier for Caterpillar branded batteries in 1985. Branded batteries include premium high output batteries needed by earthmoving machines and diesel engines, and also a line of general service batteries.

Caterpillar and East Penn have a joint product development program which has been very successful in producing new lines of flat top maintenance-free batteries and on-highway BCI Group 31 batteries. Premium high-output batteries have been developed to fit new Caterpillar compact construction equipment.

Caterpillar batteries are manufactured to special design standards. East Penn earned its first Certified Supplier Award in 1987, and has repeated that performance every year since.

Caterpillar batteries for replacement service are shipped directly from East Penn to North American Caterpillar dealers, and used batteries are returned for safe recycling.

above. **Battery manufactured on automated production line shows Cat Racing logo on new maintenance-free battery for on-highway truck service.**

left. **Batteries are packed in pallet load quantities for shipment to Caterpillar plants and dealers.**

below. **Caterpillar branded batteries for heavy-duty service supplied by East Penn Manufacturing.**

The Timken Company

below far right. **A large tapered roller bearing is fitted to the final drive for the 793 Off-Highway Truck at Decatur.**

below right. **In 1991, Timken Chairman Tim Timken (standing on tractor) uses a D6H Tractor to break ground for a new plant in** Asheboro, North Carolina, **built to manufacture a new line of Spexx™ bearings for industrial uses such as those in Caterpillar products.**

right. **Timken bearings installed on pinion gears stand ready to be fitted into Caterpillar powershift transmissions.**

Henry Timken founded the Timken Company in 1899 to produce his patented tapered roller bearings.

The use of Timken bearings in what would become Caterpillar products predates 1925, and the tapered roller bearings supplied by Timken have been essential to virtually all Caterpillar products. A good example is the planetary power shift transmission which has been the heart of the power train on many Caterpillar machines. It was made possible by the load-carrying capability of the Timken bearings in it.

Today, Caterpillar buys over 18 million anti-friction bearings annually, and Caterpillar is Timken's largest industrial customer. Joint efforts between the companies include sharing technology for manufacturing processes such as heat treating and grinding to allow each to build better products.

Since 1995, Timken bearings made to Caterpillar's design specifications are branded with Caterpillar's part number and trademark and supplied only to Caterpillar for assembly into products and distribution through the parts distribution system.

In the early '80s, Timken built a new steel mill to ensure the high-quality seamless tube and bar stock needed for their bearings. This high-quality steel permits the increase of "power density," which is the ability to carry more load in a given space with improved reliability and longer life. Caterpillar has become a major customer of Timken steel for uses such as track bushings, hydraulic cylinders and rods, gears, axle shafts and track rollers.

Said Robert Leibensperger, president and chief operating officer of Timken: "I paid my way through college by working on road construction. One of the biggest thrills I had was being told to operate a D8. Now as we begin the 21st century, the strategic partnership that has built up between Timken and Caterpillar, both in the technical and commercial sides of our business, is flourishing. We have become strategic partners to jointly develop new technology to reduce total cost for Caterpillar's customers."

Inventory Management

Caterpillar and suppliers have developed a number of innovative inventory management systems to improve service and reduce inventory costs.

ZWIP

ZWIP or Zero Warehouse Inventory Program is a just-in-time program that leaves inventory in the supplier's warehouse until needed. 50,000 items are supplied by 70 suppliers under this system.

Inbound Logistics Center

An Inbound Logistics Center was established in central Illinois to consolidate the reception and inventory of fastener commodities. The center is managed by Caterpillar Logistics Services.

Direct Distribution to Dealers

Some high-volume items such as filters, ground engaging tools and lubricants are shipped directly from suppliers to dealers to reduce freight and inventory costs.

Managing Steel Inventories

Global purchasing makes us more competitive, but it also makes inventory management more difficult… so we've developed more sophisticated forecasting, consignment programs and a variety of just-in-time delivery systems.

Letter from a Caterpillar retiree

One day my boss Bill Weber handed me a floor layout and said, "We're going to make oil coolers in this area." We had only a short time to get ready, and ran into a problem with leaking copper tubing. The day was saved when a copper tubing salesman visited the plant. He knew and understood the Caterpillar need and he also knew his company's capabilities for quality and meeting delivery dates. In less than a week, the new copper tubing was delivered and it was of fine, first-class quality.

Over six years, the copper tubing account grew to over a million dollars a year, or, in physical terms, over 4,000 miles of 3/16" copper tubing.

With the help of Caterpillar people and the supplier's input, I wrote the 1E specifications for oil cooler copper tubing for the corporation.

I was part of the team and proud of it.

John H. Shue

Chapter
75 6

Chapter 6

The Front Line

right. **Customers at The Cat Rental Store in Blanchard Machinery's territory inspect Cat compact machines. These units and other Cat products combine with work tools and allied equipment to make The Cat Rental Store a one-stop shop in Columbia, South Carolina.**

"Make Your Dealers Your Partner" is the title of an article by retired Chairman Don Fites in *Harvard Business Review.* Here's an excerpt:

"After a product leaves our door, the dealers take over. They are the ones on the front line. They're the ones the customers see. They're out there making sure that when a machine is delivered, it's in the condition it's supposed to be in. Although we offer financing and insurance, they arrange those deals for the customers.

"They're out there training a customer's operators. They service a product frequently throughout its life, carefully monitoring a machine's health and scheduling repairs to prevent costly downtime.

"These independent dealers have made huge investments in parts inventories, warehouses, fleets of trucks, service bays, diagnostic and service equipment, sophisticated information technology, and highly trained people. Indeed, our dealers, whose investments in their individual businesses range from $10 million to more than $100 million, collectively surpass our might. Their combined net worth is about five billion dollars, or about one and one-half times Caterpillar's stockholders' equity. They collectively employ almost 75,000 people, more than Caterpillar employs. And while their average revenues are about $150 million, several dealers have annual revenues in the neighborhood of one billion dollars."

March 1996

Every Caterpillar dealer has a story.

Many are stories of early 20th-century entrepreneurs, people with vision and energy who built successful businesses from the ground up. Others are stories of multi-generational dealerships, about grandchildren and great-grandchildren who have carried on family businesses and traditions over the years. Some are stories of new dealers in emerging economies where the expertise of Cat dealers is vital to economic growth.

We can't tell all dealer stories in this volume, so we've chosen a few representative ones, beginning with the story of the Yancey brothers. And we've included excerpts from a talk given by Harry Holt at a Worldwide Caterpillar Dealer Meeting in 1990. He was a grand-nephew of Benjamin Holt and co-founded—with his brother Parker— a Caterpillar dealership in Stockton, California.

Yancey Bros. Co.

Salesmanship and a Single Photograph

Here's the story from Yancey Bros. Co., Caterpillar dealer in Georgia:

"In 1914, brothers Goodloe H. and B. Earle Yancey ran Yancey Hardware Company, selling hardware, picks, shovels, and prison uniforms to government agencies—especially county prisons—for road construction. In 1918, Goodloe heard of a tractor by Holt that could do the work of '40 mules, or 40 horses and countless humans.' He and his brother traveled to Peoria to learn more about the machine. Shortly thereafter, they asked the manufacturer if they could represent the Holt line in the Southeastern United States. The reception from Holt was less than warm. They were told that there was no way that the machines could be sold for road building. They also said the machines had to be sold direct, and that a distributor set-up would be a flop. Besides, the Holt factories were tied up producing machines for the U.S. Army.

Goodloe H. Yancey, Jr., and B. Earle Yancey, co-founders of Yancey Bros. Co.

"Goodloe and Earle left Peoria after a week with only a photograph of the Holt 45 tractor and a price quote of $4,750, C.O.D., per machine.

"It wasn't long before Troup County earned the distinction of being the first buyers of a Caterpillar tractor in the Southeastern U.S. Mr. Goodloe (as he was fondly called) traveled to LaGrange to personally drive the tractor off the railroad flatcar, and people came from miles around to see this new machine work.

"Within 12 months the Yanceys had sold all the 45s Holt had in inventory, using only their salesmanship and a single photograph. When Mr. Goodloe and Earle returned to the Holt factory the following year, they were hailed as conquerors, and the first jobbers contract ever given by Holt was awarded to them. Although their original agreement had been for only a five-percent commission, the Holt officials gave them a contract with a higher commission and made the deal retroactive to their first sale. Mr. Goodloe recounted the $19,000 commission years later: 'I hadn't known there was that much money in the world.'"

left. **First Yancey facility from 1924 to 1951.**

left. **In October, 1999, Yancey opened its newest branch in Austell, Georgia. Customers toured the facility, including the showroom, parts counter and equipment rental areas.**

above. **Children of employees and customers also participated in the open house.**

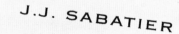

J.J. SABATIER

EXPORT DISTRICT REPRESENTATIVE
CATERPILLAR TRACTOR CO.
SAN LEANDRO, CALIFORNIA
PEORIA, ILLINOIS

Bergerat Monnoyeur Travaux Publics

Starting with a Business Card

You would be hard-pressed to find a "typical" Cat dealer. They are all different operations. They even started in different ways. This is the story of the beginning of Bergerat Monnoyeur, in France.

The year was 1929. It had been a hot summer night in Paris. Henry Bergerat had not slept well. Francis Monnoyeur, his partner, had just come in from Madrid where he was trying to sell products to the national railroad.

"Well, Henry, we've got a problem," he said. "We lost the deal. A bunch of cowboys came up with a funny-looking machine and strange name: 'Caterpillar.' The machine creeps on its own tracks."

"Now, Francis, are you serious? Yesterday a guy named Sabatier visited the office, looking for a French dealer," responded Bergerat. "He was sent by this Caterpillar company you're talking about, apparently just formed in Peoria, along the Illinois River, somewhere in the middle of the continent.

The guy was nice, but I said, 'No, thanks, we already have serious accounts, like Ruston Bucyrus for instance.' "

Francis turned pale. "Look, Henry, I think we should have another talk with him. These machines look pretty good and they seem to sell. Where is he?"

"I think I threw his card away in the waste basket," said Henry.

He quickly searched his waste basket and retrieved Sabatier's business card. They grabbed their coats and bowler hats, and drove through town in search of Sabatier. When they were able to finally track him down, it was the start of a 70-year relationship with Caterpillar.

Today, Bergerat Monnoyeur is the Cat dealer not only for France, but also for Algeria, Romania, Moldova, Poland and part of Russia. Annual sales have passed $900 million with 3,150 employees.

above. **Headquarters of Bergerat Monnoyeur Travaux Publics, Saint-Denis, France, 1999.**

left. **Francis Monnoyeur (far left, without a hat) shows Cat products to government officials, including French President Albert Lebrun (right center), at an equipment show in 1938.**

Harry Holt: **Customers First**

Harry D. Holt was a Caterpillar dealer for 50 years. In September, 1990, he spoke at a Worldwide Dealer Meeting in Peoria. Following are excerpts from his remarks:

One thing I don't need to tell you is the pride, excitement and challenge one finds in running a Caterpillar dealership. The ability to be involved in all aspects of the business, to watch your best people sell and service the best equipment, and to have second and third generations of families you originally sold to still looking to you as their supplier is an unprecedented joy.

The roots of the company you represent are deep and well documented. It goes back, as you know, to the Holt and Best manufacturing companies, both builders of large traction steam engines. In the early 1900s, the Holt Company bought the Best Company and Best left the business for a time. By 1905, Holt traction engines were using Benjamin Holt's development of an endless chain with board planks fastened to it. While these were designed for California farming, the Holt Company's international roots, from which today Caterpillar harvests half of its sales, were quick in coming.

My father, C. Parker Holt, was a vice president of The Holt Manufacturing Co. He thought that the Holt 75 Tractor would be ideal for use in Argentina, principally because Argentina had the same soil and climate conditions in South America that California had in North America. Still, my father could not convince his board of directors of that. He was so convinced otherwise that he disassembled the Holt 75 on his own ranch and sailed to Buenos Aires with my mother and my two-year-old brother, Parker. He spent three months demonstrating the tractor and at the end of that time, he appointed a dealer, Casteron Hermanos, and returned to the United States with a standing order for 20 tractors a month. He immediately transferred that order to The Holt Caterpillar Co. in Peoria.

That was in 1910. Now, two years later, let me take you to Europe—to the Hungarian town of Perdoc on the 15,000-acre farm of Dr. Leo Steiner. While at the library one day, Dr. Steiner, an engineer by education, saw an American farm journal opened to a page with an article describing The Holt Manufacturing Company's #75 Tractor. He telegraphed for more details and later wired an order for a Holt 75 to be delivered to his farm. The new tractor did everything he had hoped it would, and he negotiated a contract to represent the company in Austria, Hungary and Germany. He soon ordered 40 more tractors and two years later, he had sold 60 machines and had orders for 100 more.

It was, in fact, Dr. Steiner who provided one of the more colorful descriptions of our equipment at work. (His narrative which I'll share with you may also be the first recorded interaction between a dealer and a factory representative. I'll let you decide if factory people have changed.)

In 1912, the Austro-Hungarian war department was looking for a machine to pull its famous Skoda giant cannon used so successfully in World War I. The army set up a field trial in which it deliberately mired one of those cannons in a swamp and then had competing machines try to extricate it. A truck with a winch and cable tried, but the cable started to pull the truck into the swamp. When they chained the truck to an oak tree, the engine stalled. Next, a Fowler steam engine from England tried, and after no success, it too was tied to the oak tree. In short time, the tree was pulled out from its roots. Finally, it was the Holt 75's turn. Accompanying the machine was an always smiling, chain-smoking engineer from Peoria by the name of Hanson. It could be successfully argued from Dr. Steiner's portrayals that Hanson was the original Alexander Botts. I quote Dr. Steiner's description of what followed:

"As it was now his turn, Hanson went with confidence back to the road. He went smiling to the gun, coupled it on its lowest reachable and the narrowest possible point to the tractor, lighted a cigarette, gave full gas, let the motor race and threw the clutch in with an abrupt jerk. I stood nearby. I heard a shot-like crack, saw the tractor rear up almost vertically, saw it almost turn a somersault, but in the next moment saw it fall down in its horizontal position, at the same time lifting the gun's wheels out of their cavity in the ground and then saw it steadily drawn along the marsh behind the cozily traveling tractor driven by the smoking and smiling Hanson. It was an exciting picture, the like I never saw before. The enthusiasm of the high military committee was beyond description; the members waved their caps and the minister of war and the chief of the department hastened to Hanson and me congratulating us on this unique performance and spectacle."

Dr. Steiner concluded his story by writing that "Shortly after this most significant event, Hanson left for the U.S., not without taking along with him one of my typists as his wife."

Every dealer could use a man like Hanson. It is from these roots the Caterpillar dealer organization you represent today was born.

Soon, however, World War I intervened and, quickly, the entire production of the Holt Company was going to the governments of Russia, France and Britain and, finally, the U.S. War Department. Approximately 10,000 Model 75s were delivered to the allied governments.

During this time, Clarence Leo Best had started the C. L. Best Tractor Co., selling its famous model 30 and 60 Tractors through a small dealer network in the western United States.

In due course, the two firms merged to create Caterpillar Tractor Co. Leo Best became chairman and an outside man, Raymond Force, was named president.

As an aside here, and soon after I became a Caterpillar dealer, it was Mr. Force who provided me with an important insight into this first great president of Caterpillar. My mother and I visited him at his California ranch and found him shoveling manure in his horse paddock. I was shocked and surprised and told him that I never expected to see the president of Caterpillar doing that sort of work. He looked at me and in that deep voice of his and with almost a reprimanding tone said: "Harry, I do some of my best thinking for Caterpillar while I'm doing this." Now I'm not suggesting that all of you run out and start shoveling more manure than you

already are, but I never forgot that. And in later years, I thought of my own business problems while I raked manure in my own horse paddocks.

Anyhow, this new company, Caterpillar, was ready to begin business, but it lacked the distribution network so necessary for success. My father by this time was head of the export department for Caterpillar and made numerous trips overseas to set up a dealer network in Europe, South America and Africa. As a young boy, I can remember many long trips, one lasting nine months, during which my father sought new dealers and gave help and advice to those dealers already established.

He also did some direct sales work and I remember one instance when he told me of a sale to the Russian government he closed at the Waldorf Astoria Hotel in New York. It was a $5,590,000 order for 1,300 Model 60 Caterpillar tractors. This was in 1928 and was the largest single order the three-year-old company had ever made.

Thanks to this effective distribution network, the new company was successful. At the time of the merger, Holt was a $12-million company and Best sales were $6 million. By December of 1928, the new company was doing business of $35 million, and making a nifty 26 percent on sales.

I joined San Jose Tractor and Equipment Co. in 1936 as a parts man, mechanic and finally, a salesman. In 1938, my sales of $60,000 were enough to lead the dealership. (This was the time of $1,500 D2s, $2,700 D4s and $7,500 D8s.) Not only was it an exciting time, it was a profitable time. A 1938 *Fortune* article on Caterpillar told of the opulent lifestyle of a Caterpillar salesman who earned $6,000 a year.

That article in *Fortune* is probably the first of thousands over the years that have fostered the well deserved reputation, even legend, of the Caterpillar dealer. In later years, as president of the American Automobile Association, I had the privilege of traveling worldwide for a period of five years. I always made it a point to visit the local Caterpillar dealership and seeing that equipment always made me feel not too far from home, and I can tell you, that feeling never fades away. There really is something to that legendary "Yellow Blood" in your veins.

Still today, one of the most memorable days of my life was the day in 1939 when my brother and I started the Caterpillar dealership in Santa Maria, California. In that first year, we did a volume of $500,000 and paid ourselves $500 a month. I handled sales and marketing, and Parker took care of the financial side.

Holt Bros. was a relatively small dealership. Personally, I liked the closeness that comes with smaller size and think that added to the fun of running a business. While those of us here could have a friendly debate on what's more exciting (and I grant you that some of that "excitement" came during times when the Cat parts bill was due and collections were lousy), I think there's one thing we can agree on, the pride of owning a Caterpillar dealership. Dr. Steiner, one of our earliest predecessors, used the word "pride" first and I think it's even more applicable today.

Like many of you, we were the biggest and best tractor dealer in our territory. Others, including some heavily capitalized factory stores, came and went. Times, and the quality of that stuff you're selling against, have changed. Still, I have watched this Caterpillar-dealer partnership from its inception and I am convinced that no other group is so committed and capable. We are here this week under the banner of "Customers First." Enough said, except to note that there is more customer knowledge assembled in this room than any competitor, or for that fact, just about any business, would ever hope to have.

Of course, our customers have changed. Each new offering of a Caterpillar product brings a different type of customer. But bottom line, customers are human beings and human nature doesn't change. When the smoke clears, that fact remains intact. To lose sight of it, I think, is not to see the forest for the trees.

Customers are no different from Jake Hahn, a contractor negotiating with one of our salesmen for a No.12 Motor Grader almost 30 years ago. The salesman signed the deal in his office and he and Hahn walked past my office on the way to the front door. I waved and continued my work, only to look up a second later and see Mr. Hahn tear up his contract and storm out the door. I asked the salesman what happened and he said the contractor told him that if his business wasn't important enough for the boss to come out and thank him, he was no longer doing business with Holt Bros. We salvaged that deal, and I learned a lesson I've never forgotten. From that point on, my brother and I went out of our way to thank our customers for investing their hard-earned money with us.

The Caterpillar Family

By Luis F. Gomez Rosales, president, Importadora Industrial Agricola s.a. (IIASA), Caterpillar dealer in Ecuador, at the dealer's 75th anniversary celebration in 1999:

Caterpillar and its dealers have come far over the years, and we've learned much along the way. You need only look at some of the technology available today to get a feeling for how our knowledge has expanded. We have giant mining trucks with hauling capacities our predecessors never imagined. We have compact products that handle surprisingly large loads and easily maneuver around tight work spaces.

The technology shows up in other areas, too, such as the S•O•S fluid sampling program. All those years ago, who would have thought that such a program would not only be possible, but so frequently used? I find the technology both awesome and practical. The knowledge that has been put in our products does more than impress. It also helps our customers do business.

I am certain my grandfather, Benjamin Rosales Pareja, would be amazed to see the state of the products today, as well as the breadth of services we offer such as The Rental Store. But what pleases me are the number of things that haven't changed since my grandfather founded the dealership in 1924.

If my grandfather walked around the dealership today, he would talk to customers and recognize that they remain our top priority. My grandfather worked to build a business that would help his customers—who also

were his friends— during good times and bad. A business that only helps during good times can't last. Such an organization is part of a trend, not a business solution.

At IIASA, we are proud to say we're just the opposite. Don't get me wrong: No one enjoys the good times more than us. But they don't last forever. We all know that. And our customers need us most when they face their biggest challenges.

Almost anyone can sell a product during the boom times. But the reliability of those products becomes more crucial if economic challenges surface. We at IIASA take great pride in our preventive maintenance programs, which ensure that the customers' equipment continues to be productive no matter what the economic climate. We also are confident in the quality of the products we sell. They are built to last for years —which is longer than the life of many trends.

Today's global environment is competitive. Our customers need someone who is committed to them for the long term. We extend that commitment, and we offer the knowledge we've accumulated over the past 75 years. The family concept, another theme at the dealers, ensures that knowledge is passed from one generation to the next. We learn from our elders and teach our younger family members.

Cat dealers also share their experiences with each other, creating their own family. Those shared experiences and beliefs have created a consistency between dealerships.

At any Cat location you should find:

- Superior, advanced technology products.
- Professional expertise and advice to help in machine selection.
- Financing alternatives, including rental options.
- Superior product support through excellent parts availability and well trained, customer-oriented servicemen.

These characteristics all contribute to cost reductions for our customers, which help make Cat the superior value provider.

And that has been the goal from the start. I'm not sure my grandfather ever put it in those specific words, but the way he conducted business showed he believed it. He was fully committed to setting a standard of excellence, and he proved it by the people he hired, the products he sold and the relationships he cherished—during the booms and the challenges. This would not have been possible without the best management team and people in our territories. These top-performing individuals are fully dedicated to the Caterpillar business. A tradition of honesty and integrity along with the best products and product support have enabled us to celebrate our 75th anniversary as the market leader and to have remained a solid business through good and bad times.

We are certainly deeply satisfied to have contributed to the progress of Ecuador and are fully committed to set a standard of excellence in the business community for our country. It's a tradition we're proud to continue.

Alban Tractor Co., Inc.

Four Generations of Customer Satisfaction

Jim Alban opened Alban Tractor Co., Inc., in 1927. It was an outgrowth of an enterprise begun in 1921 known as Alban and Johnson which was a sub-dealership for Holt Manufacturing Co.

Today, his great-grandson James C. "Jamie" Alban IV is president of the company, making Alban a fourth-generation dealership.

Headquartered in Baltimore, Maryland, the dealership includes all of Maryland, Washington, D.C., and parts of Virginia and Delaware. In 1928, the first full year of operation, sales were $20,837. Then came the stock market crash.

"It was tough going in those days," said Jim Alban. "There were no nine-to-five hours. I had to keep making calls, keep servicing tractors we had sold. One year I sold five tractors in Washington, D.C., and that was our total sales for the year."

By 1940, Alban annual sales were approaching the one million dollar mark. That year, the company opened its first branch. After World War II, Jim Alban and his son Buck made a decision that, they said, "proved to be the wisest decision we ever made."

They had been handling a number of lines of construction equipment but decided to market Caterpillar products exclusively. The company continued to grow over the years. Today, Alban has corporate headquarters in Baltimore plus eight branches, three parts centers, two machining and hydraulic centers, and 13 parts drops. They employ about 500 people and annual sales have reached almost $200 million.

inset. **James C. Alban, the company founder.**

right. **Four generations of Albans have led the family business. Three of those generations include from left, James C. Alban III, James C. Alban, Jr., and James C. Alban IV.**

opposite. **Alban facility about 1940. Other photos depict current operations at the dealership.**

DEALERS 2000

NORTH AMERICAN COMMERCIAL DIVISION *United States:* Alban Tractor Co., Inc. Baltimore, Maryland • Altorfer, Inc. Cedar Rapids, Iowa • Beckwith Machinery Company Pittsburgh, Pennsylvania • Blanchard Machinery Company Columbia, South Carolina • Butler Machinery Company Fargo, North Dakota • Carlton Company Albany, Georgia • Carolina Tractor & Equipment Co. Charlotte, North Carolina • Carter Machinery Company, Inc Salem, Virginia • Cashman Equipment Company Las Vegas, Nevada • Cecil I. Walker Machinery Co. Charleston, West Virginia • Cleveland Brothers Equipment Co., Inc. Harrisburg, Pennsylvania • Darr Equipment Co. Dallas, Texas • Dean Machinery Co. Kansas City, Missouri • E. A. Martin Company Springfield, Missouri • Empire Machinery Mesa, Arizona • FABCO Equipment, Inc. Milwaukee, Wisconsin • Foley Equipment Company Wichita, Kansas • Foley, Incorporated Piscataway, New Jersey • Giles & Ransome, Inc. Bensalem, Pennsylvania • Gregory Poole Equipment Company Raleigh, North Carolina • H. O. Penn Machinery Company, Inc. Poughkeepsie, New York • Hawthorne Machinery Co. San Diego, California • Holt of California Stockton, California • Holt Company of Ohio Columbus, Ohio • Holt Company of Texas San Antonio, Texas • J. A. Riggs Tractor Company Little Rock, Arkansas • John Fabick Tractor Company Fenton, Missouri • Johnson Machinery Co. Riverside, California • Kelly Tractor Co. Miami, Florida • Long Machinery Missoula, Montana • Louisiana Machinery Company, Inc. Reserve, Louisiana • MacAllister Machinery Co., Inc. Indianapolis, Indiana • Martin Tractor Company, Inc. Topeka, Kansas • Michigan CAT Novi, Michigan • Mustang Tractor & Equipment Company Houston, Texas • N C Machinery Tukwila, Washington • Nebraska Machinery Company Omaha, Nebraska • Ohio Machinery Co. Broadview Heights, Ohio • Pacific Machinery, Inc. Waipahu, Hawaii • Papé Bros., Inc. Eugene, Oregon • Patten Industries, Inc. Elmhurst, Illinois • Peterson Tractor Co. San Leandro, California • Puckett Machinery Company Jackson, Mississippi • Quinn Company Selma, California • Ring Power Corporation Jacksonville, Florida • Ringhaver Equipment Co. Riverview, Florida • Rust Tractor Co. Albuquerque, New Mexico • Shepherd Machinery Co. Whittier, California • Southworth-Milton, Inc. Milford, Massachusetts • Stowers Machinery Corporation Knoxville, Tennessee • Syracuse Supply Company Syracuse, New York • The Halton Company Portland, Oregon • Thompson Machinery Commerce Corporation Nashville, Tennessee • Thompson Tractor Co., Inc. Birmingham, Alabama • Tractor & Equipment Co. Billings, Montana • Wagner Equipment Co. Aurora, Colorado • West Texas Equipment, L.P. Midland, Texas • Western States Equipment Company Meridian, Idaho • Whayne Supply Company Louisville, Kentucky • Wheeler Machinery Co. Salt Lake City, Utah • Wyoming Machinery Company Casper, Wyoming • Yancey Bros. Co. Atlanta, Georgia • Ziegler Inc. Minneapolis, Minnesota • *Canada:* A. Pickard Machinery (1971) Limited Charlottetown, Prince Edward Island • Atlantic Tractors & Equipment Ltd. Halifax, Nova Scotia • Hewitt Equipment Limited Montreal, Quebec • Finning Ltd. Edmonton, Alberta • Kramer Ltd. Regina, Saskatchewan • Powell Equipment Limited Winnipeg, Manitoba • Toromont Concord, Ontario **LATIN AMERICAN DIVISION** *Argentina:* Macrosa del Plata S.A. • *Bahamas:* Atlantic Equipment & Power Ltd. • *Barbados:* Plantrac Industries Ltd. • *Belize:* General Equipment Company, Ltda. • *Bolivia:* Matreq Ferreyros S.A. • *Brazil:* Bahema S.A., Salvador, Bahia; Lion S.A., São Paulo Marcosa S.A., Fortaleza, Ceará Parana Equipamentos S.A., Curitiba, Parana; Sotreq S.A., Rio de Janeiro • *Chile:* Finning Chile S.A.A. • *Colombia:* General de Equipos de Colombia S.A. • *Costa Rica:* Maquinarias y Tractores, Ltda. • *Dominican Republic:* Implementos y Maquinarias C. por A. • *Ecuador:* Importadora Industrial Agricola S.A. • *El Salvador:* Compania General de Equipos, S.A. de C.V. • *Guatemala:* Corporacion General de Tractores, S.A. • *Guyana:* Corp. of Guyana Limited • *Haiti:* Haytian Tractor & Equipment Co., S.A. • *Honduras:* Casa Comercial Mathews, S.A. de C.V. • *Jamaica:* Power & Tractors Ltd. • *Mexico:* Maquinaria, S.A. de C.V., Chihuahua; Empresas Matco, S.A. de C.V., Ciudad Obregon; Tracsa, S.A., Guadalajara; Mextrac, S.A. de C.V., Mexico City; Maquinaria Diesel, S.A. de C.V., Monterrey • *Netherlands Antilles:* Heavy Equipment & Diesel Company N.V. • *Nicaragua:* Nicaragua Machinery Co. • *Panama:* Cardoze & Lindo • *Paraguay:* S.A.C.I.H. Petersen • *Peru:* Ferreyros S.A. • *Puerto Rico:* RIMCO, Inc. • *Suriname:* Surinaamse Machinehandel N.V. • *Trinidad:* Massy Enterprises Limited • *Uruguay:* General Machinery Co. S.A. • *Venezuela:* Maquinarias Venequip S.A. **CATERPILLAR S.A.R.L.** *Albania:* Macchine Agricole Industriali Automezzi S.p.A (MAIA) - MAIA SHQIPERI SH.P.K.* • *Algeria:* Bergerat Monnoyeur International • *Angola:* Barlows Equipamentos Companhia Lda • *Austria:* Eisner Baumaschinen Vertrieb und Service GmbH • *Bahrain:* Mohamed Abdulrahman Al Bahar • *Belgium:* Tractor & Equipment Company (TRECO) • *Benin:* Benin Equipements • *Bosnia-Herzegovina:* Teknox Trading S.A. - BOSTEK Machinery* • *Botswana:* BEMCO • *Bulgaria:* Barlows Tractor International Ltd. - EKKO Limited* • *Burkina Faso:* Burkina Equipements • *Burundi:* Chanic S.A. • *Cameroun:* S.H.O. Cameroun • *Central African Republic:* S.H.O. Centrafrique • *Commonwealth of Independent States: Kazakhstan:* Borusan Makina • *South Siberia (and Mongolia):* Wagner Equipment • *North West Russia:* Zeppelin Russland • *Russian Far East* N C Machinery • *South West Russia:* Mirovaya Technika • *West Central Russia:* Bergerat Monnoyeur International • *West Siberia:* Barlows Tractor Siberia • *Ukraine:* Zeppelin Ukraine • (*Dealer Representatives - Azerbaijan:* Borusan Makina Azerbaijan; *Georgia:* Borusan Makina Georgia; *Russian Far East (South):* Amur Machinery and Service; *Turkmenistan:* Borusan Makina Turkmenistan) • *Comoro Islands:* Henri Fraise Fils & Cie. • *Congo, Republic of:* S.H.O. Congo • *Congo, Democratic Republic of:* Chanimetal • *Croatia:* Teknox Trading S.A. - CONTEK D.O.O.* • *Cyprus:* Cyprus Trading Corporation Ltd. • *Czech Republic:* Phoenix-Zeppelin S.S.R.O. • *Denmark:* Geveke N.V. - Enmaco Maskiner A/S* - Enmaco Motoren** • *Djibouti:* Anciens Comptoirs Ries • *Egypt:* MANTRAC • *Equitorial Guinea:* Tractafric S.N.C. • *Eritrea:* Eritrea Equipment PLC • *Estonia:* Wihuri oy Witraktor - Witräktor Eesti AS* • *Ethiopia:* Ries Engineering Share Company • *Finland:* Wihuri oy Witraktor - Wihuri Power Products** • *France:* Bergerat Monnoyeur Travaux Publics - Bergaret Monnoyeur Energie S.A.** • *French Guiana:* Masselco • *Gabonese Republic:* S.H.O. Gabon •

Gambia: J. A. Delmas Export • Germany: Zeppelin Baumaschinen GmbH • Ghana: Tractor & Equipment Ghana Ltd. • Greece: ELTRAK S.A. • Guadeloupe, French West Indies: Crocquet S.A. • Guinea: Manutention Guineenne • Hungary: CP Holdings Ltd. - Huntraco Trading & Servicing Co. Ltd.* • Iceland: Hekla HF • Iran: HAMKAR MACHINE Co. • Ireland, Republic of: McCormick Macnaughton Ltd. • Israel: The Israel Tractors & Equipment Co. Ltd. • Italy: Compagnia Generale Trattori S.P.A. (CGT), Milan - Macchine Agricole Industriali Automezzi S.p.A (MAIA), Rome • Ivory Coast: Manutention Africaine Côte d'Ivoire • Jordan: Jordan Tractor & Equipment Co. Ltd. • Kenya: Gailey & Roberts Ltd. • Kuwait: Mohamed Abdulrahman Al Bahar • Latvia: Wihuri oy Witraktor - Witraktor Eesti AS* • Lebanon: M. Ezzat Jallad & Fils • Lesotho: Barlows Equipment Company • Liberia: Liberia Equipment Ltd. • Libya: General Company for Farm Equipment and Agricultural Necessities • Liechstenstein: Ulrich Ammann Baumaschinen AG • Lithuania: Wihuri oy Witraktor - Witraktor Eesti AS* • Luxembourg: Bergerat-Dutry S.A. • Macedonia, Republic of: Teknox Trading S.A. - TEKNOX Machinery D.O.O.* • Madagascar: Henri Fraise Fils & Cie. • Malawi: Barlows Equipment Co. • Mali: Manutention Africaine Mali • Malta: Macchine Agricole Industriali Automezzi S.p.A (MAIA). Martinique, French West Indies: Crocquet S.A. • Mauritania: J.A. Delmas Export • Mauritius: Scomat Limitee • Mayotte, Department of: Henri Fraise Fils & Cie • Moldova: Bergerat Monnoyeur International - FORTRAC S.R.L.* • Morocco: Tractafric Maroc • Mozambique: Barlows Equipamentos Companhia Lda • Namibia: NAMTRAC Equipment Company • Netherlands: Geveke N.V. - Geveke Zwaar Materieel B.V.* - Geveke Motoren** • Niger: Manutention Africaine Niger • Nigeria: Tractor & Equipment Nigeria Limited • Northern Ireland: McCormick Macnaughton (N.I.) Ltd. • Norway: Geveke N.V. - Pay & Brinck A/S* - Pay & Brinck Motorer** • Oman: Oasis Trading & Equipment Co. • Pakistan: Allied Engineering & Services Ltd. • Poland: Bergerat Monnoyeur International - ENTRAK SP Z.O.O.* • Portugal: Sociedade Tecnica de Equipamentos e Tractores SA (STET) • Qatar: Mohamed Abdulrahman Al Bahar • Reunion Island: Ets. Camille Mace S.A. • Romania: Bergerat Monnoyeur International - FORTRAC S.R.L.* • Rwanda: SOCOMERWA • São Tomé & Príncipe: Barlows Equipamentos Companhia Lda • Saudi Arabia: Zahid Tractor & Heavy Machinery Company Ltd. • Senegal: Societe Auxiliare d'Equipements (Saudequip) • Seychelles Islands: Henri Fraise Fils & Cie. • Sierra Leone: Tractor & Equipment Sierra Leone Ltd. • Slovakia: Phoenix Zeppelin S.S.R.O. • Slovenia: Teknox Trading S.A. - AVTEK D.O.O.* • South Africa: Barlows Equipment Co. • Spain: Finanzauto S.A. • St. Barthelemy: Crocquet S.A. • St. Martin: Crocquet S.A. • Sudan: Sudanese Tractor Co. Limited • Swaziland: Barlows Equipment Co. • Sweden: Geveke N.V. - Engson Maskin AB* - Geveke Power Systems Svenska** • Switzerland: Ulrich Ammann Baumaschinen AG • Syria: M. Ezzat Jallad & Fils • Tanzania: Gailey & Roberts Ltd. • Tchad: S.H.O. Tchad • Togo: Togo Equipements • Tunisia: Parenin S.A. • Turkey: Borusan Makina Servis ve Ticaret A.S. • Uganda: Gailey & Roberts (Uganda) Ltd. • Ukraine: Zeppelin Baumaschinen GmbH • United Arab Emirates: Mohamed Abdulrahman Al Bahar • United Kingdom: Finning (U.K.) Limited • West Bank and Gaza: Palestinian Tractor & Equipment Co. Ltd. • Yemen: The Tehama Trading Co. Ltd. • Yugoslavia, Federal Republic of: Teknox Trading S.A. - TEKNOX D.O.O.* • Zambia: Barlows Equipment Co. • Zimbabwe: BARZEM **CATERPILLAR OF AUSTRALIA LTD**. Australia: William Adams Tractors Pty., Limited, North Clayton, Victoria; Energy Power Systems Australia Pty. Ltd., Melbourne; Cavill Power Products Pty., Ltd., Enfield, South Australia; Westrac Equipment Pty. Ltd., South Guildford, Western Australia; Gough & Gilmour Holdings Pty. Ltd., Parramatta, New South Wales; Hastings Deering Australia) Pty. Ltd., Archerfield, Queensland • Fiji Islands: CARPTRAC MBf • New Caledonia: Societe Caledonienne des Tracteurs S.A. • New Zealand: Gough, Gough & Hamer Ltd. • Papua New Guinea: Hastings Deering (PNG) Ltd. • Samoa, American: Hawthorne Machinery of Samoa, Inc. (administrative office in San Diego, California) • Solomon Islands: Hastings Deering • Tahiti: Tahitibull (S.A.R.L.) **CATERPILLAR ASIA PTE. LTD.** Bangladesh: Greenland Engineers & Tractors Co. Ltd. • Bhutan: TIL Limited • Cambodia: Metro Group of Cambodia Ltd. • India: GMMCO Limited, Bombay ; TIL Limited, Calcutta • Indonesia: P. T. Trakindo Utama • Korea, Republic of: Hae In Corp. • Lao People's Democratic Republic: Lao-Metro Company Limited • Malaysia: Tractors Malaysia (1982) Sdn. Bhd. • Myanmar: Myanmar Tractors & Trading Co. Ltd. • Nepal: TIL Limited • Philippines: Monark Equipment Corp. • Singapore: Tractors Singapore Limited • Sri Lanka: United Tractor & Equipment Ltd. • Thailand: Metro Machinery Company Limited • Vietnam: V-TRAC Infrastructure Development Company **SHIN CATERPILLAR MITSUBISHI LTD.** Japan: Hokkaido Caterpillar Mitsubishi Construction Equipment Sales, Ltd., Sapporo • East Kanto Caterpillar Mitsubishi Construction Equipment Sales, Ltd., Kashiwa • West Kanto Caterpillar Mitsubishi Construction Equipment Sales, Ltd., Tokyo • Hokuriku Caterpillar Mitsubishi Construction Equipment Sales, Ltd., Niigata • Tokai Caterpillar Mitsubishi Construction Equipment Sales, Ltd., Anjo • Kinki Caterpillar Mitsubishi Construction Equipment Sales, Ltd., Osaka • Chugoku Caterpillar Mitsubishi Construction Equipment Sales, Ltd., Hiroshima • Tohoku Construction Equipment Sales, Ltd., Iwanuma • Shikoku Kiki Co., Ltd., Takamatsu • Shikoku Construction Equipment Sales, Ltd., Matsuyama • Kyushu Construction Equipment Sales, Ltd., Fukuoka • Makiminato Motors Corporation, Okinawa **CATERPILLAR CHINA LIMITED** Taiwan: Jardine Machinery Taiwan Ltd. • Hong Kong SAR, Macau, and Provinces of Guangdong, Guangxi, Hainan, Fujian, Jiangxi and Hunan: The China Engineers, Ltd. • Provinces of Anhui, Henan, Hubei, Jiangsu, Shandong, Zhejiang and Municipality of Shanghai: Lei Shing Hong Machinery Ltd. • Provinces of Yunnan, Guizhou, Sichuan and Municipality of Chongqing: ECI-Metro Machinery Co., Ltd. • All other provinces, municipalities and autonomous regions are served by Caterpillar China Dealership.

*Dealer affiliates of principal dealers
**Engine only dealer
Current as of December, 1999

The Story of Product Support

Our formula for success can be stated briefly: *Find out what products customers want. Design and build them. Keep 'em running. When they wear out, rebuild or recycle. Do it better than anybody else.*

The "keep 'em running" part has always been top priority because customers depend on our products for their livelihood—sometimes for life itself, as with generator sets for standby power to hospitals. Caterpillar, dealers, suppliers—and the customers themselves—work as a team to provide what we believe is the most extraordinary product support system in the world.

Chapter 75 7

near right. **Caterpillar's Bob Spriggel (left) and B. K. Tan help employees at China's An Tai Bao Mine maintain the mine's 170 Cat machines. The two are part of a Cat work force of more than a dozen who keep the machines and engines up and running virtually around the clock.**

top right. **Cat dealers deliver parts to customers in whatever way they can, including by boat through a village in Peru.**

bottom right. **Custom Track Service was an early diagnostic program developed by Caterpillar to help customers lower undercarriage costs. Here, in the 1960s, Field Representative Steve Brown uses calipers to measure track rollers so he can recommend when to rebuild.**

1931 visionary

Every successful company needs visionaries—
people who can see their world full of possibilities
rather than confined by limitations. Virgil Unks, a
service publications illustrator in 1931, was such a
visionary. He foresaw a time when dealers could
communicate with customers in real time via video
screen, trigger parts orders by remote control and
airlift parts right to the customer site.

The methods he envisioned—and more—
have become reality.

top. **In this initial drawing,
Unks portrays a "farmer
broken down with only
one day left" to bring in
his crops.**

middle. **The farmer is on
the video phone, letting
the dealer know of his
desperate need for
replacement parts. The
dealer parts man looks
up the part number and
pulls a lever connected to
a conveyor system that
will locate and remove
the part from inventory.**

bottom. **Once on the
conveyor, the part is
loaded into the dealer
delivery plane.**

far right. **In Unks' vision of
this service scenario, the
part is air dropped within
25 minutes of the call.
The customer's crops and
profits are saved, and his
loyalty is clearly kicked up
a notch as he exclaims,
"By cracky! That's service."**

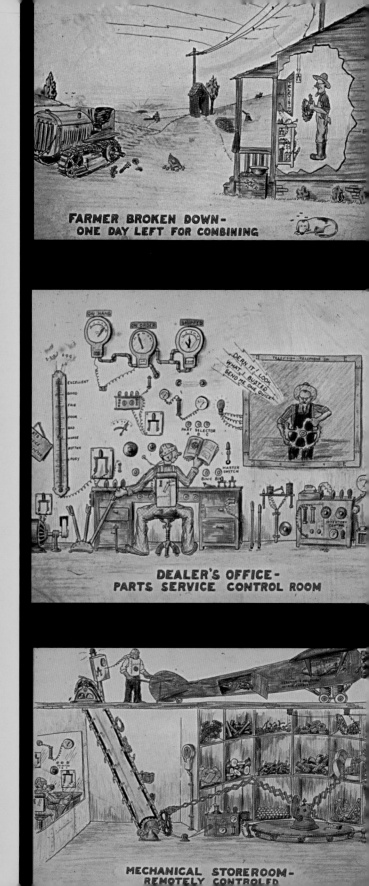

FARMER BROKEN DOWN -
ONE DAY LEFT FOR COMBINING

DEALER'S OFFICE -
PARTS SERVICE CONTROL ROOM

MECHANICAL STOREROOM -
REMOTELY CONTROLED

COMMITTED TO SERVICE

Daily Customer Orders - Entered	220,676
Daily Customer Orders Satisfied – Same Day Shipments	
■ From CATERPILLAR Dealers	196,843
■ From Nearest CAT Parts Facility	18,676
■ From Other CAT Parts Facilities	4,709
■ Customer Backorders Being Expedited	448

SERVICE SUMMARY			
TOTAL PERCENT SATISFIED	89.2	97.6	99.8

Standing behind
every product

Before the days of computers, secretary Ruth Love used this machine to compute overtime for the Morton Parts Department.

Just 10 miles east of Peoria is the heart of our parts distribution system, in Morton, Illinois. The Morton facility stocks 340,000 part numbers worth more than $1 billion. It processes 40,000 orders a day and ships to 22 other parts distribution facilities in 12 nations on six continents. Worldwide inventory is monitored by a central computer system using the most sophisticated inventory management tools available. The system is innovative because it stocks the right parts—in the right quantities—to fulfill most parts orders immediately at dealer locations while at the same time keeping inventory to a minimum. The ANTARES[SM] Parts Order Processing System links the entire distribution network online, so that orders can be filled from the nearest location.

far left. **In the 1920s, this parts warehouse in Albany, New York, was state of the art. The goal then was to have 65 percent of parts orders filled within 24 hours. To achieve this, future chairman Louis Neumiller posted the current percentage where everyone could see it. It was called the Parts Barometer, and at the time was a revolutionary idea.**

top left. **The three-million-square-foot (278 700-square-meter) parts facility in Morton, Illinois.**

bottom left. **A large electronic "Parts Barometer" in the Morton facility shows employees and visitors how parts service is doing. The numbers are updated constantly.**

above. **Parts storage at the Morton facility.**

top right. **Lobby of the 427,000-square-foot (39 668-square-meter) Product Support Center in downtown Peoria.**

bottom right. **Aerial view of the Product Support Center.**

The Product Support Center in downtown Peoria is the "brains" behind our product support efforts worldwide. Opened in 1998, the 427,000-square-foot (39 668-square-meter) building is home to service information production, repair process development, service systems, advanced training technologies, diagnostic systems, translation services and a service center large enough to handle the biggest machines and engines, with the latest diagnostic tools. The Caterpillar Service Technology Group, founded in 1985, also is located in the Product Support Center. The group develops advanced tooling. Examples: an electronic fuel flow monitoring system; an ultrasonic wear indicator; and DataView, a hardware/software advancement that replaced dozens of slow, manual diagnostic measuring devices.

. H. ZIEGLER CO., INC.

WM H. ZIEGLER CO. Inc.
CATERPILLAR
TRACTOR SCHOOL 1926

DISTRIBUTORS OF
CATERPILLAR
TRACTOR

Training

From the beginning, we've understood the value of training for employees, dealers and customers. In the 1920s, Caterpillar Schools were month-long seminars hosted by dealers for owners and operators. Today, comprehensive courses at Caterpillar Training Centers include classroom interaction with Cat experts as well as hands-on, "kick-the-tires" demonstrations.

We have developed educational/vocational programs to provide dealers with the most knowledgeable, highly skilled service technicians in the industry. The Caterpillar Professional Service Technician program includes recruitment of best-qualified candidates, complete training and education in the classroom and on the job, and hands-on experience with the most advanced technical and diagnostic tools.

In 1999, we provided funding for a service technician training facility at Illinois Central College in East Peoria, Illinois. Courses are designed by experts in the Caterpillar Service Training Department and taught by college personnel. This program, where dealers partner with local colleges by providing internships to students who complete their degrees, can be duplicated anywhere in the world.

"Across the country and around the world, Caterpillar dealers need skilled technicians to service Cat equipment. The company and two of our dealers are building on our relationship with Illinois Central College to develop a model curriculum that includes teaching materials and hands-on experience."

Glen Barton, chairman

left. **This "Caterpillar School" took place in 1926 at W. H. Ziegler Co., Cat dealer in Minnesota.**

top right. **Caterpillar parts and service representatives, as well as dealer service representatives, work in the field to help develop consistent maintenance and service practices.**

middle right. **A training class sees state-of-the-art diagnostics at work.**

bottom right. **Open house at the new training facility funded by Caterpillar at Illinois Central College in East Peoria, Illinois.**

"Those early years were exciting times. We pioneered many developments that are taken for granted today. Once we had a cylinder-liner wear problem causing high oil consumption. It was discovered that sulfur in the fuel was combining with water, a by-product of combustion, etching the top of the liner. This was corrected by a cooperative effort with Shell Oil Company in the development of detergent oil that would neutralize the acid. There were other early problems, but excellent cooperation among Service, Research, Engineering, Parts, dealers and suppliers solved problems…and we retained customers."

Elsworth Iverson, retiree

Built to Last

At Caterpillar, delivery of a product is never viewed as a final step, but as the beginning of a long-term relationship. To keep that relationship in good standing, we have to keep customers' products up and running at the lowest possible cost. We develop maintenance and service tools to enhance dealers' ability to extend product life and create greater value for the customer.

Recognizing that fluids and lubrication were the life blood of our products, we focused on the development of oil additive specifications in the mid-1930s, followed closely by specifications for transmission oils. Today, we develop fluids, filters and analysis programs along with our engines and machines. This way we know before we release a product what it takes to get the very best performance and the longest life. Coolants, oils, air filters, fluid filters and batteries all bear the Caterpillar name and meet our exacting standards.

We've used our years of experience to develop a comprehensive "repair before failure" philosophy that includes diagnostics and prognostics, controlled repair processes, computer software service tools and planned component replacement programs. Our expertise, combined with the power of personal computers and online access, has made maintenance and repairs faster and more effective than ever before.

Perhaps most innovative of all is our ability to give products a second life. Cat Reman gives customers a like-new product at a fraction of the cost of new. In a time when some manufacturers are strategically choosing to build products with single, short life spans, we take pride in making durability, long life and best customer value our priorities.

176

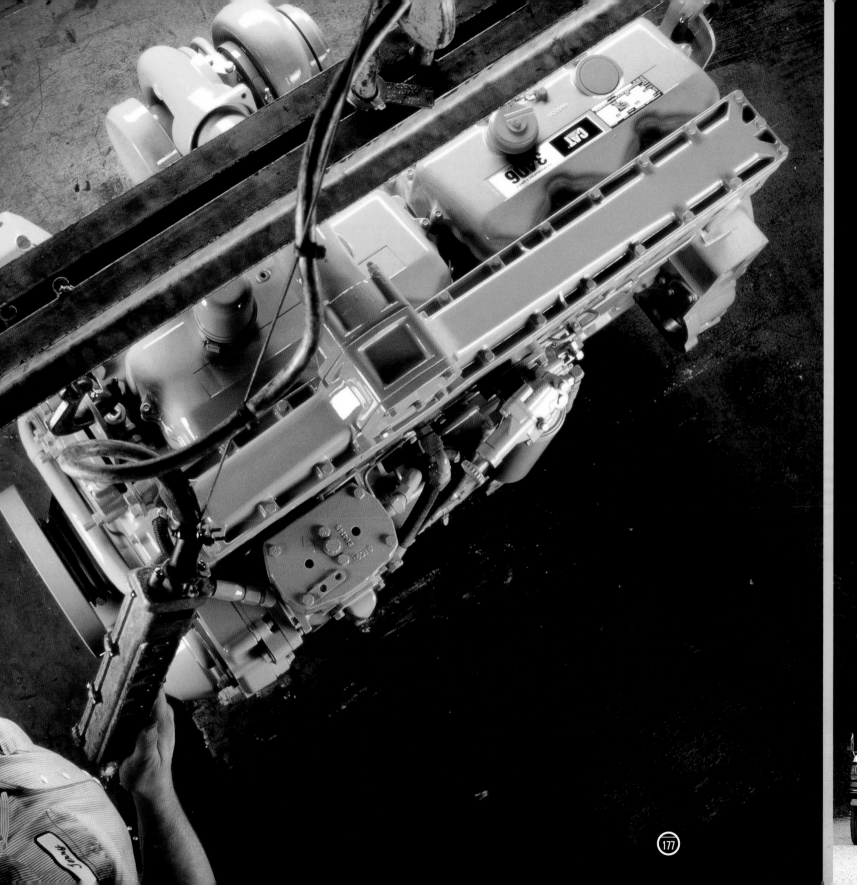

far left. **S·O·S (Scheduled Oil Sampling) is a comprehensive fluid analysis program that tests engine, drive train and hydraulic fluids. Testing provides detailed reports and trends for troubleshooting problems or enhancing performance.**

near left. **Through the development of Cat Remanufactured Products, we offer customers a reduced-cost option. Cat Reman components are remanufactured to like-new specifications and carry a same-as-new warranty. This is a remanufactured engine in the Corinth, Mississippi, facility.**

bottom. **Specialized services for hydraulic systems, undercarriage and power train can all be performed on customer sites from dealer service trucks.**

Customer Support Agreements

Customer Support Agreement: a cooperative arrangement between a customer and dealer that is designed to lower the customer's cost per unit of production.

Customer Support Agreements evolved from what used to be called Preventive Maintenance Contracts. How are these agreements different from a standard maintenance contract? They're more flexible—they can include any services the customer and dealer want, not just maintenance.

They are developed along with the purchase, not after it. Often, Customer Support Agreements add so much value that they are the deciding factor in the buying decision.

In the new millennium, parts availability, comprehensive service and support, and innovative ways to manage costs will become even more important to machine and engine users. Caterpillar and dealers will continue to provide the services that make us leaders today and tomorrow.

"Previously, we had quite an elaborate shop operation. With that you've got the cost of the shop, the physical facilities to maintain...plus, you have to hire and train and maintain qualified personnel. That's getting tougher because the equipment is changing—particularly from the onslaught of sophisticated hydraulic systems and the computerization of equipment...it's very difficult to keep a qualified and trained force of mechanics who are really capable. With a Customer Support Agreement on our equipment from Carolina Tractor, we avoid having the shop, we avoid having to worry about hiring and maintaining qualified personnel. We did some negotiating of the rates up front and then agreed to have them maintain our equipment ...make sure our warranties are in force because we've done everything...and, we worked in some conditions for buy-back on down the road. We save time. And, because preventive maintenance, repair and technical services are all rolled into it, it's definitely the cheapest way to go in the long run."

Jack Blythe, president, Blythe Construction Company, Charlotte, North Carolina

Our stories

Caterpillar is far more than product and buildings. It's people. Their stories are an essential part of our history.

Hundreds of employees and retirees submitted stories for Caterpillar's 75th anniversary. By far the largest number came from retirees in the United States. That's to be expected, since there are about 30,000 U.S. retirees, and many of them have memories of the 1920s and 1930s—decades before Caterpillar started building plants and hiring people around the world.

Some of the stories have been used throughout this book; many others are on the following pages—but, unfortunately, the majority are in a file cabinet at Caterpillar; there were too many to print. Many retirees sent in 30 or 40 pages of memories, and we had to use extracts only.

Editor's note: Deciding which stories to print was the hardest job in putting this book together. All of the stories were a great pleasure to read. They speak of pride in Caterpillar products, warm feelings for co-workers, pranks, hard times and good times. They are a true chronicle of a company and its people. Thanks to everyone who shared a story.

CHILDHOOD MEMORIES

My love affair with Caterpillar started as a young boy on my father's farm east of Brimfield, Illinois, in Jubilee Township. The Township Road Commissioner, on occasion, would park his road grader, pulled by an old "Cat 60" tractor, in our barnyard after a day's work grading the roads near our farm.

I was 12 years old in the late 1930s and I wanted to know more about this huge machine. The operator allowed me to ride along beside him in the seat while he drove. I watched as he started the engine by inserting a bar in the large exposed flywheel and cranking the engine by hand.

One day after it had been parked, I decided to see if I could start the engine. So I did as he did and gave the bar a mighty pull. The engine backfired, violently pulling the bar from my grip. The bar was stopped only when it hit the main frame of the tractor, leaving the crank bar almost 'L' shaped. Needless to say, I had some anxious moments explaining to my father and the road commissioner how the bar got bent. It also ended my brief career as an operator.

Roland Hasselbacher
ROLAND E. HASSELBACHER

I was born and raised in Addis Ababa, Ethiopia. My earliest exposure to Caterpillar, its extended family and its products started when I was a young child accompanying my father on his visits to the local Caterpillar dealer, Ries Engineering. My father was involved in different businesses, including growing coffee and wholesaling/ retailing of consumer products. My father's business relations with Ries centered around selling coffee beans to and buying soap products from Ries. During my visits to the dealership, I had many opportunities to admire the Caterpillar machines at the dealership, and to observe the quality of the machines and the product support provided by the dealer. The people we dealt with at the dealership treated us with respect and fairness. These positive experiences left a strong and lasting impression of what Caterpillar and its dealers stood for: quality, reliability, respect and integrity.

After receiving my master's degree from Thunderbird in Arizona, I had the opportunity to interview with Caterpillar and several other Fortune 500 companies. While I received several attractive offers, I chose to go to work for Caterpillar because of the company I remembered while growing up in Ethiopia.

ALI M. BAHAJ

In the late 1960s, at Christmas, I was given a gift subscription to *National Geographic* magazine. With the abundance of toys and games, this was not exactly what a nine-year-old thought of as a fun gift. However, when the issues started to arrive, I was attracted to a full-page advertisement by a company named Caterpillar. I knew that somehow those ads affected many of the lives and cultures of the people who were presented in the pages of the magazine.

Who would have thought that, several years later, I would be accepted for employment by that same company as a College Cooperative Education Trainee?

As of July 1999, I will have 17 years with Caterpillar. In that time, I have been able to secure a better understanding of the company, its culture and evolution. The products provided by this company, and its people, help shape a better world for all of us.

TOM WILCOSKY

At age 10, my childhood friend Jack Mason and I would hike over Cedar Street Bridge in Peoria and play in the tall weeds and trees out behind Caterpillar. We would look through the fence at the workers, the trucks moving and all the exciting activity, knowing both our dads were working in there. We made a vow to each other that when we grew up, we were going to work for Caterpillar like our fathers. We did just that in 1944. Jack got on as a tractor driver on the Industrial Railroad, pulling the small trains through the plant with a D4 tractor. I got on as a painter's helper.

Teddy Young
TED R. YOUNG

My Dad has worked at Cat since 1966. I was born in 1969 and attended my first Power Parade in 1974, at age five. While there, Dad took my picture next to a wheel tractor scraper. Twenty-three years later, I joined the Wheel Tractor Scraper Engineering Division in Decatur, Illinois. It must have been fate.

I was taught at an early age to recognize Cat yellow from any other yellow construction equipment. The yellow blood runs deep. *(photos then and now)*

TARA MORR

FIRST DAY ON THE JOB

The first day on the job is etched in our memories forever. Remembering the fear of getting lost or not being able to find a certain building, the challenges of starting work in a blizzard or the problems of learning a new job are common themes. For all, the first day at Caterpillar also marked the first step into a new way of life. These are some of the stories.

I was hired by Caterpillar to enter the apprentice program in Peoria in 1959. While waiting for the apprentice class cycle to start, I was given the job of sweeping around the Building X assembly line. At lunchtime I followed the others to the cafeteria with no problem. However, at quitting time, after putting my broom away and changing my shoes, everyone else was gone. I couldn't find Washington Street. First I tried one door, then another, but could not find my way out. The first day on the job and I was completely lost! Finally, swallowing my pride, I asked a 2nd-shift employee how to get out. He replied, "Out of what?" After my explanation, he pointed me in the right direction.

Edwin J. Kuhlman
EDWIN J. KUHLMAN

My first day in Caterpillar was August 31, 1998. That day, I became a new employee of AsiaTrak (Tianjin) Ltd. in China. The groundbreaking ceremony for the new AsiaTrak facility was September 18, and everybody had an opportunity to put their names on the first piling. That gave me a feeling: I am a member of AsiaTrak's starting team! During my first month, I felt strongly Caterpillar's culture: its teamwork, spirit, its mutual respect and its emphasis on continuous improvement deeply impressed me. I concluded that Caterpillar definitely has a vigorous future. It is just the place I have been looking for.

STANLEY GE

I remember my first day in the Planning Office, Building TT, in Peoria in July, 1942. Filing blueprints was the job a starting employee was given. I remember that white shirts, ties and suits were the dress code for men. The women could wear dresses, suits, skirts and blouses and anklets to match. I was very happy to have my job at Caterpillar. I respected our company and I had a feeling of ownership, even though I wasn't buying stock because we didn't have the employee stock plan at that time. I was paid $75 a month in 1942. You could get a plate lunch in the cafeteria for 26¢. Ice cream cones sold for 5¢ and candy bars were 5¢. We didn't have air conditioning, good lighting or new furniture, but we were happy.

MILDRED BURY BROOKSBANK

I went to work for Cat in June, 1947. I had just turned 17 and was fresh from the farm, not really knowing what a factory was. I went to work in the foundry. At that time the foundry was in East Peoria. As I was taken into the foundry to go to work on the third shift, the second shift was finishing pouring iron. I looked at the smoke and gas fumes and decided this was no place for me, but I would stay that night. Thirty-eight and a half years later, I retired from Cat.

JOHN L. LORTON

On my first day at Caterpillar when I walked into Building KK in East Peoria, I had two thoughts: first, being straight off the farm, I thought this building was so big it must cover 12 acres of ground (which was as big as one of our corn fields); second, and with a few modifications, they could make this into an indoor stock car race track.

EARL L. STALTER

I was born and raised on a farm four miles south of Tremont, Illinois, 15 miles from Peoria. However, I had only been in Peoria one time when, at the age of 18, I started working at Caterpillar on March 21, 1949, in the foundry cleaning room. As

most know, it was a dirty place to work. I didn't want to lose my job, so I didn't leave the area until the noon whistle blew. As you can imagine, I desperately needed the restroom. As I entered, I saw this large granite bowl with water running into it. It was in the center of the room and you could stand all around it. I had never seen anything like this, but I thought it was pretty neat. As I started using it, I soon found out it wasn't a urinal, but a washbasin. Needless to say, I didn't do that again.

RICHARD F. LUICK

I began my career in Peoria on June 1, 1999. When I came in for interviews in October of 1998, I had to come in early to Medical and give a urine sample to be drug-tested. Well, I couldn't go! The medical staff was very kind to me and told me not to worry, that that sort of thing happens all the time. They suggested I try again later, after I had drunk lots of water. For the next five minutes, I drank what seemed like three gallons of water, thinking to myself, "I really want this job. If I don't get it because I can't go to the bathroom, this will be really bad!" Finally I was able to offer up what I could and I proceeded to my three interviews. I was very nervous

about the interviews but I made it through the first one just fine. But, along came the second interview and it didn't go as well. It took place about two hours after I had consumed all that water. I had to go really bad! I thought to myself, "I shouldn't leave right in the middle of an interview. This is really important and I don't want to blow it." I had to abruptly interrupt my interviewer and have him rush me to the nearest restroom.

The story has a good ending. After it was over, all parties involved had a big laugh over the ordeal. Better yet, I got a phone call a couple of days later and they told me that they liked what they saw and that a job offer was in the mail.

My mentor encouraged me to let you know about my unusual early experience at Caterpillar.

GREG ANDREWS

On Dec. 6, 1935, I received notice to report for work as a foundry apprentice. I arrived bright and early to wait for my job assignment. After waiting several hours, I was introduced to my foreman and was told my job was to unload steel racks of core plates after the cores were removed from the plates. For removal, the racks were run through a 500-degree oven to bake the sand

cores. The plates were hot, heavy and very hard to handle. I stacked them on skids in a storage area, ready to be used again by the core makers. The empty steel racks were then delivered to the core makers by an overhead crane. Being so unfamiliar with the work made it difficult but I soon learned. My foreman would stop by and give me a hand and upon leaving would say, "Well, kid, you're caught up now. Let's see you keep it that way." This was the longest night of my life. I thought 8 o'clock would never come.

MAURI G. ELWOOD

My first day at Caterpillar in Peoria was one I will never forget. I could not find the place. In 1955 there were engineering groups all over town. I was to report to a Main Street address that was referred to as "the varsity dress shop." Having attended Bradley, I figured that I knew the area pretty well. After finding a place to park, I started walking down Main Street. No signs were marked "Caterpillar" but there was this place with the windows painted black that told me to stay away. After several passes up and down Main Street and starting time getting very close, panic set in. Then someone grabbed me and said,

"Get in here." It turned out to be a friend from my high school. My first supervisor was my shop teacher. They were expecting me and were watching the whole time over the top of those black painted windows.

JON K. GREUTER

I will never forget that day as long as I live, but I need to give you a little background information. I arrived in Peoria on January 23, 1975, from Gadsden, Alabama. There were about a dozen other new hires from the Southern states arriving at the same time. We met that weekend at an alumna's apartment who had been working for Cat for a few years. We all mentioned how cold it was that weekend, but the streets were clear and there was no snow visible. On Monday morning when my alarm clock sounded, I arose and looked out the window and saw the ground completely covered with snow. As a matter of fact, the snow was continually falling on the ground. I was excited about the snow because I had never seen such a beautiful sight, and I was trying to figure out what to do that day. Well, most of us had acquired an apartment in the same area that weekend. So we called each other and decided to meet at my apartment to spend the day with each other, since we all knew we didn't have to go to work because of the snow. In the Deep South, we were accustomed to everything (including schools, malls, factories) closing whenever it snowed. At about 9:00 a.m., one of the girls was cooking breakfast in the kitchen when the telephone rang. I answered the phone and my supervisor asked if I was having problems getting to work. I asked if he had looked outside because it was snowing. He said, "So?" I replied, "So, what?" I knew then that we were on different planets. To make a long story short, he told me that it's rare if anything shuts down in Peoria because of the snow. I was so distraught and scared because I had never driven in the snow. He reassured me that the roads would be clear and gave me directions. After I hung up the receiver and smelled the bacon cooking, I gave the news to my friends who had become my new family in Peoria. We were all shocked and asked who knew how to drive in this kind of weather. Since none of us had ever driven in snow before, we decided to drive in pairs. We were so nervous. We took

the wrong turn and drove half way to Galesburg before we realized that we were going in the wrong direction. I don't believe our speedometer went past 20 mph. About 1:30 p.m. we finally arrived at Caterpillar and were totally shaken.

BEVERLY JOHNSON THOMAS

When my start date came on January 16, 1979, in Aurora, Illinois, so did a blizzard. The snow blew so hard that it packed the underside of the hood of my car solid with snow. In spite of everything I tried, the car refused to start so I missed my first day of work. My first day turned out to be my second scheduled day as I had to borrow my girlfriend's car to drive to work on Tuesday the 17th. It was a challenging beginning but I have managed to continue the journey with Caterpillar for the past 20 years.

JON WRENCH

It was May 18, 1964. I was 19 years old on that first day, along with 14 others at Caterpillar. It was a warm spring night and everything was in bloom. After reporting in at

employment, they took us to the safety store where we got our first safety shoes. With shoe boxes under our arms, someone led the group of us out into the shop of "J court." As we walked, the leader would stop along the way to drop someone off at his assigned line. And so we went winding through Buildings J, H, P and X, where I was the last person to leave. I had no idea where I had ended up, or even how to find my way out and back to my '55 Pontiac in HH lot. I thought I was lost in this place forever.

RICHARD CLEAVER

"FIRSTS" AT CATERPILLAR

In 75 years, a growing global company and its employees experience many "firsts," as machinery becomes more sophisticated, as unimaginable technologies and computers develop, as new cultures are encountered, and as business relationships change with the times.

I recall when they were getting ready to hire the first females into the factory at

Aurora, Illinois. The manufacturing manager came up to me, asked me to take my shoes off and stand up. When I did, he asked me how tall I was. I told him 5'2", and he said I had just established the initial criteria for the height requirement for the ladies being hired into the shop.

MARION WALTERS

We built ten D10s before they were put into assembly line production. Although I didn't actually assemble these D10s, I watched every one being built from start to finish. My job was to record special parts put into these machines to help engineers understand what failed and why. I had my approved license to drive equipment, so I got to operate the D10 and test it for decibel noise limits for the EPA. I really felt big up there, knowing that people were looking at me! I'm not a show-off. But, hey, not everyone got to operate this monster of a machine, especially when it was first born!

GARNET J. MEISCHNER

In 1942, I was one of the first 12 women to be hired by Caterpillar as a timekeeper in the shop. This was during World War II when women were replacing the men who had gone off to war. And it was the first time I wore slacks to work. In those days women did not wear slacks!

(photo below)

ANGELINE OHLSEN

One of the funny stories of my time with Caterpillar involved the move of Production Control Division of Manufacturing General Offices into the Corporate Administration Building in downtown Peoria in the summer of 1967. We were one of the first groups to move into the new building, and it wasn't quite finished. The air conditioning was not in operation, and the warm temperatures made it necessary to have the windows open. The Cilco coal-burning power plant across the river was operating at full blast in those pre-EPA days with smoke pouring out its stacks.

Unfortunately, the wind was in our direction that day. You may remember that mini-skirts were the rage at the time with lots of leg and hose exposed. The women didn't realize what high sulphur ash would do to their hose. There were many "holely" stockings at the end of the day. We also had to de-ash our desktops every morning before beginning work.

WILLIAM H. HOUNSHELL

My most rewarding memory involves building and shipping the first low ground pressure tractors. In April, 1955, I was on special assignment and Jim Munro asked me if I thought it possible to make a September 15 ship date. I thought so, but not through the normal systems. We agreed that three of us would take care of the engineering releases, create factory work orders and purchase orders.

I took care of the paperwork. Glenn Pease and Jim Johnson coordinated the shop work and Corb Alexander handled purchasing. I can pick out these names because we were first in line; but everyone got into this thing, and what a job they did! Names do come back: Amy Heisel and Dick Franks, Engineering; Louis Luthens, Assembly; Bob

Schaub, Mfg. Bldg. LL; Pat McElwee, Inventory Control; and John Elwood, Manufacturing. There are so many more.

Well, we made it on the last possible day (freeze up at Antarctica), even though we had to hand-carry a D8 water pump from Bldg. KK to replace one that started leaking as it was loaded on the rail car.

WILLIAM I. CUSSON

I am very proud to be distinguished as the first black man to receive a 50-year pin which was pinned on me by Jim Despain, vice-president.

HORACE LEE

The most memorable event that I can remember is the "OK" [for women] to wear pant suits. (right)

VAL MOSS

The last few years of my time at Caterpillar were spent working in the "new" Building SS where I enjoyed one of the biggest highlights of my career. I had the opportunity to paint the first D10 that was built. What a thrill!

EARL M. BEASLEY

In 1955 I started working at the temporary downtown offices of Caterpillar. Many things come to mind about those first months. I was a member of the first Manufacturing Training class for women. At that time, no women worked in the shop.

This course allowed us to become familiar with shop terms and operations and was a big help in our jobs. I remember the several bus trips to the new plant site for downtown employees to view the progress of our future home—beginning with a trip to see the steel framework on the prairie and culminating with a trip in June to watch the first motor grader come off the assembly line at the new Decatur plant.

MARY MENDENHALL

I was the first and only Chinese engineer at Caterpillar for many years. My boss at Caterpillar helped me 40 years ago obtain residency. Then, to obtain residency you had to be sponsored by your company. Thanks to Cat and Congressman Bob Michel, my wife and son came in 1959.

We were reunited after four years and it was the first time I was able to meet my son.

HWA JUH SHEN

About 1964, a sheet was circulated offering testing to anyone interested in computers. I signed up and tested in the top 12 and was offered a job in the soon-to-be computer center. The first computer center consisted of tabulator, collators and sorters. Data was keypunched on IBM cards. I had the privilege, along with others, to design, test and install the EDS–Engineering Data System. This was the largest software in the country, controlling 10 million part facts, and took eight years to develop. When it was finally installed, it ran without a hitch. This was the early 1980s and it was built to be Y2K compatible. A cornerstone of computer graphics, the system made it possible to construct and test tractors before actually building them from steel.

ROBERT CRADDICK

The first time women were allowed to smoke at their desks in the offices (Parts Department), one woman lit up a cigar.

DONALD ZERWEKH

After World War II, Caterpillar expanded facilities and marketing throughout the world. "Innovation" and "flexibility" became the words of the day. Entry into Japan was no exception. The government there had raised barricades to imports and foreign investments. But in 1963 these restrictions were overcome when a 50-50 joint venture called Caterpillar Mitsubishi Ltd. was formed.

What a revelation for our employees (and for the Japanese recruited to this enterprise.) Every business phase had to be derived "from scratch," and the two groups certainly came from different life backgrounds and business systems.

Every day was a cultural learning experience for all. One example occurred when the Japanese promised to erect a greenfield plant on a timetable unheard of in Caterpillar circles. But in 17 months, the first Cat product, a D4, rolled off the assembly line. That D4 became party to a Shinto ceremony as priests blessed the results, and executives planted trees as good omens for the future. (They're still growing!)

KEITH G. JOHNSON

I started at Cat in a four-year machinist apprentice course in 1955. That same day, the first No. 12 Motor Grader built at Decatur plant rolled off the assembly line. That machine has been repossessed, restored and now sits in the Visitor Center in the Decatur plant. It looks as good or better than it did 44 years ago. I, on the other hand, show the effects of 44 years of wear and tear!

WILLIAM M. MCCLURE

I began my career with Caterpillar of Canada Limited in 1981. I was hired as the first female management employee out of about 100 management members. This presented some challenges and many rewards.

DAWN EGLITIS

I started at Cat in '39 or '40. I started the tank line. I built the first motor grader fuel tank by myself. There were 82 piece-parts. They gave me a print and said, "Do it."

ANTHONY JOHN WYSOCKI

I joined Caterpillar in 1979, less than two years after emigrating from China to Hong Kong. In 1982, I accompanied Len Kuchan and Jim Martin of Product Source Planning and Steve Weckel of

Caterpillar Far East Limited Sales Development on a visit to Fujian, China (a southeastern coastal province), for discussions with provincial and factory officials. This was the beginning of a long, eventful and rewarding career of participating in Caterpillar's efforts in establishing a permanent presence with China.

In those early years, China was still "opening up" and people were wary of anything foreign. It took many trips, meetings and presentations to explain Caterpillar's way of doing business and to build understanding and trust.

In August, 1984, a delegation of 16 persons from China came to Peoria and we signed our first technology transfer agreement on powershift transmissions. Then in December, 1986, we signed a 10-factory multi-product technology transfer agreement in Beijing. This agreement was considered a milestone in Caterpillar's relationship with China. The signing ceremony was held in the Great Hall of the People. The Chinese Minister He Guangyuan officiated at the ceremony and held a reception with over 200 guests attending.

ARTHUR HSIEH

My wife, Lois Mae Garton, started work in the Metallurgical Laboratory as a chemist on October 1, 1942. She was the first female to be hired on the hourly payroll in the bargaining unit. Her badge number was 20000. *(photo above)*

NORMAN L. GARTON

The assembly people in the East Peoria plant would complain that the hydraulic valve assemblies received from the Joliet plant were not clean.

That nite, on the *Jack Paar* (NBC) *Tonite Show*, he had a demonstration of a "skin packaging machine." I'll never forget it.

The operator put down a piece of cardboard on which he laid a raw egg, a bottle partially filled with Coca-Cola and a fish bowl half-filled with water and a gold fish swimming around in the bowl. This machine completely covered these three items with a sheet of thin plastic. Then the operator took hold of the cardboard, turned it vertical and the egg didn't break, no

Coke came out and the fish kept swimming in the bowl.

I "saw" valve body assemblies inside that plastic. I wrote the producers of the show ... and, to shorten the story, ... we NEVER got another complaint about dirty valve bodies.

Milton B. Jensen
MILTON B. JENSEN

HUMOR HELPS

Working at Caterpillar can be demanding and few jobs get done without some level of stress. As the challenges loom larger, employees sometimes use humor to ease the load, build community and deal with change. Some of the stories in this collection have become company legends.

One of the funniest moments that ever occurred at the Mapleton Foundry took place about five years ago during a training session. At the time, violence in the workplace was a growing concern all over North America. Our class was designed to train us for what to look for and what to do so as to eliminate the risk of violence in our workplace.

Our instructor was experienced, well informed and interesting. He was walking about the room, in

between our desks, looking about our group and talking about the power of observation. As he gazed about us, we were educated about physical traits to look for that a high percentage of violent people have been known to possess: tattoos, body piercing, etc. In addition, he stated that cowboy boots are an excellent hiding spot for weapons, such as knives and small handguns.

After about 10 minutes, he wheeled about and pointed a finger at one of our fellow supervisors who happened to be wearing cowboy boots and proclaimed that he was concealing an article in his boots!

The instructor asked our fellow supervisor and long-time friend to empty out his boot. Charlie pulled a "Hostess Twinkie" out of his right boot. Holding the Twinkie high in the air, he claimed, "I thought it would be a long session and knew I'd get hungry. I got another Twinkie in my other boot!"

We all laughed so hard that several of us were gasping for air.

Tom Shipley
TOM SHIPLEY

In the early to mid '50s, Karl Mason was an assistant director of the Research Department and became one

of the first employees to invest in a foreign car, a Volkswagen Beetle. It was love at first fueling! Karl was delighted with the fuel economy demonstrated. In a day when most of us were content with 17 miles per gallon and only a few got 20, Karl got closer to 30 miles per gallon.

Needless to say, Karl was only too willing to gloat over his ability to pass fueling stations that others visited often. As his VW was broken in, the mileage moved into the '30s and Karl became evangelistic.

Even though fellow researchers agreed that the mileage was remarkable, some felt it could become even better. To accomplish this, they took turns at lunch time in the parking lot, adding a little gasoline to Karl's tank. Karl's fuel economy improved still further, and he was only too willing to discuss the matter. As it moved into the '40s and '50s, Karl became so enamored of the vehicle that he returned to the dealer to compliment them. They felt that, although the mileage was exemplary, it just testified to the precision of German manufactured parts.

In due time, the noon additions ceased. Karl took the loss of fuel economy in stride, but gave the engine frequent

tuneups and talked less about the performance. It was only after his Research "friends" started noontime trips to siphon gas out of the tank that Karl went back to the dealer.

Such skullduggery is difficult to conceal and Karl soon found out about the noontime entertainment. Some claim he eventually forgave them!

Don Zook
DONALD ZOOK

Competition between the Advertising Department and the Sales Department reached an all-time high during the Christmas season of 1949. Each department claimed it alone was responsible for the sale of Cat products, and the other was no more than costly overhead. Advertising was headed by Hy Cox, a talented and creative fellow who enjoyed the practical joke. Bill Ziegler managed sales and was a legend with dealers and customers. Each was a target for the other.

As part of Christmas tradition, each department would decorate a tree, complete with an abundance of cookies and candy. One year, our Sales Department tree was smaller than usual. Advertising saw this as an opportunity.

We arrived one morning to find our small tree replaced by a giant specimen. It was over 15 feet tall and mounted in a large box filled with advertising literature. The tree was decorated with life size facial portraits of each member of the Advertising Department. On each of our desks was a letter saying, "We came down from our higher position (they were on the second floor) in Advertising to find your small tree struggling for life, struggling for its very existence, as you are struggling for your life and

existence. As you can see, through advertising, we have given it life and growth, as we will continue to give you life and growth." The letter was a masterpiece of creative writing, and it called for an immediate response.

Sales Training Division was given the job. Many of us had just completed a one-year "factory training" program and were now sales trainees, working toward assignments in other sales areas. We were ready for some action. Our boss had said, "get even, make it good, and keep me informed." We decided to present Advertising with an "advertising machine." The idea exploded into action. One of the group had an uncle with a farm. He had what we wanted: an ancient manure spreader (circa 1919). It had large steel wheels mounted on a solid axle, a heavy wooden body bolted to iron brackets, a massive metal "flinging device" at the rear and a long tongue for a team of horses. We bought it on the spot for $25 and hauled it to the back of Building HH. We worked most of the night taking it apart, piece by piece. It was hard work. Most of the nuts and bolts were stuck with rust.

The next night we hauled all the pieces to the entrance of Building HH and started the task of hauling it up the stairs to Advertising and putting it together. Desks and other furniture were moved aside to make way for the monster. The nuts and bolts, as well as the large steel axle, were "peaned" on assembly, making

it impossible to take apart. A large sign labeled it as *Advertising Machine—Easy to Operate*, and a large caricature of Hy Cox, shouting through a megaphone to his people, was mounted in the wagon. Advertising literature, strung on wires, was seen as being flung out the rear end. The large tongue extended from the spreader into one of the offices.

Bill Ziegler came by about 2 a.m. to admire the finishing touches. He was pleased. About this time, a plant security person came up for a routine check. He looked around, went to a phone and dialed a number. "This is Jones, plant security, second floor, Advertising, and there are some fellas up here with a manure spreader … No, it ain't no toy, it's a real manure spreader. I don't know how they got it up here, or what it's for, but they're here." He left saying, "Why do they ask me all these silly questions?"

Word spread quickly. By 6:30 a.m., people leaving third shift were dropping by to see "the manure spreader in the Advertising Department." One person did not drop by that morning. That was Chairman Louis B. Neumiller. He normally visited all departments to extend his

Christmas greeting, but this time he skipped Sales and Advertising.

The next day, we were summoned to his office for a little chat. We thought our careers were ended, but we were wrong. In a fatherly way, he suggested Sales and Advertising "bury the hatchet," and complimented us on our creative talent and energy. "But I strongly suggest, that in the future, you direct these resources toward beating our competition." We got the message.

A "hatchet burying ceremony" was held the next day. Both department heads shook hands and placed a large hatchet in a small coffin which was sealed and carried off for burial.

And how was the spreader removed from the second floor? Advertising hired a private welder to cut the thing apart so it could be hauled down the stairs.

Nick Humy
B. G. 'NICK' HUMY
(THE PARTICIPANTS I CAN REMEMBER ARE DEAN BLOMEYER, ART HARTWIG, CLARK CHAMBERLAIN AND ROMIE PITZEN. THERE WERE MORE BUT I JUST CAN'T RECALL.)

A gentleman named Ev Davis was manager in one of the old office buildings (about 40 years ago). He went to Peoria and bought a new hat and wore it back to work. When he got to work, he hung it on a hanger and went back to his desk.

Jim Munro and Lloyd Ely went to Peoria and bought two hats identical to Ev Davis' hat—one hat one-half size smaller than Ev's and the other one-half size larger than Ev's. When the two guys got to work, one put the smaller hat on the hanger and took the one Ev had bought. At the end of the day, Ev put the hat on and wore it home. The next day, Ev wore the hat to work, put it on the hanger and went to his desk. During the day, one of the guys put the larger sized hat on the hanger and Ev wore that one home.

Eventually, Ev went to the doctor and told him he had a problem. He said, "One day my head shrinks and my hat sits on top of my head, another day my hat is resting on my ears."

Jim and Lloyd finally told Ev what they had been doing.

RUSS SAURS

A humorous event I remember involved the large coffee pot that the people in the computer room used to make coffee. The pot was used for some time in the start-up and testing of conveyor elevators until a management directive came down to get rid of the coffee pot. The coffee pot was missing for two to three months. I was perusing an inventory listing one day and noticed an unusual part number. I informed my supervisor, and he said to bring it out. We all waited patiently to see what was coming out on the conveyor. In the middle of a large pallet was the coffee pot with a tombstone epitaph which gave the date of birth and death with flowers adorning the pot.

Thomas J. Tracy
THOMAS J. TRACY

When we first moved into the new Administration Building in downtown Peoria, we had trouble getting the air conditioning to work correctly. Also, in those early days in the building, Chairman Bill Franklin declared coffee machines off limits until after 9 a.m. In those days, it was expected that people would have their coffee at home and they wouldn't need another cup as soon as they reached the office.

One Friday afternoon Bill Franklin called Wally Bornholdt, who was in charge of the building, and said, "Wally, you've got to do something about the air conditioning in this office. It's over 85 degrees and sweltering." Wally got the air conditioning people and they worked all weekend.

First thing Monday morning, Wally got another call from the chairman: "Wally, you've got to do something about the air conditioning up here. It's 65 degrees and I'm freezing."

The exhausted Wally replied, "Well, wait until nine o'clock and go get a hot cup of coffee," and slammed down the telephone receiver.

JIM WOGSLAND

I took a trip calling on dealers in the Midwest and went out to dinner with some dealer people. When I got back to the hotel, I went up to my room and had some trouble opening the door. A bellboy was coming down the corridor and I asked him for help. He tried the key in the lock with no success, then looked at the key and said, "You're in the wrong hotel."

BILL LAMBIE

Editor's Note: When he heard this story, retired President Bob Gilmore said: "For those of us who know Bill, this sounds exactly like him. But we also know that he was one of those rare, true visionaries. As vice president of Parts and Service, he could see needs far into the future and propelled the company in that direction.")

FAMILY TIES

Entire generations of families comprise part of the Caterpillar family. As one author writes, "My association with Caterpillar reads much like a family tree."

"Gram" was 103 on June 25, 1999. She retired July 1, 1962, at age 66 (at that time you had to retire at age 66). She worked in Building X in East Peoria, third shift, in Heat Treat, lifting 35-pound track links into a furnace until the day she retired. (As a worker on the farm with her in my teenage years, I knew from experience that you didn't want her to pop you in the head!)

My mom retired from the photo lab after 32 years service. My dad retired in 1975 after 36 years service. He and his team of buddies were the designers of the first new "Basic Engine" plant at Mossville. His father was in plant protection for about 15 years. My father-in-law retired from East Peoria as an external grinder operator in 1976 with 30 years.

I'm in year 36 of a career that I hope makes it to 40 years or more. (Oh, yes, and my wife worked here when we were married 35 years ago and two of "Gram's" other grand-children have Caterpillar history. Larry Burchell was a commodity group manager at York, retiring in 1995 with 42 years and Don was in the IS field for 12 years. "Gram's" second husband Elmer was a plant protection officer for some time.)

I am proud of this Caterpillar history.

DICK WRIGHT

Our children grew up saluting Caterpillar tractors and we all joked that we had yellow blood. Things were different then, and I believe the kids felt a connection to their parents' work and took pride in the fact that they built a well-known American product. My son worked at Cat in the '70s. As I did, he made deep long-lasting friendships with fellow Cat employees. It's about the people. Caterpillar is still a huge part of my life almost 20 years after my retirement.

Jack Trowbridge
JOHN W. TROWBRIDGE

My association with Cat reads like a family tree. My family has been with Cat longer than I have been alive! My maternal grandfather, Harry B. Tapp, began with Cat in the early to mid-1930s. I am not certain what position he held before I was born; however, I know he was a millwright in East Peoria in the mid-1950s. My mother took great pride in pointing to the "Caterpillar" sign on the side of "SS" and telling us, "Your grandfather made that sign before he retired." My mother, Ann Tapp, now deceased, worked here during the war years making tracks for army tanks. She "retired" when the boys came marching home. For years I listened to family members talk about Caterpillar over Sunday dinner and family gatherings. My deceased uncle Earl Tapp, a supervisor at the Aurora plant, often joined in the occasional heated discussions. Today, my brother, Dale Duncan, holds 20-plus years and works the paint line in Building BB, continuing the tradition.

More importantly, my father, Clarence C. Duncan, was a repairman on the Transmission Line in East Peoria. My father was 57 years old when I came along. He retired in 1966 when I was 11. I sat many hours and listened to union stories, Cat stories and many opinions. It was my father's work ethic and respect for Caterpillar which I most remember and admire. The relationship my father had with his peers and management remained a source of pride for him, lasting until his death in 1976.

For as long as I can remember, every "payday Friday" my mother, two brothers and I would walk from Fourth Street and MacArthur Blvd. to East Peoria, crossing the Cedar Street Bridge and on to the guard shack to wait for my father. We would all ride home in his shiny teal Mercury, on to the bank, and then dinner at Sandy's Hamburgers on Western Ave. We lived for Friday!

I remember the pride I felt watching my father appear from the large brick building, walking tall, dressed in his blue work shirt and creased dungarees. When asked why he wore pressed work shirts and pants, especially in the factory, he always said, "It's a matter of pride, in yourself and your job." I think that still holds true today. I have worked for Caterpillar five years, starting in the factory and now working in EPD Marketing Services, as supervisor of the Targeted Marketing Group. Daily, I try to approach all I do with a remembrance of loved ones who created what I now enjoy. I remind myself of why I am here, and I try to inject the passion and respect I have for Caterpillar in whomever I meet, and to continue the "vision" my family has enjoyed for three generations.

MELANIE J. HUXTABLE

From 1928 to the present, four generations of my family have benefited from mostly steady employment, outstanding wages, unmatched benefits, challenging work, retirement security, long lists of lifetime friends and the pride of being a Caterpillar employee. As children were born, hospital bills were paid and as the first two generations passed away, flowers arrived from the company that had given them a livelihood. Two generations remain. May the second 75 years be as great at the first!

JOYCE NORDHIELM

I will have 47+ years when I retire in August 2000. My wife, Judy, had 33 years. My brother, Don, had 43 years. My sister, Flo Webster, had 42 and 1/2 years when she retired. Also, several years ago, we had three uncles— Nelson, Clarence and Harry Kent—who had a total of 77 years between them when they retired.

RICHARD A. GARSKE

My father, Pascual Mendoza, came to America in 1927 at the age of 19. He made it through the Great Depression of the '30s and worked several jobs in the '40s and '50s. He got a job at Caterpillar in Joliet in 1952. He retired in 1974 as a crane operator.

CATERPILLAR COMBINES

He was from Mexico and had no education but learned to read and write himself. He is 90 years old now and still talks about how good it was to work at Cat. Caterpillar and America are the best places in the world to work. I worked for Cat for 30 years and retired March 1, 1999.

FRANK MENDOZA
FRANK MENDOZA

Editor's note: Brian Millar, retiree from Great Britain, and his wife Jo, from Switzerland, adopted two Indian children and then started a day care village in Madras, India.

After Mina and Bablou arrived, we wanted to learn first-hand about India, so in 1979 Jo and I traveled extensively on the Indian subcontinent and visited numerous children's projects, firstly to meet the people we had been trying to help and with whom we built up a friendship through regular correspondence, secondly to see how well the funds or clothes we had sent were being distributed. We visited a children's village in Usthi, 30 kilometers from Calcutta, run by a Swiss couple. That started us thinking about a day care village.

BRIAN MILLAR

I have married into a family with a Caterpillar history, and we wanted to share it with you. My husband, Ron, and I made this list of family members who have worked at local plants. He is one of eight children, and all six of the boys in his family were fortunate enough to work for Caterpillar. These 15 family members with three generations have worked more than 375 combined years for one of the greatest companies in the world! *(see chart below)*

PATTI L. HAUK

Relationship	Name	Years and Current Status
my husband	Ron Hauk	30+ (retired)
his father	Frank Hauk	31+ (deceased 1993)
his half-brother	Earl Johnson	39+ (deceased 1999)
his brother	Virgil Hauk	43+ (retired)
his brother	Melvin Hauk	30+ (retired)
his brother	Allen Hauk	10+ moved to Iowa
his brother	Robert Hauk	2+ moved to Washington
his brother-in-law	Floyd Jackson	41+ (retired)
his brother-in-law	Gary Eaton	30 (retired)
his wife (me)	Patti Boucher Hauk	25+ (Morton Parts–Int'l Orders)
his stepson	Jeff Boucher	4+ (TTT–EP apprentice grad. 1998)
our daughter-in-law	Sharon Boucher	2+ (Morton Parts - IS)
his uncle	George Johnson	40+ (retired)
his aunt	Vernice Johnson	21+ (retired)
his uncle	Robert Johnson	29+ (deceased)

SOCIAL LIFE

Over the years, friendships deepen and grow. The threads of these friendships are woven into the fabric of our social life as well. Over the past 75 years, these social times were both formal and informal as leagues, teams, groups and parties marked what it meant to work at Caterpillar.

To me, Caterpillar Tullamarine in Australia was the crossroads of the world. Multiculture at its best—a work force of so many nationalities, sharing duties in manufacturing, parts and general offices. There was intense pride in products and parts manufactured. The parts warehouse foreshadowed any supermarket we know today. I was amazed at the bulk shipments of parts on those big semi-trailers most every day.

I remember the children's Christmas parties, pony rides, train rides, ice cream, lollies and, of course, presents to many hundreds of employees' children. There was always a choice of ready-made Santas available.

FRANK LIND

I started my official employment with Caterpillar in June, 1943, but actually started working with them in the late 1930s chasing foul balls hit out of the ball park for Pat Doyle. The pay was a used softball (rarely a new one) and the broken or unwanted bats. As we got a little older, they let some of us post the scores on the scoreboard. This was when the Diesels and the Dieselettes were contenders for national softball titles. My family followed these teams wherever they played. I remember going on the bus with the team for the National Softball Tournament in Detroit.

More than one Caterpillar employee found employment at Caterpillar because they had talents in softball or basketball.

Jack J. Clatt
JACK J. CLATT

In the mid-30s we organized the Caterpillar Brass Band. I played clarinet. I did lead the band a few times. We played concerts in the HH Show Room. Mr. Neumiller was head of the Sales Department so we would go to the train station at 7 a.m. and play while the train came in with Sales Dealers. In the evening, members of the band were guests at the Pere Marquette Hotel banquet for Sales Dealers. The band also played for soldiers leaving for World War II.

Walter D. Bristow
WALTER D. BRISTOW

In the 43-plus years I worked at Caterpillar, there were many good memories: the 25 Year Banquets at the Shrine, the big bands we enjoyed hearing, and the Caterpillar Operettas. They were all great!

Ralph L. Gross
RALPH L. GROSS

Every year on the first Monday of February, we have a Cat reunion here in St. Petersburg, Florida. Cat folks who live here or are here for just a few weeks or months come to the dinner and we get to see old friends and remember the good old days.

Bob Cooper
ROBERT N. COOPER

In 1945, I was playing basketball in the Inter Plant League. Marv Hamilton asked me to try out for the Diesels Team which I did. I played regularly until 1950 when I went into the army. In 1952 when I returned from the army, I rejoined the team for that successful season. I worked for a short time in scheduling for Bob Gilmore while I was playing. As captain of the team for a couple of years, it was always a pleasure on Monday mornings to be stopped by Mr. Neumiller on my way to Building HH to brief him on the weekend games.

William E. Dempsey
WILLIAM DEMPSEY

In 1957, I was the vice president of the Caterpillar Girls' Club [in Joliet, Illinois]. The purpose of the Girls' Club was to help needy employees until they could get back on their feet. Caterpillar helped the Girls' Club in many ways to be effective with their work, but the Club raised the money and decided who needed assistance.

When Clinton Kimble's house burned down in December 1957, the Girls' Club went into action. As vice president of the Club, it was my responsibility to check on situations such as this and arrange for assistance. I received so many calls offering clothing, furniture, etc., that I was overwhelmed and wondered how to handle it. We would need a truck and help loading and unloading. As usual, Caterpillar came to the rescue. The Public Affairs Manager arranged for a Caterpillar truck and personnel to help with the work.

Ann L. Rigg
ANN L. RIGG

Caterpillar Girls' Clubs were very active during the pre-NOW years of our company's history. I was fairly active at one time in Aurora's Club.

The Girls' Club at Aurora was the social glue for the plant in our growing years of 1960 through the '80s. It helped create a social environment for Caterpillar among office personnel, management and shop personnel.

KATHY WEEKLY

CHANGE AND CONTRASTS OVER THE YEARS

The past 75 years have been marked with substantial change. Some of the changes have been dramatic for those whose responsibility is the practical implementation of technical advances. Some of the changes have been dramatic for those who have worked hard to bring Caterpillar products into new areas. Other changes have been profound as new organizational and professional values continue to evolve.

When I started work, we were using slide rules, paper and pencil. The computer was a central computer that used fed keypunch information. We had few computer programs, so if we wanted to run data through the computer we usually had to write a program to handle the information. The language, FORTRAN, was very crude and difficult to use.

A few years later we got one calculator for the whole division, so we had to take turns using it. It cost about $450 and was capable of about as much as a $10 calculator today. We had no copy machines. If you wanted a copy, the secretary had to make extra carbons when

typing it originally, or you tried to run a copy through the blue print machine.

Our data was recorded on a galvanometer, or displayed on an oscilloscope and photographed, and then had to be digitized manually, one trace at a time. Then you used your slide rule to calculate the stress, engine performance or whatever you had recorded. Today, with digital recording tape, workstations on your desk and much better computer programs, an engineer can analyze results thousands of times faster than I could as a young engineer. Plus, the data is much more accurate and more encompassing.

What will it be like 30 years from now? One can't even imagine!

Jack W. Dennis
JACK W. DENNIS

The biggest event in my Accounting Department years was sales reaching one billion dollars. That happened in 1965 or 1966. In those days, electronic calculators had not been invented. We had big Marchant adding machines, almost as large as a typewriter. They would only total to $999,999,999.99. Reaching one billion in sales increased the complexity of accounting, but only during

November or December, when accumulated sales reached that total. Now Caterpillar sales exceed one billion per month.

John Orton
JOHN ORTON

On a cold, wet morning in 1935 I left Hooperton, Illinois, in my 1928 Chevy and drove to Peoria and Cat looking for a job. I got in a line which was four-foot wide and at least two blocks long. When I got to the employment window, Ray Weaver asked about my credentials. I was given a paper to read and sign. I was ushered down to the office Building M and introduced to Jay Martin in charge of hiring for the physical inventory. I was told I would be paid 50¢ an hour with a 3¢ night bonus, and the job would be temporary. It turned out to be the best and longest temporary job I would ever have. It lasted almost 38 years.

D.S. Ehvall
D.S. EHVALL

On June 9, 1937, I began my 45-year career at Caterpillar in the Building Q blacksmith and sheet metal shop. A drop forge machine located about 20 feet from my drilling machine shook the floor and rattled the windows with each stroke. This was a radical change from the quiet horse powered farm life I was accustomed to.

My first check for three days' pay ($7.60) helped me decide to endure the noise and stay with Caterpillar. After experiencing droughts, chinch bugs, 10¢/bushel corn and 15¢/pound hogs in the 1930s, this was a lot of money.

Cliff
CLIFFORD C. GILLETT

In 1923, I was just out of high school and was hired to work in the Engineering Department of Holt Manufacturing Company. There were six girls in our department: two blueprint machine operators, one in charge of the vault, a typist, a senior clerk and a secretary. I believe there were 125 girls in the whole office. Mrs. Holt, wife of one of the founders of the company, came from California once in a while and checked to see if the girls were being treated properly. I started at $12 a week.

My sister worked for Louis Neumiller in Spare Parts. We lived in Peoria and rode the streetcar to work. Sometimes we missed connections with the East Peoria car, but we were able to flag down one of the "Jitneys" that cruised in the area of the Franklin Street bridge. These were vintage touring cars painted gray.

We rode for a nickel. They got us to work in time to punch the clock.

In 1925 we were typing: "Caterpillar Tractor Co., successor to Holt Mfg. Co." at the top of the bills of material. Then the changes began.

I was married that year and in those days not many girls worked after marriage, so I quit. I was then making $14 a week! In 1952, I decided to see if Caterpillar would give me a job. The employment interviewer called to check on my old record and the girl was having problems finding my old records. She had to check before the Flood. Then, I was hired.

Velma F. Evans
VELMA EVANS

I can remember the days when it took all day, using a slide-rule, to determine a design equation. Today it can take less than a minute.

Larry
LARRY BERG

When I began my job in 1954, engineering drawings were being converted from India ink on linen to pencil on mylar. When CAD was introduced, drawings were again printed with ink but now on special paper. I believe that today some engineering designs go directly to the manufacturing area without a drawing.

PAUL C. ROSENBERGER

I worked in the Division of Data Processing General Offices (DPGO) starting in 1967. I went through the first internal Entry Level Training Program for DPGO. The course was taught by Kenniston Lord and included 1401 Autocoder Programming Language, COBOL Programming Language, Job Control Language (JCL), IBM System 360 Operating System and Guide 1057 Systems Development Methodology. The programs were written on coding pads and keypunched into cards. You desk-checked the cards to detect key-punching mistakes. This was critical because turnaround time between keypunch and the computer center might take one to two days. The computer center was located on A2 and housed two IBM Model 30s, one IBM Model 40, a lot of tape drives, a few disk drives and printers. Other machines to support running 1401 Autocoder programs and Electronic Accounting Machine (EAM) programs were also part of the

environment. Everything that ran on the computer was ultimately converted to paper in some form or another to view the results. Programs could not be any larger than 64K bytes. A short time later an IBM Model 60 was added and I believe programs could be as large as 128K bytes.

When you compare that environment with the powerful PCs of today, it is amazing that we ran our entire corporate portfolio of systems with less computer power than currently sits on our desks. The creation of programs is now on-line and turnaround is almost instantaneous. The storage medium has migrated to various forms of disk storage with very little magnetic tape in use. Paper reports are basically printouts of information that is available on-line. Computer technology is changing at such a rapid pace today, it would be difficult to envision where we will be in another five years.

THOMAS D. MCMAHILL

I started working at Caterpillar in June, 1928, when the Two-Ton tractor was being replaced by the new Twenty. My first job was assembling shoes on the track. We worked 44 hours per week for 50¢ per hour,

which I considered a good wage for a kid just out of high school. I was laid off three times during the Great Depression but had steady work from 1933 until I retired on January 1, 1973.

I was there when the transition was made from gasoline to diesel engines.

MAURICE H. BRADEN

It was an extremely cold January, but I don't recall the year. My desk in Accounting [Decatur] was at the top of the stairs on the second floor. Each time the front door to the Reception Room was opened, a blast of cold air went up the stairs directly to my feet and legs. It was an extremely uncomfortable situation and I received no sympathy.

I decided to take matters into my own hands, so I wore a heavy slack suit and boots to work. Of course, I was advised by my supervisor to not wear slacks to work again or I would be sent home and risk losing my job.

I had a passion pink slack suit with a tunic top which I wore the next day to work. All my co-workers, aware of the circumstances of the previous day, questioned my sanity.

Before I went to my desk, I carefully removed my pink slack pants and nonchalantly strolled to my desk to the amusement of "some" of my co-workers. I had made a statement that "pant" restrictions for females was discriminatory and senseless.

Even though it took many months before my "statement" was honored and women were allowed to wear slacks, I think my "statement" was the impetus for the policy to change and it was definitely a welcome relief to women employees at Cat.

BETTY J. CEARLOCK

The tough years were the first three, starting in 1931. As nearly as I can estimate I earned $1,238 in three years. Some wages!! Compare that to today. My retirement pay is nearly the same per month.

ALVIE L. RICE

I recall how Dr. Wang put on a demonstration of the first computer that displayed numbers and letters on a screen. It must have been in the mid-'60s in the Accounting Department Conference Room. This first demo was a failure. The numbers kept rolling because the power frequency

was different. However, in two weeks Dr. Wang was back to put on a successful demonstration.

E. ROGER STREID

The first computer-controlled machine that I remember coming into the factory was what was called a Burgmaster "Turret Drill." This thing had a turret you could load with tools and a moving table upon which you could mount your work piece. You loaded the instruction into the machine via a paper-punched tape. Once the tape was read into the machine, you could hit the "start cycle" button and a miracle occurred. The machine table would actually move the work piece to the proper location under the correct tool in the turret. The machine was so advanced we did not know how to predetermine production work order times for it. The technology simply blew everyone away.

BRIAN J. KOSINSKI

When I started at Caterpillar in 1934, all machines ran from pulleys from overhead power, the jack trucks were all run by raw hand power, the yards were mostly unpaved and covered by cinders and it took three or four men to move a jack truck loaded

with iron! It's a new world down there today!

C. BRUNENMEYER

People followed the flow of yellow equipment around the world as established and emerging national economies expanded. As the tractors covered new ground, employees found themselves facing new cultures and solving problems in creative new relationships based on mutual respect and an appreciation of differences.

In April of 1989, Jim Duke of Product Division, Fred Spiegel of East Peoria Engineering and I traveled to the Siberian Pipeline to follow up on a group of tractors and pipelayers which had been sold to the Ministry of Oil and Gas. After five days in a pipeline camp in the vicinity of Yamburg where we lived in steel tubes about three meters in diameter and 10 meters long, we made our way south to the city of Urengoy which sits right on the Arctic Circle to meet with the ministry people in charge of the Urengoy Region. Following the meetings, they took us to dinner at a club on the outskirts of the city. As we approached the club, Duke commented that this was the same club he had been to during his visit to Urengoy in 1988 and that he had taught the band to play "Dixie." My reaction of course was, "Sure you did, Jim." When we entered, we were greeted by a hostess who escorted us to our table and as we passed the band stand, they all pointed and waved at Duke and began to play "Dixie."

BOB EMMERT

One of our greatest marketing challenges can be convincing a customer to replace a proven, trusted Cat product with a new, improved one.

In 1985, the dealer invited me to speak at a customer marine engine seminar in the Indian coastal city of Visakhapatnam. "Visak," as it was called, was home port to a large number of vessels that fished in the Bay of Bengal. At the seminar, we were highlighting the features and benefits of the 3400 Series marine propulsion engines. In the course of the seminar, we learned that the Cat D353 was widely used in the fleet. As I recall, the D353 was introduced in the early 1960s, a 1200 rpm, inline 6-cylinder design, producing 425 hp in a propulsion engine configuration.

Later in the day, a customer was describing his experience with his D353. He explained that they affectionately called it "the stupid engine." I wasn't sure how to react to the statement, so I asked him to explain. He went on describing the tough conditions under which the engine worked, their efforts to maintain them and the tight economics that prevented them from always buying the genuine spare parts they needed. But in spite of all this, the "stupid" engine kept on working reliably, taking them fishing and bringing them home safely.

At that point, I could see that the 3412 was up against a tough competitor ... the "stupid" old D353.

DAVID A. NOELKEN

A field report from Afghanistan by Jay M. Fetters, dated May 11, 1932, was found in Caterpillar files in Geneva, Switzerland. Here's an extract from that report. Submitted by Merv Rennick.

The Thirty arrived in Kabul on May 4th. The War Minister was notified and we were asked to bring it to the War Office for inspection at four o'clock that afternoon. By the time we arrived, all the officials from the army and the civil departments were on hand as well as several hundred soldiers and other people.

The War Minister looked the Thirty over but did not seem much impressed. I took it without any load and did some maneuvers for a few minutes. He then asked me to try to pull a heavy steel wagon, loaded with a big gun, that was standing behind the office. The whole load must have weighed 12 or 14 tons and the wagon had been standing for months. It had settled several inches into the ground. The wheels looked as if they had not been lubricated since the wagon was delivered.

We had no chain to make a hitch but someone said we could get some chain from the elephants that were working nearby. Someone else said to bring the elephant and let him try to move the load so they could see how strong the machine was. This is the kind of a show that appeals, so the minister gave the order for the elephant to be brought. The crowd was still gathering from every side and by the time the elephant arrived, the compound and the street outside were full of people.

The elephant was a big one and knew how to make his weight help. With much shouting and advice from the crowd, he was soon hitched. He first leaned into the load slowly to find out how much he was going to have to pull and after he had tightened the chain and the load did not move, he backed up one step, bent his legs both front and back, and went into it with a snort, with all his strength and weight but—he couldn't move it an inch. He tried three times, the crowd yelled "Shabash, Shabash." Mr. Elephant pulled and grunted but it was too much for him so they unhitched to give the Thirty a chance.

The crowd settled back to watch us fail because to them an elephant personifies power and strength and as they had seen him fail, they felt sure the "Caterpillar"—that looked so small beside the elephant—could not move such a load.

I backed the Thirty up and took a short hitch, put it in low gear, opened the throttle, took up the slack in the chain and took a hard steady pull. The load moved about a half inch and then the tracks spun so I backed up about six inches, opened the throttle again and slammed the clutch in, taking no chances to fail in front of the Minister and that mob—and off walked the Thirty with the load behind.

"Shabash, Shabash, Shabash." The crowd yelled and cheered good and proper this time.

The next day I repeated the demonstration for the King. In excellent English he told me how impressed they all were with the tractor, thanked me for coming to Kabul to show it, and then said: "Mr. Fetters, you will be pleased to know that I have just instructed my prime minister to purchase 12 of your machines."

They will use the tractors in many ways in their development scheme. First and foremost on roads, there being no railways in the country and no money with which to build them for some years to come. In addition to roads there will be drainage schemes, snow removal and agriculture which will be aided by state plowing, etc.

If you are unable to supply Thirtys and so advise me I will try to get them to take Thirty-Fives and if that is not successful will go back to Twenty-Fives.

Yours very truly,

J. M. FETTERS,
DISTRICT REPRESENTATIVE

I met the project manager for the dam at the Central Hotel in Kano, Nigeria. Together we set out in a borrowed four-wheel-drive vehicle, with a driver who spoke English and Haussa, hoping that the dam site would be dry enough for access. The dam site, on the Bunga River, is actually closer to Bauchi, a four-hour drive from Kano. A huge tree fallen across a creek caused us to search for another crossing place. After hours of involuntary sightseeing, we found the dam site and did our inspection. Then we got stuck trying to return to Kano. First one tribesman came, then another, and we put branches and stones under the wheels, to no avail. One of our helpers suggested that we Europeans should come to his village, stay there and wait for the car, which he would get out of the water before nightfall with the help of the villagers. Darkness came, and with it an endless amount of mosquitos. Then the lightning came. The villagers couldn't move the car. The little village could not accommodate us, so our guide took us on foot to his village. We almost ran for an hour, through bush, high grass, and sometimes water, trying not to lose sight of the guide in almost total darkness. Only the lightning helped, as we would never have found our trail again if we had lost it. When we got to the village, we were given a three-by-three meter hut in a complex of huts belonging to the chief. The hard earth was not exactly comfortable, but cleaner than the hotels in Kano. At the crack of dawn we organized the four bicycles of the village, three for us and one for a guide who was to lead us to the highway. All bikes had twisted frames and none had brakes. Three boys started running as soon as we left the village, to bring the bicycles back from the highway. We soon discovered the difficulty of cycling through the savannah. Our wheels spun and we slid right and left as we tried to stabilize our progress with our feet on the ground—the only way to brake the bicycle. To ford the creek—where we had trouble with our vehicle the day before—we took off our boots, rolled up our trousers and shouldered our bikes in true sporty fashion. It was getting warm when we reached the highway. Here we left the bikes with our guide and

thumbed our way to the next town. That evening, a resident engineer told us that what we went through is sold at a high price in Germany as an "Adventure Holiday."

CARLOS MIHALKA, AS REPORTED IN THE *COSA ECHO*, A PUBLICATION OF CATERPILLAR IN GENEVA, SWITZERLAND

In 1977, after having worked at Mentor, Dallas and Toronto, I was offered the opportunity to work in Brazil. My wife and I spent a month in immersion language training before we left for Brazil. In Brazil, I bought a used car. It was a late model Ford and was cute and powerful. On our first drive with this car, we ran into a rainstorm. The mud started packing, the exhaust system loosened and the car started to sound like a race car. I promised my wife I would get it fixed right away.

The next day I spotted a billboard that read "amortecedores" and showed the picture of a muffler. I went to the shop and pointed at my car and said, "amortecedores." The man working there shrugged his shoulders and went to work on the car. I went and had a cup of coffee. Later he gave me the bill and I was surprised to find that I had

bought four amortecedores. He went over to the car and pushed down on the fender smiling at me. I then realized I had bought a new set of shock absorbers! On the way out he called to me that next time I might consider buying a "silenceador," a muffler. It was a good lesson for me in language skills in my early days in Brazil.

JOHN G. BARRY

In 1952, I got my first field assignment to Lima, Peru, to cover the west coast of South America. In Lima, there were no phones in homes and Peoria was 4000 miles away, so communication was by letter and an occasional cable.

There was the thrill of getting to know countries new to me, making new friends through shared experiences (we still keep in touch with many friends from South America whom we met in the '50s) and exploring lands of contrast (geographic, historic, ethnic, cultural). I recall the first multiple D397 El setting installation at 16,000 feet in the Andes; the development of Southern Peru Copper's giant Toquepala open pit mine;

working with contractors building the first pipeline over the Andes; and a 500 kilometer highway from Cochabamba to Santa Cruz, Bolivia, across the Andes and through jungle.

These experiences, together with helping dealers to do their jobs better, made this initial overseas period the most interesting and enjoyable part of my career. The downside of this period was the time I had to spend away from home and family. It was a huge territory, and transport was by road or in DC3s and DC4s, so my trips averaged three weeks at a time. Much credit to my well-being and success is due to my wife's understanding and willingness to put up with my absences, and take care of a

young family on her own during those times.

Blair
BLAIR L. MANNING

For four years my territory covered New South Wales and Queensland in Australia and two major projects were Mount Isa copper mine open cut and the Snowy Mountains Hydro project. I was proud to represent a company which had such an important presence with such major projects. Caterpillar did well and had an enviable reputation. It was not easy, either. One week in 40 degrees Celsius in Mount Isa and the next week in -5 degrees in the Snowy. Still, that's how the company got its reputation —its people would be wherever they were needed. Another extreme for me was to be in Marble Bar, the hottest place in Australia, and then within a few months to be in Prudeau Bay on the north coast of Alaska.

HOWARD NEILSON

In 1955, I had the wonderful opportunity to join a group going to Scotland to set up a factory in Tannockside, Scotland. What an incredible opportunity for a Missouri guy, gal and four children. Our children ranged from

seven to 15 years old. We all had mixed emotions but in retrospect, we also all benefited from the experience. We traveled from Peoria to Liverpool, England, and then to Scotland. What an adventure. Our lives certainly would never be the same. For four years we all experienced things that would never have been possible had we not been offered this chance. We all saw the Continent, traveled throughout Great Britain and made true friends with the Scots. We've all returned to visit. The kids' excellent schooling experiences made adjusting to a new country well worth it. We feel we owe Caterpillar a debt of thanks for this invaluable experience.

Roley G. Stephens
ROLEY G. STEPHENS
"STOVE"

I was sent to Grenoble, France, in 1963 to manage the Caterpillar plant there.

One of the first things a manager has to do in a new job is to learn how to work with his secretary. My secretary worked with our lawyers to set up board meetings—sent out proxies—prepared the registry—and did a multitude of things connected with corporate matters. She spoke five languages and had exceptional administrative perception. If a job had to be done and she considered it important, she would stay half the night and even came to work on Sundays when necessary. On the other hand, she consistently arrived late for work, then immediately disappeared to apply her face. When cautioned about this habit, her reply was that a French boss wasn't supposed to arrive until an hour after the rest of the work force and that if I would behave like I should, she would be there before I was and I would never know she was late. I never was able to separate her from this philosophy.

BOB GILMORE

In February, 1966, only a few days after I started working at Caterpillar France SA in Grenoble, I was standing at the bus stop waiting for my bus to go downtown. A car stopped next to me. The window on the driver side opened, and Mr. Gilmore, our American managing director, leaned out and asked me where I wanted to go and offered to drive me there! I was very surprised to hear

Mr. Gilmore knew who I was and the division I was working in, in a plant with over 1,300 employees! One must keep in mind that it was 1966, and it is not that common that a plant manager offers to one of his employees to drive him somewhere. Was it the starting point of our Common Values implementation?

SAUVEUR
SCOTTO

As a traveler to foreign lands, one of the things we tried to do was to partake of the local cuisine and in some areas this was difficult. I remember Don Coonan, who held many positions outside of the United States, telling about getting the goat's eyes in the Middle East where both of us traveled. We also got caught one time in Iraq during one of their skirmishes in the '60s and were sequestered in a hotel for a few days while the shooting was going on in the streets. In Iraq I also remember being served a fish which had been cooked in the ground when we visited shipbuilders on one of the Iraqi rivers. It was a bit

difficult to think about eating green salad and fish from the ground with one's fingers but we did our best to accommodate our hosts. There were, of course, other stories from the Middle East, such as the beautiful city of Beirut which was, at the time, our sanctuary as we traveled throughout the Middle East when we were not in Geneva. The city today is no comparison to that of the early '60s.

Wayne Coon
WAYNE COON

After my first tour of duty as a field engineer stationed in Beirut and Tehran, I was asked to visit the UK operations on my way back to Tehran. Our first visit was to the London Office, where Ross Adcock, then district representative for the UK, met my wife and me. We were invited to have lunch with Ross and his family at their cottage on the Thames near Windsor.

After lunch, the favored activity was punting on the Thames, and after Ross got us started, I asked for a turn at the pole. Naturally, on the third push off with the pole, it got stuck in the mud and I couldn't pull it out. Therefore, we drifted aimlessly down the Thames

for several miles until a powered boat brought our pole back to us. Now I know what it means to be up the river without a paddle.

RODNEY D. PAGE

I moved with my wife and three preschool daughters to Mexico City, Mexico, in October, 1960. It was a first foreign assignment as a sales field engineer.

After settling the family in an apartment, the district representative suggested a first trip, accompanying a Rome Plow Rep to deliver a D7, KG Tree Shearing Blade, and heavy disc plow to a sugar plantation. First we flew in a DC-3 to the nearest city, then by car (two flat tires) to the plantation headquarters. By Jeep we bounced to the river landing. Our river boat was a roofed launch powered by a Ford car engine/transmission. We used poles to navigate tight river turns. I spent the trip lying on the roof practicing Spanish with a Mextrac salesman.

Arriving at the landing nearest the area to be land-cleared, we were transported to the site by sugarcane wagons pulled by small tractors and accompanied by horsemen.

Headquarters at the site was a dirt-floored shack, home of the lady cook who shooed chickens and young pigs away from the cook pot. I soon got the worst case of the "Aztec Two Step" (diarrhea) experienced by humans. After much labor to mount the KG Blade and assemble the disc plow, we showed them how to use it. Four days later, we headed back to the ranch across country on horses, fording rivers. Six different modes of transport in one trip. It was quite an initiation into the life of a field representative!

C. RODNEY BOYNTON

I was present for the start-up of the plant in Piracicaba, Brazil. There were a number of problems. The first was learning a new language. The second was overcoming the ill feelings of most Brazilians. When you live in a large house and drive a new car and your Brazilian boss lives in a three room apartment and drives a six-year-old car, you can understand his resentment. But when the people learned you were sincere about helping them get a new plant started, you could get the job done. I used to tell people in a weekly meeting, "Caterpillar e Caterpillar, Brasil and

Estatos Unidos mesmo!" As processing supervisor, I tried to anticipate all the needs of moving from São Paulo to the new plant in Piracicaba, but when the new chains for the Steel Bay came in, I learned they didn't have heat-treated chains in Brazil. I received a dressing down for buying chains nobody could lift. We also had quality problems with weld wire. The weld engineer, Marion Scott, ran down the problem, which was gaps of no flux in the center of the weld wire. When I discovered they had no standards for weld wire in Brazil, we developed a second source and the competition improved the quality of the wire. You soon learned that people in Brazil were just as capable as people in the United States. Just their priorities were different. Piracicaba has its 25th anniversary in the year 2000.

Charles C Morris
CHARLES C. MORRIS

In 1963, I was working at a warehouse in Lapa, Brazil, without air conditioning and with a metallic roof that almost roasted us inside. A recently arrived American was working there and I invited him to have a soft drink in the front bakery. He accepted and when I asked him what kind of soft drink he wanted, he said "siete up" in Spanish. I said we did not know such a drink and he accepted a Coke instead. While drinking the Coke, he saw someone else drinking the one he asked for and complained, asking me how we called that drink. I said, "Seven Up." He laughed and told me he was translating it to Spanish to make it easier for me to understand.

One of the American wives told me that she learned in Brazil to cross the red light when driving late at night and she enjoyed it so much she was going to adopt the same procedure in Peoria.

FRANCISCO MARCELLINI

Editor's note: Following is a postscript from his wife.

As the wife of a Caterpillar employee from 1960 to 1990 here in Brazil, we were always seeing the possibility of constant progress in his job, we were able to give not only school but also a comfortable life at home to our three children, and now, both of us being retired, we still have medical care and monetary help. We thank you for all this and pray for Caterpillar to continue giving such living conditions to all employees all over the world.

MARIA LUIZA MARCELLINI

I progressed to the Engineering and Research Departments, eventually becoming chief engineer of the Glasgow, Scotland, plant in 1958. This was one of Cat's early manufacturing ventures overseas. One of the first things we had to develop was a communication system. We were tooling up for the D8 tractor which was to be the same machine worldwide regardless of where it was manufactured. This required close cooperation between Engineering Departments, which didn't always occur.

One day the Engineering Department in Peoria reviewed the latest lab reports on the engine air cleaner and decided it was too small. This was at 4 p.m. at a meeting with the U.S. supplier, who immediately telephoned his home office, who, in turn, cabled their licensee in Wales, who telephoned us in Glasgow. The production date was close upon us and we needed the blueprints for this change.

At that time Russia had launched the first satellite orbiting around the earth and it was in all the news. We sent a cable to Peoria: "Sputnik reports change in D8 air cleaner. Please send details."

The cable arrived in Peoria during the night and was on the engineer's desk the next morning. They were amazed at how we knew of their decision so quickly. Anyway, it helped to develop the kind of communication systems so necessary for a worldwide multinational corporation like Caterpillar.

ROBERT V. LARSON

CHALLENGING TIMES

Part of a quality company is its performance under stressful circumstances. These stories share the human side of the Caterpillar community facing challenging times. The stories include memories of the 1943 flood of the Illinois River, reflections of World War II and Caterpillar employees pulling together in times of tragedy and loss.

FLOOD STORIES...

During the 1943 Illinois River flood in East Peoria, many factory employees worked at sandbagging the levees to prevent the Caterpillar factory from being flooded. All ground floor offices were shut down, but Engineering, being on the second floor, was requested to work. We were warned if the levee broke we

were to evacuate immediately, a whistle was to be sounded. It did sound and we ran like scared rabbits—only to find out it was malfunction due to the wet weather.

BETTY M. RUSSELL

During the flood in 1943, I was on third shift as an instructor in the Training Department and my boss was Hugh Bush who was working on third shift this particular night. We were directed to go down to Farm Creek at West Washington Street to help with filling sandbags. We alternated with shoveling and holding the bag. We were working away like mad when we heard someone call out in a loud voice, asking if anyone could drive a tractor. We both stopped and straightened up just to see who was calling and he assumed we were volunteering. He said, "Follow me." We hurried around the other side of a building which stood there. There sat two tractors hitched to four-wheeled dump wagons loaded with sand. I said, "We'll drive the tractors but I don't know how to start these with the gasoline starting engines." He proceeded to start them while I instructed Hugh how to drive a Caterpillar Track-Type Tractor.

My dad had let me drive the city's No. 60 Caterpillar when I was in high school, so I knew how to use the brakes and the steering levers. When the tractors were started, he instructed us to take them down between Building HH and the Foundry. We were about halfway down the length of HH when we met Jim Munro. He yells out, "Where are you going with those?" When I told him we were following instructions, he said, "This is where all that sand came from and they need it over between building N and building P." I was able to wheel my rig around and head back out to Washington Street, but Hugh was unable to maneuver his and get it turned around so they held him for a relief driver. When I arrived at the north side of buildings P and N, where they had instructed me to go, they wanted the dump wagon of sand backed into Building N to be dumped. This is where I met my Waterloo as I could not get that four-wheeled wagon to do what I wanted it to do. I was really sweating when somebody yelled, "Here comes the regular driver." So, I happily turned it all over to him and went back for another assignment.

ROBERT BAYLESS

My employment started with Caterpillar in 1941. I had moved to Peoria from Nebraska ...as a direct result of Depression days and drought on the farms of Nebraska. After seven straight years of crop failure due to the weather, it was time for a life change.

Having sold my old Model A for $10 in the farm auction and with little money left, I chose to hitchhike across the country to find a reliable place of employment. Caterpillar had a good reputation and did not rely on the weather for success or failure ...a welcome relief. I stood in line many mornings until I was finally interviewed and accepted for a job in the Parts Department.

Just as I felt relieved to have a job that did not depend on the weather, what happened? We had huge amounts of rain and the Illinois River was on the brink of flooding, threatening the entire Caterpillar plant and the city. Along with everyone else on third shift, I worked countless hours on the dike putting sandbag after sandbag in place.

This threat of flood and work on the dike was one of my most traumatic experiences at Caterpillar. It was dark, cold, rainy, and we could feel the dike shaking under foot—on the brink of giving way and potentially resulting in drownings and flooding the plant. I can remember thinking, "Maybe I should have stayed on the farm where at least I was safe." But we kept working hard and, with the Lord's help, prevailed over the river—saving people and helping the Cat plant keep her feet dry.

Fritz Dalluge
FRITZ DALLUGE

In 1943, Caterpillar stopped production for two weeks to combat the flood. I was assigned to watch duty in Building P. I was told to keep an eye on two sandbags covering a sewer manhole. Two men on eight hour shifts. We were told if we saw water seeping out from under the sand bags to notify the foreman immediately. It was a tiresome job. After the flood scare was over, we removed the sandbags and had a good laugh and surprise: no manhole.

John Stepzinski
JOHN STEPZINSKI

WORLD WAR II STORIES

On June 6, 1944, when I landed on Utah Beach with my division, we were being struck by German planes. I took refuge and hid under one of the Caterpillar tractors that was being used to pull our invasion equipment onto to the beach.

Maybe I had supplied the tools to this tractor in Building HH just a short time before.

Robert D. Reeves
ROBERT D. REEVES

Caterpillar sponsored a Heavy Shop Company for the U.S. Corps of Engineers. Their job: maintenance and repair of equipment, especially Track-Type Tractors. The 158 volunteers from Caterpillar were inducted as a group in 1942 and trained together in Louisiana. Their major work was on the Ledo Road in Burma. Jean Walker, who had been a Caterpillar field representative in South Africa, was captain of the company. Here's an extract from a letter he wrote from Burma to a friend in Peoria on December 1, 1944:

Dear Mac:
Your letter was one of the nicest events that's come along the Ledo Road for a long time. To have you say that Kitty has never looked better helps a lot. You see, she'll never say whether she's fit or ill ... always O.K. So, thanks.

The outfit is really doing a grand job. I didn't know what I was tackling when I said yes to this job. Sometimes they act like a bunch of two-year-old kids. You are mother, father, teacher, disciplinarian, all rolled into one. I'm 20 years older than I was two years ago, but Lord how they do work.

They have set a record, that for real accomplishment, can't be beaten anywhere. As you probably guess, I'm rather proud of them, but I will be very glad when I can say "dismissed" for the last time.

SUBMITTED BY DEARL MORRIS

October 26, 1943, was my first day at Caterpillar. It was World War II and women were helping the war effort. I was to be in the Foundry Office for six months until the return of Swede Peterson. I remained there on various jobs until 1970. Many men resented the presence of women. Others were understanding and helpful. Even the good men liked to pull jokes on us sometimes.

Frank Shipley was Foundry Manager for a long period of time. We sometimes bantered about politics. He was a Republican, and I a Democrat. Mr. Shipley admired Herbert Hoover. I remember the days when President Hoover kept telling us to tighten our belts while his own waist line became even larger. One of the several times President Truman "blew his stack" at a music critic who was unkindly critical of Margaret's ability, Frank Shipley paused at my desk and said, "What do you have to say about the pipsqueak now?" I replied, "The same thing I say when I hear unkind remarks about you. Mr. Shipley: Until I can surpass your achievement I'll withhold unkind comment." He went on into his office and closed the door. As a last resort he would always do that. I really missed him when he retired."

Ethel Freant
ETHEL G. FREANT

During World War II, I was the manufacturing manager at the San Leandro plant. At that time, Caterpillar was important to the military. We were asked to convert our parts manufacturing production lines to lines that produced rifle case dies, bomb fuses and 37 millimeter armor piercing shells.

On one occasion, I was asked to go to Stanford University to get the details required for the production of a five-inch rocket. Caterpillar was asked to produce as many rockets as possible. We had to borrow machinery from various production lines in order to produce 100 rockets a week in three weeks time. It was a real rush job. In fact, with the plant working three shifts, we were able to increase the production to 250 rockets a week. It was a real war effort.

During the war years, we hired 850 women to work on the lines. These women were hired to replace the men who were drafted. They played an important part in keeping Caterpillar going. One day I received a phone call from the owner of Friden Calculator, a San Leandro company, asking me not to hire his women. The women came to Caterpillar looking for work at better pay. I told him I would gladly stop if he would stop hiring our top tool and die and automatic screw machine workers. He made no response as he hung up the phone!

ALAN PARRY

It was June, 1944, in the Tuscany region of Italy. At the exit of my small village, about 61 kilometers from Florence, a small bridge was dynamited by the retreating German army. Miraculously, after a few hours, some soldiers of the Allied armies materialized, followed by huge machines which laid big tubes on the bottom of the stream. Tractors, loaders and motor graders did the rest.

Presto! The way was open to let most of the troops pass. The work to recover the bridge began just after lunch and it was finished just before dark.

I was seven years old. I watched the entire operation, fascinated by the movements of the men and machines. It was a big show. A name printed on one of the machines was engraved on my mind: CATERPILLAR.

20 years later, July, 1964— São Paulo, Brazil. I had been approved to work as a machine operator for Simca do Brasil, an automobile factory in São Bernado do Campo and also for Caterpillar Brasil, a tractor factory in Santo Amaro. The salary offered by the French factory was 40% more than Caterpillar's offer. I had to make up my mind between the two companies in order to "set my future."

The 20-year-old image of an earth mover rebuilding the bridge in my little village made me choose Caterpillar, even though it was less money.

The French company closed down its activities a few months later. And Caterpillar became the gigantic industrial complex that we now know. It was the best choice of my life!

ANDREA MATTESINI

HELPING FAMILIES AND COMMUNITY ...

Born in 1924, I spent the first 21 years in Indonesia where my father had a construction company. The last 3 1/2 years of this time the men in the family were in a POW camp. In January, 1946, we repatriated to the Netherlands. During the 10 years there I worked and attended university where I received my bachelor's and master's degrees.

In August, 1956, my wife, children and I emigrated to the U.S. sponsored by the First Presbyterian Church of Decatur, which had taken care of housing for my family and a job for me at Caterpillar Tractor Co. I started as a draftsman in Engineering. We were awed by the help and friendliness of all the people! We received assistance with shopping and recipes. The children (ages 9, 7 and 5) were supplied with picture dictionaries and toys. They started school three weeks

after we arrived and were helped with the language and customs. It was the same at work. In no time they made me "one of them."

GENE EASTERLING

In the early 1950s, the Caterpillar company officials who controlled the purse kept it tightly closed and didn't spend money freely. Chief Forbin wanted a new fire truck but knew the cost for buying one would not be approved. He decided to purchase an Army Jeep and make our own fire truck. I recall one evening a small industry on Highway 6, a couple of miles from the Joliet plant, had a fire. Caterpillar's training stressed that they wanted management to promote good relations and be good neighbors. We saw the flames shooting into the sky and heard the Joliet city fire trucks on Highway 6. I made the decision to go help our neighbors. The little Jeep was so loaded we could only get about 45 or 50 miles per hour out of it. The big fire trucks from Joliet and other cities would roar past us blowing their horns and flashing their

lights. When the fire was extinguished, although they didn't need our help, they were amused at our little Jeep fire truck and thought it was real funny. It was equipped with about all the emergency equipment that goes on a regular fire truck except a water tank.

W. W. "BILL" MINGS

My son Joseph and his family moved to Monterrey, Mexico. We all hated to see them leave for many reasons but mostly because Joe was the special one who everyone turned to with their problems. His love of life and people seemed to dictate his every move and thought.

Joe loved Mexico and its people. He tried to learn everything about them and their culture.

Just as dawn broke on Monday, March 19th, my husband and I were awakened by banging on the front door. Our daughter, Phyllis, and her husband entered. She was wearing her robe and the expression on her face told me something bad had happened. I said, "My God, did your house burn down?"

She put her arms around me and began to cry. Her next words tore at my heart as she said, "We've lost him."

Believing she meant my oldest son who had a heart condition, I said, "Buster?" She answered, "No mother, it's Joe."

Staring at her in stunned disbelief, I entered into a mental twilight zone. Our world, as we knew it, would never be the same. We learned later that he had a blood clot that entered his heart, killing him instantly. As Joe's family waited for the ambulance, Joe's friend, Lee Edwards, was called at the Caterpillar plant. He told her he would be there as quickly as possible. Lee arrived with others from Caterpillar who were authorized to help. Caterpillar contacted the American Embassy and my worst fears, that his body would be detained, were put to rest.

People at Caterpillar and local friends requested a chance to say goodbye to Joe so by that evening a memorial was held at the mortuary chapel, arranged by Caterpillar, including the priest and family friends. After the memorial a gathering was held at their house where food and refreshments were furnished by Caterpillar and friends.

The next morning a car arrived from Caterpillar to pick up Joe's family and drive them to the airport. Lee Edwards met them as he accompanied them home. Customs had been cleared in advance, so all, including Joe's casket, boarded the plane without delays. Arriving in Houston, Texas, the U.S. Customs treated them with the same courtesy. I'm sure Caterpillar had contacted them also.

Although I wrote a thank-you letter to the Monterrey plant, I realized corporate offices were also involved and hope this story will let them know of Joe's family's appreciation.

PEGGY TUCKER

On July 18, 1994, Jana Rockey, Shirley Kon, and I were hit by a drunk driver in front of Caterpillar's corporate headquarters. The driver came up on the sidewalk and on the wall in front of Cat and knocked Jana over the wall and pinned Shirley and me under the car. A pillar in front of Cat stopped the car.

Jana had minor injuries. Caterpillar nurse Martha Belford was there immediately to see that Jana was O.K. I was thought to be dead as I had no pulse but gurgled (probably trying to say "get this car off me"). The Cat

receptionist called for emergency help and within minutes fire fighters and ambulances were there but it took them awhile to lift the car off.

Cat's medical director, Dr. Crane, tried to reach Bob Scroggs, my husband, who was in Denver pulling parts. He finally got through to Bob. On the way to the airport, they got a phone call informing them to go to a different airport where a Lear Jet was waiting to fly Bob back to Peoria. Bob flew back and when he landed in Peoria, Jim Baldwin, his vice president, and Jerry Kenney, director of compensation, met him. They told him they knew no details and drove him to St. Francis Hospital. He went to my room where he hardly recognized me as my head was huge (swollen) and there were all kinds of tubes running into me.

At the hospital, Marci Carballido, Janie Copeland, Mike DeWalt, Bill Martin, Bob Gallagher and others gathered to see how their co-workers were doing.

I was given only a 20% chance of making it but I fooled them. I was in a coma for six weeks and then in rehab. I am blind in the left eye, the right eye doesn't work right because the right side of my face is partially paralyzed. I have a palsy in my right leg, a third degree burn scar on my right leg and my right hand doesn't work quite right. Because I feared that returning to corporate life would cause me to lose the little sight remaining, I decided (after a long debate with myself) to go on permanent disability.

The day after the accident, Sally Malmberg, Don Fites' secretary, called Jana and offered a car and driver if Jana needed help getting to her doctor appointments. She also called Bob and asked if he needed anything. He requested a cell phone so he could keep in touch with work and the hospital—the next day, Donna Frank and Jim Baldwin brought him one.

According to Paul Buchanan, the day after the accident, Cat brought in Sue Kirk, a psychiatrist, to talk to employees who were either scared about walking in front of the building or who were traumatized from the accident which injured three of their co-workers and/or friends.

All levels of Cat came to the hospital and have stood by these three employees through their surgeries and rehabilitation. Jim Owens, now a group president, came over to check on Jana and welcome her back when she returned. Jana says for months after the accident people would stop her to ask a question about the accident or check on my medical status.

Employees might not realize the acts that Cat does in situations like this and we thought they should read about a terrible situation made good through the care and kindness of Caterpillar's employees.

Shirley still works for Cat. Jana works in Corporate Accounting as an analysis clerk. Bob retired from Cat in 1997 and he and I live in Sun City Grand, Surprise, Arizona.

MARY SCROGGS

WORK STORIES

These stories about working at Caterpillar speak of affection for machinery, adapting to new technical problems and cultural situations, practical innovations and solutions, a sense of personal and organizational progress and pride in one's contribution to making Caterpillar a high quality global company.

My neighbor George Heiser, originally started working for Mr. Oscar Starr on his experimental ranch testing many different kinds of tractors in the 1930s. George repaired and operated all kinds of equipment and eventually went to work in the Machine Maintenance Department of Caterpillar where he remained on the job for 37 years.

George worked up in Vasco on Mr. Starr's ranch, testing all kinds of tractor functions from bulldozing to grading. Mr. Starr's ranch was approximately 3,000 acres. According to George, Mr. Starr was a common, hard working man. His motto was, "If I can do it, you can do it." George said he was a wonderful and nice man to work for. Mr. Starr was the largest shareholder of Caterpillar in those days.

Mr. Starr personally hired George to work in his factory. How this happened was out at the ranch Mr. Starr told George to go and fill out an application. So he did. The personnel boss told him they didn't have any work, but when Mr. Starr found this out he told them to put George to work anyway.

FRANCINE NOVICK ON BEHALF OF GEORGE HEISER

Working on an oil drilling rig in the Persian Gulf in 1976 had its striking aspects. Being picked up from a boat in some kind of a basket dangling on a steel rope, itself suspended to a seemingly fragile crane and landing on the rig's platform is quite an experience. On the rig itself, working with people of various nationalities, cultures and creeds is an ever-fascinating adventure. Overall, being the representative of a well-respected equipment manufacturer can put the man on the spot, but if taken in the right perspective this responsibility is a mine of knowledge and of enriching human contacts.

MAURICE MONTJOVENT, AS REPORTED IN *COSA ECHO*, A PUBLICATION OF CATERPILLAR IN GENEVA, SWITZERLAND

In 1941, I graduated from the University of Illinois and reported for work at Caterpillar. At that time, all new employees went through a two-day orientation program without pay. Les Lord was our guide, teacher and mother hen. He did his best to fill us full of yellow paint by telling us about Caterpillar and the predecessor companies, Holt and Best, each of which built Track-Type Tractors and combines. I shall never forget his telling us about the fierce competition between the two companies prior to their merger in 1925. The Best Company advertised its machines with the following jingle: "Buy the Best; the Best is best."

In a short time however, the Holt Company countered with a jingle of its own, as follows: "Buy the Holt; the best is none too good."

ROGER M. SMITH

From Japan with flowers to Caterpillar. Living in Japan in one of Caterpillar's greatest competitor's locations, it was difficult to understand the culture of Caterpillar after joining the company, difficult to hear "English" from American bosses, difficult to understand U.S. and European plant/marketing needs. But now I am really enjoying this multicultural Caterpillar.

It's time to cast off the skin to be a new age butterfly flying over beautiful flowers.

MASA YAMAGUCHI

As engine product service rep for Italy, Tunisia and Morocco, I was called on to run the long awaited sea-trial on M/S Le Printemps, a trawler built by MECANAV, a shipyard at Sfax, a Tunisian port on the Mediterranean Sea. It was the first Tunisian vessel to be powered by a Cat-built engine: a 3408 Marine Engine. That morning not only the engine but also the boat had to demonstrate its seaworthiness. Quite honestly, both were doing much better than myself, the dealer personnel and some of the fishermen. Many of us were sick and we were thrown around the various quarters like logs. The boat itself was bounced and pounded by the waves like a nutshell and the captain had a hard time preventing the boat from tipping. The engine performed well during that storm and the boat truly proved its seaworthiness.

TONY JAGGY

I retired after 35 years with Cat. My last working day was September 16, 1995. I remember that about a week before leaving, my supervisor asked me if I had ever driven a tractor. I responded that I hadn't. He said it would be bad to retire without having that experience. He assigned a qualified employee to me to "show me the ropes."

I drove the 988. I felt like a little fly atop such a huge unit. It handled like a dream. The bucket was not attached, but I drove around and raised and lowered the front end. My escort asked what I would like to drive next. I was so nervous (as well as contented) and I responded that I just drove the "ultimate machine" and that was enough for me.

JAMES E. METZGER

Our first Director of Research Department was C. G. A. Rosen, to us in Building W, just Art Rosen, who was liked and respected by all, a man who knew good minds in Europe and U.S. as well. He believed in using together the analytical and experimental approaches in research whenever possible. More than once we have heard him urge us not to fear failure but think freely and act boldly. He believed that to create better products we also had to think

boldly and not fear being wrong. "We work in the region of failure," he used to say, "so, you may even expect to have failures."

ALEX GOLOFF

We had many successes, but there were failures also. We tried to incorporate what was called a "sealed for life" pin into the large wheel loader Z-bar linkage. This required a bolted joint at the pin location. Unfortunately, high tension forces were imposed on the linkage when the bucket was dumped. During the initial test the bolts failed, the linkage collapsed, and there we stood looking at our hands—work that now looked like a limp hand shake. Back to the drawing board! What a terrible feeling of disappointment. We eventually solved the problem.

JIM REISEL

I came to Peoria from Springfield in the spring of 1937. A good friend, Neil Fisher, provided me with food and housing, as I was penniless. In those days, it was customary to line up at Cat's employment office, file past the employment manager, and hope that you would be chosen.

For three weeks, early in the morning, and again in the afternoon, I walked over the Franklin Street Bridge, got in line, and smiled at the selector. Finally, at the end of the third week, I was chosen to unload castings in Building X Receiving, at 64 cents an hour. From then on, I was able to afford the street car to ride back and forth to work.

For the next 43 years, I traveled from Building X to HH, to the Industrial Division, to São Paulo, Brazil, to Building LL, to the Technical Center, from which I retired in 1980. I started as a penniless high school graduate and retired to a financially comfortable life style many years later.

I have many happy memories of my career at Caterpillar, as well as bizarre happenings. One incident I will never forget occurred during my tenure in Building LL.

Space to store material became a serious problem, so some visionary in the Planning Department decided that we could use the great outdoors to store the steel tubs of parts. So he purchased an enormous plastic tent, kept aloft by a huge air compressor. We stored our overflow storeroom in this monstrous balloon outside Building LL.

Unfortunately, the balloon had two enemies—high winds and snowstorms. On at least six occasions, I was awakened from a sound sleep and called to work because the tent was collapsing. It became the laughing stock of Building LL employees, some of whom referred to this monstrosity as "England's Bubble."

BOB ENGLAND

One incident I will never forget unless I would be stricken with Alzheimer's disease. It was about 1965 or 1966 in Peoria in Building KK. I was a foreman on second shift and I had a line inspector who was having problems by not catching bad set-ups on machines. This particular evening about 30 minutes into second shift I was going to have a trucker pick up a load of bad parts approved by this inspector and we were going to look at the part he approved. The weather outside was stormy and as we walked by a wash tank that vented through the roof we heard a whistling noise coming from that wash tank. I told the trucker there was a tornado coming. About that time it hit right above the ceiling where we were. I was told later the tornado sucked the cinder tile up and then dropped it. Parts of the roof

started falling in. I had nothing to hide under but put my head between two tote boxes. Only one person in the area had a piece of the roof that hit (him in) the back of his neck. The rain poured in the hole and I finally realized that where I was, was not a good place to be. Our assistant chief inspector was still in the building. He came out and sent me to first aid to get my eyes cleaned out. I was black from all the gray iron dust that came down from the overhead steel structure. I was told to go home and take the night off but we already had one of three foremen off so I went home, showered, ate dinner and went back to work. I was really shook up and did very little that night. The people on the line were mostly trying to contain the water. I was paid for a white shirt and a new tie. A line foreman told me he would bring something in that would clean the dirt and rust from my shirt. After I used it and went back to work, he asked me if it worked. I told him it made my shirt real white but I couldn't get the brown streaks out of my shorts.

I worked for a contractor before I worked at Caterpillar. I was angry at him so I applied at Caterpillar. I decided to keep the Caterpillar

job until I found a better one. I started in August of 1950 and retired January 1, 1985. Best thing that ever happened to me.

HARLEY FISHEL

My most beloved assignment was in air export orders in Peoria. If there's such a thing as loving a job, I did this one! I had a Selectric IBM typewriter which I fondly told, "There's no BM like an IBM." I prepared documents for parts to be flown from O'Hare in Chicago all over the world. Each country's paper work was different. One of my favorites was Fiji Islands because I could hum, "Oh say, Oh see, has anyone seen my GiGi from the Fiji Islands."

I am so proud of Caterpillar. I live in Arizona now where there is lots of building. So when I see all that road equipment, I clap my hands and say, "Thank God for Caterpillar" and please bless all the dear people who work there.

BETTY FULLER

I was a landscape architect at Caterpillar from 1965 to 1982, and worked all over the world. One of my favorite jobs was putting in natural landscaping —prairie grass—at the Technical Center and then at

Mossville and Mapleton plants. This is one of those win-win situations. It was handsome to look at, provided good erosion control, returned the land to its natural state and was cost-effective. In those days, it cost $300 per acre per year to cut the grass, but only $25 per acre per year for prairie grass. I was proud of that achievement.

WALTER BRAKEMAN

After spending six months in the factory, one of my shop foremen convinced me that I should try to enroll in the Caterpillar training program. After completing the two-year machine shop training program, I graduated into tool design in Building TT. What a change from the shop. I thought I had died and gone to heaven. After spending five years there, I decided that I would like to be a data processor. I put in a transfer for the Data Processing Department and became an analyst in April 1973. In 1976, the company decided to send me and my family to Gosselies, Belgium, to install several systems at that facility. This was probably one of my most memorable experiences

during my employment with Caterpillar. There we were, from living in a small town in central South Dakota; moving to a bigger city of Peoria, Illinois; and now living almost halfway around the world in Belgium (the international capital of the world). Whew, what a whirlwind ride this has turned out to be.

RICHARD E. DOLLY

I recall an occasion when the insufficient command of a foreign language caused a hilarious situation. Larry Warren was assigned as Brazil's chief engineer. By 1972, he had made a good impression among Brazilians due to his ability to use basic Portuguese words. But when Larry first arrived in Brazil, he didn't yet have a good command of the language. He saw thieves trying to break into his neighbor's house. Combining the best words he knew he told me what happened. I tried to help with some English words but he insisted on speaking Portuguese. I understood everything except "the police were playing soccer on the roof of the house."

The confusion was due to the fact that "shoot" sounds like "chute" which means kicking. "Bullets" is translated by "balas" which sounds like "bolas" which means balls. He said, "The police were playing soccer on the roof of the house," when he meant to say, "The police were shooting bullets against the roof of the house!"

CLAUDIO LUCCI

I hired in [at San Leandro] straight out of high school at the age of 17. I knew I wanted to be a machinist when I was in the eighth grade.

When we knew our plant was to be closed, my heart cried. I knew that I would be losing good friends to layoff and retirement. My job became the layoff foremen. I would move to a new department as the work came to an end.

My last day of work was very sad. Normally, it took 10 minutes to drive home, but that day it took an hour because it is hard to drive with tears in your eyes.

WILLIAM SHAVER

I retired January 1, 1984, after 30 years of service at the York plant. Our first two plant managers, Mr. Allenbrand and Mr. Breese, could not have been a more charismatic choice by the company to instill Caterpillar within the community and in the hearts of the employees.

In the mid-1960s, the Fourth of July holiday was approaching and one of the girls (that's what we were called in the good ole days) had the idea that we should all dress in red, white and blue for the last day worked before the holiday. We never dreamed the impact this would have on Mr. Breese.

He was like a father watching his family emerge as a patriotic spectacular happening. After realizing we were all dressed that way, he toured the entire plant, looking in on all the small shop offices, the met lab office and the credit union office. This pleased him to no end.

We continued this dress code for every Fourth of July until Mr. Breese's tenure in York came to a close.

NORMA L. NEUMAN

While working for Caterpillar as an engineer, I was taken to a job site about halfway up a rugged mountain of stones. The only way to get to the lone D8 working there was to walk up the narrow, zig-zag path the tractor had made. The tractor was working back and forth on a ledge that wasn't even twice the length of the tractor; it was dislodging huge boulders, pushing them over the side, then leveling the fine material left behind to inch its way up.

Tex, the operator, stopped to talk to me while the engineer I was with took a turn at the tractor controls. I asked Tex what he was building and he told me a road, which would extend from the top of the mountain to the valley below.

"Wouldn't it be easier to start at the top and push everything downhill?" I asked.

"You're right!" said Tex. "I can tell you'll make a good engineer some day; just tell me how to get that tractor up there!"

Instead of laughing at me, Tex told me what he thought about as he slowly worked his way up the mountain. He told me the D8 was like a person, and the mountain was like a company: Caterpillar Tractor

Company. In order to achieve a better position at Cat, a person, like the tractor, must start somewhere at the bottom and plan a path. As advances are made, large obstacles, like boulders, must be overcome by pushing them aside.

"Be careful not to push the obstacles onto the path below or ahead," Tex advised. "And save all the little things you learn; they are like the footing the tractor compacts as it earns its way up. And one more thing," continued Tex, "even when, and if, you reach the top of the mountain, remember, the fuel is still at the bottom; so those on top depend upon those at the bottom, plus everyone in between.

"There aren't many companies, and no tractors, as good as Cat," Tex concluded.

So, the next time you drive down a mountain incline or through a mountain pass where the earth has been cut away, remember this: the first Caterpillar tractor on the job didn't start at the top.

PAUL T. HULING

I started at Caterpillar Brasil in 1961. Caterpillar was one of the best companies because it offered very attractive wages, a good work environment and health insurance. People came from everywhere, even the immigrants living in Brazil like Italians, Hungarians, Germans … along with Americans. They all had the language of work in common.

In the '70s, there was a great concern about industrial espionage. I remember that I was working on a layout and I had to take pictures of each department. There was a small American guy, with the look of a CIA agent, who came to me and tried to take my Polaroid away. It took a great deal of talking to convince him I wasn't a spy.

In the '80s, we had a rough time; nothing was sure. Even though times were uncertain, I decided to marry Leonice. There were many strikes, and we had to be careful. There were parking lots full of new tractors, we were selling nothing and buying only what was absolutely necessary. Caterpillar opened new internal jobs just to keep their employees busy to avoid firing them. We were in the red. I even thought Caterpillar was going to close down in Brazil. But in the middle of all that, something very important happened in my life. My son was born in 1983.

At that time, things were very mysterious at CBSA. There was a group of Americans assigned to work for a kind of "Vanguard Plan." I remember that I was called to pick up two of them at their hotel. What a nightmare! They were so big that they almost could not get in my tiny little Volkswagen Beetle. I was so ashamed that I could speak almost no English to them.

Moving to the new plant in Piracicaba started in 1987. Factories, offices, shops and warehouses were emptied in a consistent rhythm. I had a strange feeling of loss … the price for progress.

I left Cat in May, 1991. I was there 30 years. I learned the importance of perseverance, tolerance and balance. I thank God for this experience.

MARCELO ALVES MARTINS

In the early 1960s we began "budgeting" in the East Peoria plant. We created the first budget [which was divided into sections] by building and department. As the supervisor, I was elected to review and obtain reasons for the budget-to-actual differences. In the case of the manufacturing buildings, we had budgeted base hours, performance percent, indirect ratios and scrap per base hour.

First stop was Building J through X. Now, John Elwood was indeed an exciting factory manager. However, he had a somewhat colorful vocabulary. John told me as politely as he could that since we had prepared the budget, it was our job to determine the differences.

We also budgeted year-end production stores inventory. Dowell Kimmel was production manager at that time. He looked at our figure and then, on the wall behind a picture, he wrote his figure. Prior to year-end he had transferred to Australia, and when I looked behind the picture his number was closer to actual than ours! I wrote him about this and in his return letter the words, "of course," were neatly typed!

ROBERT M. BROWN

Ray Greenan tells the story when Kennedy was running for President, he came to the gates of Cat and was shaking hands. One old-timer asked if Kennedy ever worked a day in his life. Kennedy answered no and then the old timer said, "You ain't missed a damn thing."

JACK J. LUSCHER

Around 1990, Caterpillar became involved in European truck racing by loosely supporting a team that was using the 3176 engine. The support was minimal, only software and a few parts. The engineers who supported the effort did most of the work in their spare time. As the sport became more popular, the support slowly grew and Caterpillar became recognized as a presence in European supertruck racing. In the early '90s, the 10 liter 3176 engine was frequently beating the larger 18 liter Mercedes powered trucks.

Around 1994, the classes of trucks became more defined and supertrucks were limited to 12 liters. This fit well with Caterpillar's development of the C-12 (12 liter) truck engine. One of the C-12 development engines was provided to the Chris Hodge racing team as a "probe test." The C-12 was being developed for the 350-425 hp on-highway market but in the race truck power output was eventually increased to 1400 hp.

The Hodge team refined their chassis and improved their finishing places in the races. They won the European supertruck championship in

the 1997-1998 season and finished second in the 1998-1999 season. Caterpillar currently is providing a full sponsorship for the team. COSA sets up a full hospitality pavilion at each race and uses the truck racing as a brand recognition and sales tool.

My involvement began in the early '90s and I was the engine performance engineer involved in the development of the C-12. There were also several other dedicated people involved in supporting the race engine development over the years.

TRENT A. SIMPSON

I can't forget a night on a weekend in 1959 when our plant in Brazil was invaded by cattle. There was a railway station near the plant, and from time to time wagons with cattle were brought to a lot nearby. The train used to arrive at night and wait until dawn for the cowboys to unload the cattle. But that night, they got out and invaded the plant. It was a very hectic night as we had to

wait for the cowboys to arrive on horseback to subdue the animals and remove them from the plant. I have many other stories, but I'll save them for the 100th anniversary of this company that's part of my life.

SEBASTIAO RODRIGUES DO PRADO

In 1957, we had a machine named "Big Bertha." She was located at about LL3E. "Big Bertha" was a Cat built machine, designed in Tool Design and built in the Tool Room. She machined the bull gear faces, axle bores and the transmission faces and bores on the D9 case. I forget what the exact output was but I think it was about 1 1/3 cases per shift. I do know that "Big Bertha" was the controlling machine and determined how many D9 tractors we could build each week. "Big Bertha" ran 24 hours a day, 7 days a week. She was not shut down during lunch or shift change. Breakdowns were rare but when she broke down, all of the needed crafts were there and there was no stopping until she was running again. This machine is truly a credit to the people who designed, built, maintained and operated her. I speak of this machine like she is one of the family, and in those days she was. But like all good things there has to be an end. Better technology, a fabricated case and the need to produce more D9s was her demise.

I think she was dismantled and sold for scrap.

Vern Mall
VERN MALL

The job that I remember was making a four foot dial bull gear for a 200-ton mold stripping press—90 teeth 2 pitch 20 degree pressure angle. 46" O.D. to be exact. This was made by me and my people at the request of Harmon Eberhard, president of Caterpillar, for the president of Keystone Steel & Wire to avoid plant shutdown. We built this in 4 1/2 days and avoided their shutdown. This was a challenge to me, and I enjoyed it.

Bill Cole
BILL COLE

I started working at Caterpillar in 1935 and retired 50 years later in 1985. I took out two years during World War II for the Marine Corps and took night and extension courses. Through Caterpillar, I've visited every state in the United States, as well as Canada, Mexico, Ireland, Scotland, England, France,

Germany, Switzerland, Japan, Hong Kong, Singapore and communist China. I have been to the bottom of the Columbia River, the fourth sub-basement of the telephone company in Denver, down the Ohio and Illinois Rivers on tugboats, at the bottom of Hungry Horse Dam in Montana, lived in logging camps and army camps, all in pursuit of my Caterpillar job. I don't regret a moment of it; I loved it.

Ray Bessler
RAY R. BESSLER

I clearly remember the ceremony in Louis Neumiller's office when I received the $100 check for coming up with the winning name [Danny Diesel] for the animated tractor. I was earning $60 per week as a trainee, so $100 looked pretty big. One thing that really impressed me was that when the photographer was taking a lot of pictures, LBN asked him how much it cost each time he took a picture. The photographer said he didn't know, and LBN said, "Don't you ever come into my office again to take a picture without knowing how much it costs." *(photo above)*

Pete
PETE DONIS
(PRESIDENT 1985-1989)

Being a line foreman has to be the best job I had at Caterpillar. The pressure from above and below, the one or two percent of the people who don't want to work, the demand to meet schedules and the ongoing effort to have a safe operation are all offset by earning the respect of the people you work with and watching a quality product go out the door.

DEWEY J. EDWARDS

I remember an incident in 1948 (my second year with

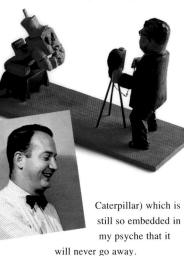

Caterpillar) which is still so embedded in my psyche that it will never go away.

We were having a downturn in business and the word went out that we had to, among other things, cut waste. At the time I was assigned to the Sales Department in Building HH in Peoria.

One afternoon we were astonished to see Louis Neumiller himself come into the office along with a man from the Carpenter Shop. The latter carried a box of hand crank pencil sharpeners. The two of them, without saying a word, went to every electric pencil sharpener in the place. The carpenter removed the electric pencil sharpener and installed a hand-crank unit in its place. You could have heard a pin drop. We were dumbfounded. But we got the "cut waste" message loud and clear. This high visibility action by the top man made a strong impression on everyone, even those who only heard about it on the grapevine.

Electric pencil sharpeners were new to American business at that time. But for us they became a case in point. They cost more, they used electricity and they didn't improve on anything.

LLOYD F. "ANDY" ANDERSON

In the early 1960s I was District Sales Rep. for Minnesota and Wisconsin. We lived in Edina, a suburb of Minneapolis. The lot behind us was staked for a new home.

At breakfast one fall morning a lowboy truck pulled up to

the vacant lot and unloaded a bright green wheel loader. I was aware that much of our development was on uncompacted peat moss. To no one in particular, I suggested there was no way to dig a basement with a wheel loader in those conditions. I mused about all the reasons why. Quietly munching her oatmeal, our precocious four-year-old daughter hung on daddy's every word.

I went off to work and my wife sent the four-year-old out to play. She sat on a rock in our back yard to watch the operator start his dig. Soon he stopped for a smoke and approached his young observer. She spoke first. "Hi, mister," she said. "You may not know it but you're digging in fill over an old bog. Pretty soon you're gonna be up to your hubs in muck." "What you need," she went on, "is a Cat 955 Power Shift. Better yet would be a long undercarriage excavator."

Well, sure enough, 10 minutes later, the bright green loader was completely mired in the dark black goo. When I got home that evening, my wife couldn't wait to tell me about it. "The operator came to the back door," she said, "and asked to use the phone." He dialed his office and said,

"Morrie, you ain't gonna believe this, but I've just met a four-year-old kid who knows more about digging basements than anybody we got."

The next morning the lowboy was back...with a Cat LGP 955 Power Shift Loader.

Ron
RON PILON

I began to work for Caterpillar Brasil on June 18, 1956. Although I lived near the company, there wasn't public transportation so I had to go on bicycle or on foot. It was a problem when it rained because it became nearly impossible to walk in the mud. I had to change shoes at the entrance before I went into the office. Being pioneers was very difficult as we had to move to the new plant in Santo Amaro and new obstacles had to be overcome. Our bus had to first go downtown which used to take us about 75 minutes. Communication between the office and the factory was by radio; telephones were very undependable at that time. Our office was temporary, with no air conditioning; when the heat was intense, and the rain and wind were strong, it was nearly impossible to work. At times I had to go to Santo Amaro by truck.

One of my happiest days as a professional was the day the first motor grader was assembled in Santo Amaro. I have always been proud of working for Caterpillar, and during this 34 years of work, I have always tried to reach Caterpillar's goals.

ADILSON NUNES CAMILO

As a Parts and Service Sales Representative I moved to the Pacific Northwest in January 1977. My territory also included Alaska. The Alaska pipeline was just being completed. I was in Anchorage calling on N C Machinery in June 1977 when the "pig" reached Valdez marking the completion of the project. (A pig is a device that was run the length of the pipeline to verify that all welds were secure.) I still have the Anchorage newspaper with the headline, "Pig Arrives at Valdez." I was very proud that Cat equipment and dealer support helped complete this enormous project.

FRANK J. SCHERBING

My name is George H Y Wang. I am an employee at AsiaTrak (Tianjin) Co. Ltd. Before, I didn't have an English name. Since I got a job at an American company, I felt it was necessary to have

an English name, because my Chinese name is difficult for some Americans to speak. After thinking, I decided to use "George" as my English name.

One day, the secretary of the general manager came to me and gave me a piece of paper and said, "The general manager wants you to work on this and give him a report. By the way, do you have that English name yet? If you don't, the general manager suggests 'Harry.'" I said, "Oh, sorry, I already have an English name, George."

A few minutes later, the secretary came back and told me lightly, "Do you know why the general manager suggested 'Harry' to you? It's his father's name. And do you know who is George? You will be surprised to know that is the general manager's grandfather's name!"

GEORGE H Y WANG

In West Australia, sometimes in construction booms the servicing facility does not get built before the job gets under way, and when things have to be repaired you have to use what is available. When the transmission of a twin engine 657 Scraper has to be changed, you need a strong support to hang the crane

on. So, the biggest gum tree was the dealer workshop for a while!

MARSHALL MCKELSON

REFLECTIONS ON GRATEFULNESS

These stories reflect a gratitude for a life filled with work where people felt valued and appreciated, where contributions became common goals and where special needs were handled with care.

Caterpillar has been, and is, the source of our livelihood, lasting friendships, satisfaction of accomplishment and extreme pride for having been employed by the greatest company on this planet. My wife holds her hand over her heart every time she sees a Caterpillar product!

Oak Sloter
OAKLEY H. SLOTER

At 94 years of age I have only words of praise for my time with Caterpillar. Starting in 1929 and retiring in 1967, I was one of the lucky persons to find employment with the best company in the world, where quality counted. With 1,200 employees at that time and ending with over 80,000 in 1967, I can only wish them success in the future.

KLAAS J. DE VRIES

I remember when the Safety Department in Peoria hired George Pople, who had been blind from birth, to repair safety glasses. This is probably one of the first severely handicapped people to be hired by industry. George remained employed in the Safety Department until he retired.

RUSSELL WAUGHOP

Having started working at Caterpillar at age 29, I decided to quit early at age 62 after almost 33 years of a truly enjoyable career. In describing my Caterpillar experience, I usually say, "I can't remember a time when I dreaded a Monday or yearned for a Friday." I don't know if it showed as much as I felt it inside, but I was one happy employee for each of those 33 years. I still give thanks for them.

Bob Hancock
BOB HANCOCK

I had a wonderful career with Caterpillar as managing director of Caterpillar of Australia and chairman of Caterpillar Mitsubishi. I retired as a director and executive vice president of the company in 1987. The company provided many opportunities to me and my family, both professionally and personally.

EDWARD J. SCHLEGEL

My grandfather, Owen P. Jones, worked at Caterpillar in East Peoria until he retired in 1961. As I was growing up, I remember him telling me what a great place Caterpillar was to work and that I and my siblings should all try to work there if we could. Grandpa was right. Caterpillar is a wonderful place to work. It has helped my brothers, sisters and myself raise our children. The outstanding benefits have helped when we faced medical problems. It has helped all of us to be challenged, to further our education and to grow personally by all the relationships we have developed at Caterpillar.

PATRICIA L. BENKO

While learning the ropes as a tool designer, I'll never forget how Mr. Price, then the president of Solar, would walk thru the plant talking to employees and when he came over to me and said, "You must be new. I'm Ed Price." And just asked how I was doing and welcomed me to Solar—What an honor—I never stopped loving Solar for 36 1/2 years as I advanced thru the ranks.
Glen C. Paape
GLEN PAAPE

I am afraid that at my present age of approximately 93 and one half years,

I have forgotten most of the funny things. My memory isn't as good as it used to be. Naturally, in looking back over those early days, there were incidents that I wished could have been different, but I consider myself to have been very lucky and there is little I would want to change. There are very few people at Caterpillar that I know now, but I sure grew up with some fine ones…and the benefits are great.

HARRISON WELCH

Editor's note: Harrison Welch (right) received his 40-year service pin from Lee Morgan (center), who was later president and chairman, and Bill Lambie (left), vice president of parts and service. A number of Caterpillar retirees sent in photographs of themselves receiving service pins. Clearly these are treasured memories.

I traveled to Peoria from Brazil at the end of November, 1998, to attend a coordination meeting. Tim Chally (CIS-Peoria, Illinois) invited me for Thanksgiving dinner with his family, at his brother's residence in Geneva, Illinois, near Chicago. During the meal, everyone including me was asked to say a prayer. After the meal, they told jokes about the Irish and asked me which country we joked about and I said it was Portugal, but I could just remember the simple ones—and it was a success since they were so similar.

After the joke session, they taught me how to play American football and we played until 8 at night. I got to kick the ball to start the game no matter the team.

They treated me just like family; everybody (the parents, the uncles, the nephews, the children) wanted me to stay in their houses and come back the next day.

HENIO PETRINI

It is hard for me to explain all of my feelings for the company. Maybe the best way is to just say that I have a replica of a Caterpillar end-loader scraper mounted to the front of my house here in Mesa, Arizona.

CURTIS L. SOUTH

In 1966, Caterpillar Overseas S.A. was looking for young Europeans willing to relocate and travel a lot. I became a trainee in Geneva, Switzerland.

In the spring of 1967, I was sent to Peoria for training. As in our Geneva offices I was surrounded in Peoria with great friends, hospitable, helpful and above all hard working. Visiting the East Peoria plant impressed me … and so I started to better understand what it takes to build Quality.

This was my first time in America, and I had some adapting to do. I learned on one of my first dates all about a "doggy bag" and about hamburgers, and I still love the "Steak and Shake diners."

As I developed a liking for the American life style, I found very good friends who went out of their way to invite Europeans to their homes and introduced us to their friends.

I worked initially in Building HH and later in 1967 we moved to our new headquarters downtown. Everything in the new office was somewhat sterile. Dress code was really conservative: white shirts and dark suits, plus all men had very short haircuts. I was the only European in my training class.

When I showed up with a blue blazer and dark grey pants, I really did not fit the mold.

I loved it that these great Americans would be so formal. During a business day they would have only ice water for lunch (at night, drinking alcohol was allowed). But during lunch it seemed a cardinal sin. Difficult to comprehend, but reality. So my glass of Beaujolais for lunch was replaced by American Beaujolais or Coca-Cola.

Now I have been with Caterpillar 34 years. I have had 18 different jobs—moved to 12 different locations—moved my furniture 17 times. I had the opportunity to live in great places like Geneva, Peoria, Athens, Johannesburg, Brussels, Stockholm, Paris. Each and every move helped me develop further; each time I had the opportunity to work with great Caterpillar colleagues as well as great dealer associates.

PIERRE P. GHEYSENS

Editor's note: Ken Gerber, now retired, for many years portrayed Alexander Botts at various company events. Botts was a fictional tractor salesman invented by William Hazlitt Upson for a series of short stories in The Saturday Evening Post *in the mid-1920s. In 1936, the movie* Earthworm Tractor *starring Joe E. Brown had its world premier in Peoria.*

I had the great honor to participate in well over 100 equipment shows all over the U.S. My assignment was to provide the comedy relief, and I got to work up-close to many employees, their spouses, kids, grandparents, etc. I estimate, in all, we presented our shows all over the U.S. over the years to more than 300,000 people … think of that. Every event involved entertaining and rewarding employees for producing the finest products in their industry … to dealers who sold the products … to friends in our plant communities who got the chance to feel our pride and excitement for our products.

Of course, I hid behind the masks of Toby the Clown and Alexander Botts, but my pride got through to everybody and their pride got through to me. What a great partnership it was!

Ken Gerber
KEN GERBER

Back in 1957, I was working in the shop and was offered the opportunity to enter the two-year machinist training course. It was a tough decision. I would have to take a 50-cent-an-hour pay cut to go into the program, and I'd have to buy my tools—at a cost of $8 a month for two years. I had two kids and, in those days, that was a lot of money. Fortunately, I completed the program (even though it took three years instead of two because of layoffs in the middle) and after graduation the company reimbursed me for the entire cost of the tools and box.

I still have my original tools and tool box *(photo above)* and I proudly display them in my office in the CV Building today. They're a reminder of good times and a smart decision. And, for me, they represent what is possible

at Caterpillar for people, regardless of where they start with the company.

JIM DESPAIN, VICE PRESIDENT

CATERPILLAR, Wow!
I don't know if that name means as much to the ordinary person as it does to those of us who are members of the "Caterpillar family!"

As a youngster in north central Iowa, Christmastime was a time to look forward to. The celebration of the birth of the Christ child—and the gifts! Among those gifts was always a windup Track-Type Tractor which we called "Caterpillar." Hours were spent playing with these tractors, challenging them to climb steep inclines, etc. Unfortunately the manufacturer of these toy crawlers was not as quality-conscious as the company we named our tractors after, as the windup mechanism did not last very long. Just like in the real world, a tractor that is not a quality machine is discarded.

Years later, while in the military and traveling between bases, I saw a Caterpillar machine doing some dozer work and thought to myself, not even knowing where a plant was, "I think I would like to work for Caterpillar." As it would happen I ended up near Joliet, Illinois, and hired-in May 18, 1962, and became a member of the Caterpillar family.

For 30 years I shared joys and sorrows with other members of this great family. For 30 years these family members helped me solve problems from shingling a house to overhauling an automobile engine. For 30 years I was both the recipient and executor of practical jokes. In those 30 years I was fortunate to meet some of the best people in the world and make lasting friendships.

Now retired and back in rural north central Iowa where I played with those windup tractors 50 or more years ago, I am reminded of the Caterpillar family and Caterpillar quality every day as a growing number of Challenger tractors work the fields and change the color of the landscape from "John Deere green" to "Caterpillar Yellow!"

HENRY MEYER

CAT YELLOW

Years ago, Virgil Unks told me this story of "Why Construction Machines Are Painted Yellow."

A lot of people were involved with the decision, but the man who got it going was a district engineer for the Minnesota Highway Department.

On the morning when it all began, word came down of another smashup between two Highway Department vehicles in his district. It was the third such collision in as many months. This time a truck driver backed into a tractor parked in the equipment yard.

Sometimes a tractor would get side-swiped. Sometimes a truck would run into a moving tractor. One time a tractor and truck smashed up head-on in broad daylight. Each time the operators said the same thing: they didn't see each other.

The district engineer's response was also the same, "How could he not see a 10-ton machine sitting out in the open in full daylight?"

It was the weather that caused the problem. The overcast skies and short days of the winter months of the North cut visibility sharply.

Then there was the color scheme of the tractors. Most were painted a shade of gray with dark trim. That color scheme looked classy polished

up on the showroom floor. But in the fog and gloom of wintertime Minnesota the machines melted into the background and were hard to see.

It was a problem that reached all the way to the sign shop at the district garages. Their business was making signs that were easy to see day or night, in all kinds of weather.

"You can't beat yellow for visibility," said the sign shop foreman. "If they want people to see road machines, they should paint 'em yellow."

That's why, in the early '30s, the Caterpillar dealer in Minneapolis got an invitation to bid on 30 tractors for the State of Minnesota Highway Department with this stipulation: "All machines to be painted in the color of Bright Highway Yellow."

The sale of 30 tractors was a sit-up-and-take-notice event. (It still is.) But to paint 30 machines yellow presented a hang-up: any color except standard gray was a special order and called for an extra $35 charge.

The Minnesota dealer feared that a $35 per machine special order color charge would push

the price beyond reach. The dealer wanted Cat to make yellow a second standard color at no extra charge.

The company was attracted by the size of the Minnesota order but the special paint job required an expert opinion.

So, according to Virgil Unks, the then company president buzzed in his secretary to ask her.

The girls who became executive secretaries were no dumbbells. She told the president, "If machine users in Minnesota have trouble seeing machines on gloomy days, you can be sure other people in the northern tier states do too. And so do Canadians. And possibly Europeans. And private contractors as well as government buyers."

Then she suggested Caterpillar do all those customers a favor and make yellow the standard Caterpillar machine color!

"Yellow would be easy to see. It would stand out from competition. It would make the company look bright and aggressive."

The president thought for a moment, said, "Good thinking!" and the standard color changed.

The president's secretary was right. Machine customers did like the bright yellow color. Before long yellow became so closely identified with Caterpillar the color was known as "Caterpillar Yellow."

DON AXT

Editor's note: The University of California at Davis has a letter (dated December 7, 1931) with a slightly different version of how "Hi-Way Yellow" was introduced:

Beginning Monday, December 7, all Caterpillar Tractors and all Caterpillar Road Machines shipped from the factories will have as their standard color Hi-Way Yellow. This is a rich golden shade of yellow, bright and lustrous. Trade-marks and trimmings are black. A very thorough study of the subject of paint on the part of our own organization and the country's leading color and paint authorities resulted in the choice of Hi-Way Yellow as the standard color. It has been chosen with full consideration of every factor—attractiveness

of appearance, the safety factor on high visibility value, the legal requirements in certain localities for machines used on the highways, durability of paint and protection of the surface.

THE LETTER IS SIGNED BY J.C. FLETCHER, EXPORT SALES MANAGER AT THE TIME.

Editor's note: Ted Halton, dealer from Portland, Oregon, and president of the Antique Caterpillar Machinery Owners Club, supplied this story about the switch to "Hi-Way Yellow":

A committee came up with three new paint options: bright orange with black engine and black trim; metallic silver; and yellow. Management chose the orange and black combination. But Oscar Starr, who ran the San Leandro, California, plant, hit the ceiling! Using two colors would cost at least $25 more per unit. This was 1931! Starr was not about to endorse that kind of waste.

Their second recommendation: metallic silver. But the paint shop foreman pointed out that paint guns would have to be replaced because they couldn't handle metallic paint. Cost to replace the paint guns: $1,500. Solution: yellow, the third choice.

"There is but one Caterpillar and wherever it is, you will find it reaching for high levels of integrity, achievement and quality—standing first and foremost for the rights and dignity of the individual and wishing to make association with the company a life-satisfying experience."

LOUIS NEUMILLER,
CHAIRMAN 1954-1962

seventy-five years

of Caterpillar

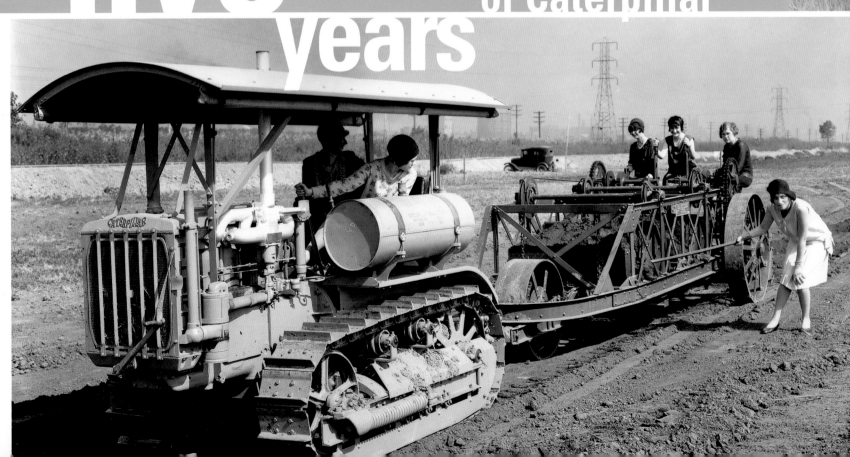

Timeline
1925-1999

1 9 2 5 - 1 9 3 4

By 1929, the East Peoria plant had 25 acres under roof— more than double its space of just four years earlier. Employment had grown to more than 4,000 people, from about 1,600 in 1925.

Sales were booming, reaching nearly $52 million in the high-water year of 1929. And then came the Depression. The company had been warning its dealers: "Our experience of the past few years has made us little more than order takers. The business for the most part has come to us. From now on, we will have to go after it."

How true that was! Sales fell to $45 million in 1930 as the Great Depression engulfed the world. The company was in relatively good health, though, largely due to export sales—in particular, sales to the Soviet Union, which amounted to $12 million between October, 1929, and May, 1930.

But there was a definite limit to the number of machines that could be sold to the U.S.S.R. and other overseas customers. Sales fell to $24 million in 1931, then to $13 million in 1932, when the company failed to earn a profit for the first time.

Early Caterpillar ads in *The Saturday Evening Post* listed prices—$1,850 for a 2-Ton and $5,000 for a Sixty. Colorful copy offered a reward for the Snow Bogy who was wanted for blocking traffic, interference with the U.S. mail, murder, arson, thwarting education and banditry.

Caterpillar Milestones

1925

1928

1925 - Holt and Best combine to form Caterpillar Tractor Co. Because of geographical advantages, administration and manufacturing came to be centered in Peoria, Illinois, formerly Holt's branch factory.

Raymond C. Force, first company president

1926 - Five-for-one stock split.

C. L. "Leo" Best leaves active operations soon after the Holt-Best merger. He continues to chair the executive committee.

1928 - Acquisition of the Russell Grader Manufacturing Company accelerates Caterpillar's entry into the road machinery business.

1929 - First foundry opens in East Peoria, Illinois.

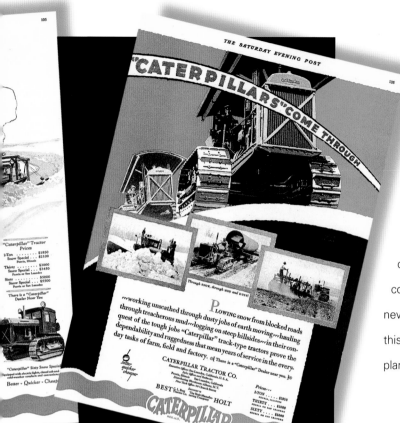

Cost-cutting measures included pay cuts up to 20 percent for top executives in 1933. The work week fell to four days. A number of employees at all levels lost their jobs.

Factories were consolidated so the company could operate more economically. By late 1929, combine production had already been moved to a new factory at East Peoria. Known as Building HH, this factory also became our main road machinery plant early in the 1930s.

Headquarters was officially moved from San Leandro, California, to East Peoria, Illinois. A new Research Division was organized. Despite the Depression, we continued to emphasize research and to introduce new products that would eventually revolutionize the industry. By 1933, we had a completely new product line—every model of tractor, engine and road machinery had been redesigned since 1930. Production of combines was dropped by the mid-1930s so we could concentrate resources on tractors and engines.

1925 through 1934

1930 - World population reaches two billion.

First frozen vegetables (peas) marketed by Clarence Birdseye.

Planet Pluto discovered.

1931 - Empire State Building becomes world's tallest building.

"The Star Spangled Banner" becomes U.S. national anthem.

Julius Arthur Nieuwland develops synthetic rubber.

1932 - First automatic dishwasher introduced.

Sydney Harbor Bridge in Australia opens after seven years of construction.

Sulfa discovered.

1933 - Adolf Hitler takes power.

British airplane flies over Mount Everest.

Automatic control of auto traffic begins in Piccadilly, London.

1934 - Mao Zedong begins Long March in China.

Great Britain introduces driving tests.

Radar successfully demonstrated in Germany.

1931

1934

1930 - Byron C. Heacock named president.

Heacock's badge to enter Ordnance plant during World War II.

1931 - Caterpillar pioneers use of diesel tractor power; with increased sales of its tractors, becomes the world's largest diesel manufacturer.

Introduction of the revolutionary auto patrol, with engine positioned in back of the operator.

Decision made to change color of products from gray with red trim to Hi-Way Yellow with black trim.

1932 - Caterpillar is first diesel manufacturer to mass-produce its own pre-calibrated fuel pumps and injectors.

1933 - The diesel tractors—the Seventy-Five, Fifty, and Thirty-Five—now outsell gasoline-powered models.

L. J. Fletcher on a state farm in the Soviet Union, 1929. Fletcher represented Caterpillar in Russia in 1929. Recognized as an international authority on agricultural affairs, he was president of the American Society of Agricultural Engineers in 1931 and 1932. In 1951, he was elected a Caterpillar vice president.

Caterpillar and Russia

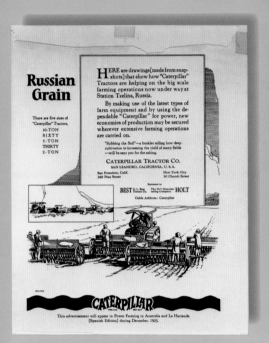

Holt tractors had been used in Russia as far back as pre-Revolution days. In May, 1913, at St. Petersburg, the Imperial Automobile Club under the patronage of Czar Nicholas II held an exhibition and plowing contest to help celebrate the 300th anniversary of the Romanov dynasty. A Holt "Caterpillar" track-type tractor won gold medals.

Starting in the late 1920s, large state farms were organized throughout the U.S.S.R. The Zernotrest (Soviet Grain Trust) ordered 20 Sixty tractors to work on the largest farms. These were so successful that in the fall of 1929 they ordered 1,350 more. More orders followed.

These sales to the Soviet Union helped us stabilize output of factories adversely affected by the Depression. By keeping our assets working, we were able to earn a profit while reducing tractor prices.

In discussing sales to the U.S.S.R., the company's Executive Committee stated, " … at such a time as the present, when there is much evidence of serious unemployment in the country, it is deemed the duty of those in charge … to keep as many employees as possible steadily at work."

Sales to the Soviet Union ended in the mid '30s and we made no significant sales there until 1966.

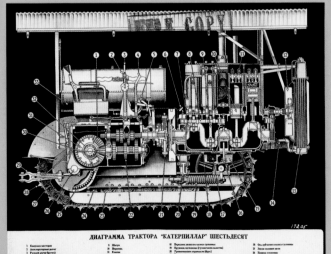

upper left. **As indicated by this 1925 ad, tractor sales to the U.S.S.R. were growing at about the same time Caterpillar was formed.**

left. **Page from a catalog in Russian for the Sixty Tractor.**

right. **Assembly of canopy for a Thirty upon its arrival in Moscow.**

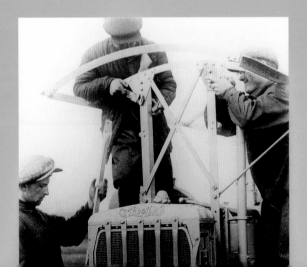

above. **Stretching back to the turn of the century, Best, Holt and, later, Cat machines were well accepted in Russia. One milestone was this 1913 appearance of Holt's "Caterpillar" track-type tractor at an exhibition and plowing contest.**

right. **A model Thirty hauling wagons loaded with wheat sheaves during harvest time at Petukhovsky State Farm, U.S.S.R.**

Sept. 1930

Expositions and Demonstrations Then and Now

above. **In 1930, employees, dealers and customers gathered on a field in East Peoria, Illinois, to view the latest in Cat products.**

below. **1990s machine demonstrations at Tinaja Hills, Tucson, Arizona, (left) and Málaga, Spain (right).**

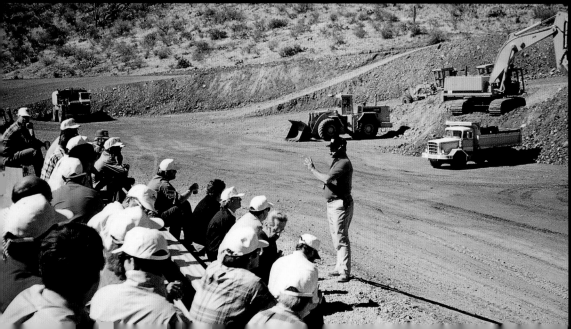

below. **At the CONEXPO-CON/AGG '99 show in Las Vegas, Nevada, customers inspect the new line of compact construction equipment including skid steer loaders, mini hydraulic excavators and compact wheel loaders.**

1 9 3 5 - 1 9 4 4

Sales in 1935 were $36 million, a 53 percent increase over the previous year. An additional 3,000 people came on the payroll, bringing total employment to 9,000. We had been unprofitable only one year, 1932.

But the Great Depression still had a tight grip on the world economy. Recovery was slow, with a setback in 1938. With the advent of World War II, almost all of our production went toward the war effort. Civilian needs would have to wait.

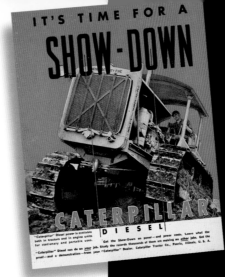

Saturday Evening Post ad from 1935.

below. **In November, 1935, Caterpillar passed a milestone— its 10,000th diesel engine, built at East Peoria plant.**

Caterpillar Milestones/World **Events**

1935 - U.S. Social Security Act signed.

World's longest bridge opens over lower Zambesi in Africa.

1936 - First vitamin pill.

Boulder Dam (Hoover) completed on Colorado River, creating world's largest reservoir, Lake Mead.

Mercedes produces first diesel-powered automobile.

1937 - Golden Gate Bridge opens.

First jet engine built.

Insulin used to control diabetes.

1938 - Ballpoint pen invented.

Nylon introduced.

New York City has 20,000 TV sets.

1939 - World War II begins September 1.

Movie *Gone with the Wind* hits screens.

China's Yangtze River floods, killing between 500,000 and 1,000,000 people.

1935

1935 - RD8 Tractor introduced. The "R" was later dropped.

The first Cat diesel engine not designed for tractor use—the V8 D17000—introduced.

Caterpillar uses first detergent lube oils as a result of cooperative research with major oil companies.

1938

1938 - No. 12 Motor Grader introduced.

1939 - Major engine developments include a complete line of marine engines; the first complete generator set with matched engine and generator sold and serviced by a single manufacturer; the D468, Caterpillar's first truck engine (discontinued with the advent of WWII).

Shift change at East Peoria, Illinois, 1943.

1940 - Prehistoric wall paintings from about 20,000 B.C. discovered in Lascaux caves in France.

Jeep (from GP—general purpose) introduced in U.S.

First successful helicopter flight in U.S.

1941 - Pearl Harbor bombed, December 7.

Beginning of Manhattan Project.

Polyester developed in the United Kingdom.

1942 - World War II rages. Bataan falls. Allies invade North Africa.

Enrico Fermi splits the atom.

Henry J. Kaiser develops technique for building 10,000-ton Liberty Ship in four days.

1943 - Battle of Stalingrad turns the tide of the war.

Streptomycin discovered.

1944 - Allied invasion of France, June 6.

Teflon invented.

Cost of living in U.S. rises almost 30 percent.

1941

1944

1940 - First Caterpillar rubber-tired tractor, the DW10. The war interrupts introductions of other rubber-tired models.

1941 - Louis B. Neumiller elected president.

1942 - Caterpillar Military Engine Company formed to manufacture diesels for tanks. (The subsidiary was dissolved in 1946.)

1943 - Major flood in Peoria jeopardizes production.

1944 - Service Awards program begun, honoring employees for years of service with the company.

"The four machines that won the war in the Pacific were the submarine, radar, the airplane, and the tractor-bulldozer."

Admiral William F. "Bull" Halsey, Commander U.S. Third Fleet

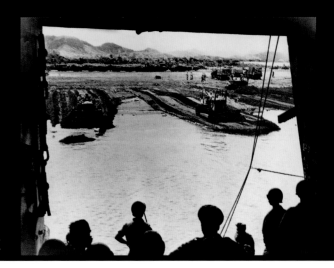

above. **D7s are building approaches for landing craft at Leyte, Philippines.**

Chapter 9

Ads in the *Saturday Evening Post* showed Cat products in war zones. "Little Peoria" (right) was a sign posted at a construction site on the Burma Road. The 497th Heavy Shop Company of U.S. Army Engineers—most of whom were Cat employees—helped build the road.

The Caterpillar Girls Club organized charity work for servicemen and fellow employees. It was originally formed as the Patriotic League to sell Liberty Bonds during World War I. Today, the club continues as the Caterpillar All Employees Club.

World War II

In July, 1941, the U.S. government asked us to convert a gasoline-powered radial airplane engine to diesel for use in tanks. By February, 1942, the Caterpillar Military Engine Company subsidiary was formed to make 1,000 of the new RD-1820 engines a month. Decatur, Illinois, was chosen as the plant site.

We also started making tank transmissions and final drives; shells and bomb fuses; howitzer carriages; and high-speed and armored versions of standard tractors.

By mid-1943, the U.S. government had become convinced of the need for more construction equipment for the war effort. We were asked to phase out most of the special products and step up production of standard products, especially the D7 Tractor. We had made only 120 of the

RD-1820 tank engines when production was stopped so we could focus on construction machines.

Cat engineers found they could actually improve quality while saving strategic materials. For example, new methods of high-frequency electrical induction hardening of steel were developed so parts formerly made with scarce nickel or nickel-chromium steel could be made with plentiful carbon steel.

Because the crawler was often paired with a bulldozer blade, both soldiers and civilians took to calling the whole machine a "bulldozer." Returning from the South Pacific, one serviceman said, "They could have sent us all the airplanes in the world. But if they hadn't sent us bulldozers, too, we might just as well have stayed home."

Both in the South Pacific and in Europe, Caterpillar machines were used in battle and to carry out tasks like building airstrips and clearing bombed-out areas.

Milling cylinder-head castings at East Peoria, 1943. About 85 percent of employees working in the aluminum foundry were women. Company-wide, women made up about 30 percent of employees at the war's peak.

General George Patton said that if forced to choose between tanks and "bulldozers" for an invasion, he'd take the roadbuilding equipment every time.

Throughout the war, plants operated three shifts, six days a week, with many employees volunteering for an extra four-hour "Victory Shift." Vacations were suspended. By the end of the war, nearly 6,000 employees were on military leave and employment grew enormously at the East Peoria plant. Caterpillar people comprised 25 percent of all those employed within a 30-mile radius of Peoria.

Less than 24 hours after retreating troops blew up this bridge in Sicily, traffic was again passing over it. A D7 with bulldozer cleared debris and built new approaches.

The railroad crossing sign serves as a yardstick to measure the depth of the water next to a Caterpillar building.

The view from Peoria across the flooded Illinois River. Caterpillar buildings are in the background.

At 10 a.m. one day, U.S. engineers at Decatur promised 500 big tarpaulins for use on the levee. They were delivered by 3 p.m. the same day.

The Peoria Flood of '43

On June 11, 1943, *News and Views*, a publication for employees in the Peoria area, put out a special flood issue. Here's how the story began:

"'Come hell or high water'—Caterpillar didn't expect either but received plenty of each for more than one week. Starting May 20, the Illinois River went on a rampage and soared to a crest of 28.82 feet—17.22 feet above normal—and shattered a 99-year flood record by 2.52 feet.

"More than 15,000 Caterpillar employees battled weakened levees, which were watersoaked and spongy, and reinforced them with over a million and a half sandbags. Over 250 pieces of earthmoving equipment were rushed to critical areas and operated 24 hours a day until the crisis had passed on Sunday, May 23.

"The plant was saved. President Louis Neumiller said: 'Neither words nor pictures can fully describe the events which took place when we faced, fought and licked the worst flood threat in the history of this part of the country.'"

Later, levees were built and the Farmdale Dam was constructed to prevent a repeat of the flood.

Sandbags were piled around the walls of East Peoria plant in an effort to keep the factory running.

More than 250 pieces of heavy equipment were used 24 hours a day to stem the mounting waters. This is the street leading to Franklin Street Bridge and downtown Peoria.

1945 - 1954

Peace came at last in 1945.

Backed-up demand, all over the world, was enormous. Customers had been making do with obsolete equipment for years. Destruction wrought in the war called for construction equipment—lots of it. Many of the machines shipped around the world during the war became available for reconstruction work, but they needed parts and service. Cat's European and Asian dealer organization needed to be rebuilt.

We launched aggressive expansion plans, both in the United States and abroad. Sales amounting to $231 million in 1945 climbed to $407 million in 1954.

A TYPICAL VETERAN IS CLYDE STOKES, PICTURED HERE WITH HIS FAMILY. READ HOW HE AND HIS BUDDIES ARE GETTING THEIR CHANCE, BACK IN CIVILIAN LIFE. PAGE 4.

In the first issue of *Dealer Magazine* in 1946, Editor Burt Powell wrote: "Like any kid, this magazine must have its didies changed regularly, can use a good spanking from time to time, and don't forget, it has to be fed often.

"These are crazy times. Everybody wants machines. There aren't enough to go around. (We're telling you!) But we feel that a Dealer's magazine isn't built just to push sales. It's a common ground for the exchange of ideas—a friendly medium of goodwill for Caterpillar dealers around the world."

1945 - Atomic age begins.

United Nations founded.

International Bank for Reconstruction and Development (World Bank) founded.

1946 - Winston Churchill coins phrase "Iron Curtain."

Xerography process invented.

1947 - Edwin Land introduces Polaroid Land Camera.

Marshall Plan to rebuild Europe begins.

First flight at supersonic speed.

Bell Laboratories invents the transistor.

1948 - State of Israel proclaimed.

Velcro developed in Switzerland.

Idlewild Airport in New York dedicated. Later renamed John F. Kennedy Airport.

1949 - First Soviet atomic bomb.

TV receivers in U.S. top one million.

North Atlantic Treaty Organization established.

1945
1948

1945 - Announcement of plans for a complete package of earthmoving tools, including Caterpillar-built bulldozers, rippers, scrapers and cable control units.

Arizona Proving Ground opens.

1946 - Largest expansion program ever attempted by the company up to that time; contracts let to increase manufacturing facilities by 50 percent.

***Dealer Magazine* launched.**

1947 - Peoria Proving Ground opens.

1948 - Ten new products announced, including a V-12 diesel engine, as postwar expansion moves forward.

East Peoria hourly employees choose a new bargaining agent: United Auto Workers.

1949 - Building LL (850,000 square feet/78 965 square meters) opens in East Peoria plant. The diesel engine factory (Building KK), opened in 1947, now in full production.

Two-for-one stock split.

Clear the way for Santa Claus

CATERPILLAR DIESEL

WHEN YOU THINK OF HIGHWAYS, THINK OF THE BIG YELLOW MACHINES THAT KEEP DIGGING DOWN

In the postwar period, Caterpillar continued its longstanding ad campaign in the prestigious *Saturday Evening Post*.

At the January, 1950, all-management meeting in Peoria, officers reviewed results of operations. Shown left to right: R. M. Monk, W. J. McBrian, A. T. Brown, L. B. Neumiller, G. E. Spain, H. S. Eberhard. The assembled managers (all male in those days) from all Peoria facilities filled the Shrine Mosque in Peoria.

SALES	$ 254,900,000
COSTS	
MATERIALS	142,400,000
WAGES	76,800,000
DEPRECIATION	4,900,000
INTEREST	600,000
FEDERAL INCOME TAX	11,400,000
	236,100,000
PROFIT	18,800,000
DIVIDENDS	7,000,000
PROFIT EMPLOYED IN THE BUSINESS	$ 11,800,000

1950 - Korean War begins.

2,200 drive-in movies in the U.S.

Credit cards introduced.

1951 - Chrysler pioneers power steering.

Color TV broadcasting introduced in U.S.

1952 - Jonas Salk discovers polio vaccine.

U.S. explodes first hydrogen bomb.

First tranquilizer developed.

1953 - Queen Elizabeth II crowned.

Stalin dies.

Korean War ends.

1954 - First nuclear submarine, the Nautilus.

Boeing 707 introduced to commercial air service.

First successful kidney transplant.

U.S. Supreme Court outlaws racial discrimination in public schools.

1951

1954

1950 - First production of the four-wheel DW20 Tractor and W20 Wagon to be followed shortly by the two-wheel DW21 and No. 21 Scraper.

1951 - Joliet, Illinois, plant opens.

Caterpillar Tractor Co., Ltd., in the United Kingdom, formed in 1950, moves into its first facility—the beginning of Caterpillar's expansion outside the United States.

Trackson Company, Milwaukee, acquired.

Harry H. Fair named chairman.

1952 - Caterpillar Foundation created.

No. 6 Traxcavator introduced—a new concept in track loaders.

1953 - Production begins in York, Pennsylvania, plant.

Separate engine division created—solidifies commitment to engine market.

1954 - Denver, Colorado, parts depot opens.

Louis Neumiller elected chairman of the board. Harmon Eberhard becomes president.

Brazilian subsidiary announced.

In 1950, Caterpillar President Louis Neumiller (front row, second from right) served on a national Junior Chamber of Commerce committee to select the outstanding young men of the year. The winners went to Peoria for a banquet. Joe E. Brown (front row, second from left) spoke at the banquet. He starred as Alexander Botts, a fictional tractor salesman in the 1936 movie *Earthworm Tractor*. Standing behind him is Jacque Mercer, Miss America of that year.

Others in front row: Harold Russell (left), Academy Award winner for his role as a handicapped veteran of World War II in "The Best Years of Our Lives" and Franklin D. Murphy, another of the outstanding young men.

Back row: Outstanding young men Robert L. Floyd; Charles H. Percy, future U.S. Senator from Illinois; John Ben Shepperd; Gerald R. Ford, future U.S. President; Charles E. Hastings; and Kenneth S. Pitzer.

Food for Thousands

"During all my years at the East Peoria plant in the 1950s and 1960s, Wednesday was my favorite day to go to the cafeteria, because Wednesday was 'Bean Soup Day.' Pearl's navy bean soup was the best I've ever eaten, and turned me into a connoisseur of bean soup. To this day I have bean soup wherever and whenever I can. None ever quite matches Pearl's bean soup!!!"

Fred Simpson, retiree

Menu for Today
WEDNESDAY, MAY 12, 1954

Soup, Juices
Tomato Juice.....5 & 10¢   Orange Juice.....5 & 10¢
Fresh Grapefruit.........10¢
Cup of Beef Bouillon.........................10¢
Bean Soup..15¢

Meats
Roast Prime Rib of Beef, Au Jus................45¢
Individual Chicken Pot Pie.....................45¢
Barbequed Spareribs
Diced Ham and Navy Beans
Goulash
DeLuxe Salad Plate W/Tuna Fish, etc.

Sandwiches
Cold Roast Loin of Pork Sandwich
Bologna on Whole Wheat
Ham Salad on Bun
Brick Cheese on Rye

Vegetables
Boiled Cabbage.........10¢   Baked Dressing.......10¢
Buttered Peas.........10¢
Mashed or Au Gratin Potatoes.................5¢

Salads
Molded Banana Salad.....
Shredded Lettuce Bowl (Ch. of Dressing).........15¢
3 in One (Cottage Cheese, Jello & Egg).........15¢
Macaroni Salad.........10¢   Sliced Onions,Cf. Dressing10¢

Breads
Corn Muffins, each.............................5¢
Parkerhouse Rolls, each
Butter, per patty.............................3¢
White, Rye or Whole Wheat Bread, each slice....2¢

Desserts
Fresh Strawberries...........................1¢
Strawberry Jello, Peaches or Prunes..........15¢
Vanilla or Black Cherry Ice Cream............10¢
Pineapple Sherbet............................15¢
Chocolate or Butterscotch Sundae.............15¢
Custard, Gooseberry or Cherry Pie............20¢
White Cake W/Chocolate Nut Icing

Drinks
Milk............................10¢
Coffee.........7¢   Buttermilk.....5¢
Iced Tea, Coffee or Lemonade.....10¢   Hot Tea.....5¢

CATERPILLAR TRACTOR CO., PEORIA, ILLINOIS

Fibber McGee and Molly being served in the Caterpillar dining room. The Peoria natives were national U.S. radio stars in the 1940s and '50s.

Pearl Tullett (center) managed food preparation and serving throughout the Peoria-area facilities for many years.

SUPPOSE NOBODY CARED?

COMMUNITY CHEST CAMPAIGN

LILLIAN O. TITUS

left. **Poster promoting the Community Chest, an early name for the United Way.**

Caterpillar supports such well-known organizations as United Way, Red Cross and Habitat for Humanity, as well as a wide variety of local, national and international organizations. The Caterpillar Foundation, launched in 1952, funds education, health and human services, civic and community programs, and culture and art. Over four decades, the foundation has distributed more than $100 million to these causes. The Caterpillar matching gift program doubles employee gifts to qualifying organizations.

Left to right:
Coach Warren Womble,
Howie Williams, Dan Pippin,
Ron Bontemps, Frank
McCabe, Marc Freiberger.

Caterpillar and the Olympics

In 1952, five Caterpillar basketball players led the U.S. Olympic team to gold medals in Helsinki. It was a proud moment for all Caterpillar people.

The five men played for the Caterpillar Diesels, a team in the national Industrial Basketball League. Team members were all employees who received no extra compensation for their basketball efforts. The Diesels won the National Amateur Athletic Union tournament for three years running—1952, 1953 and 1954.

Frank McCabe's basketball jersey and Olympic gold medal.

Caterpillar "Diesels"

1951–1952 National U.S.A. Champion Basketball Team
Olympics contenders, July 19, 1952, Helsinki, Finland.

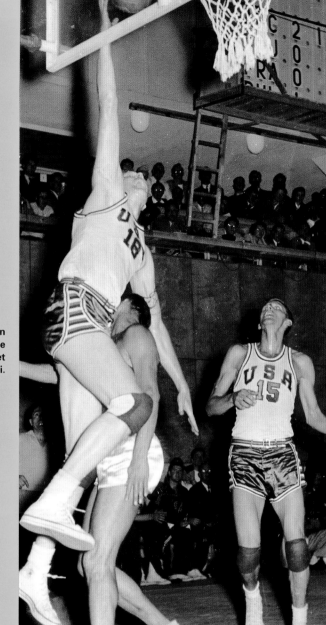

Ron Bontemps in action at an Olympic game against the Soviet Union team in Helsinki.

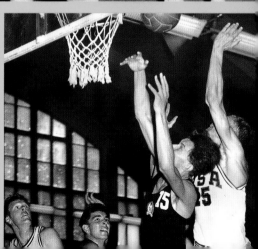

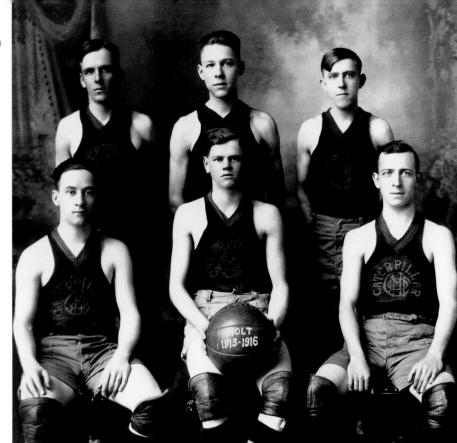

left. **Future Chairman Louis Neumiller played on the 1915 Holt basketball team. He's in the second row, center.**

Sports Involvement

Participation in sports has been characteristic of many Caterpillar people over the decades—so much so that sports involvement could be identified as an element of Caterpillar culture. Countless employees are involved in company-sponsored bowling leagues, soccer teams, golf, baseball, rod and reel clubs, volleyball and many others.

below. **Holt's "Caterpillar" baseball team won the Commercial Saturday Afternoon League championship in 1916 in Peoria.**

"I was the first woman to join the golf club at the San Leandro plant and the first to make a hole in one. That was November 12, 1968, on the fifth hole at Silver Pines Golf Course. I'm now 84 years of age and enjoying my retirement."

Caterine "Kay" Beatriz

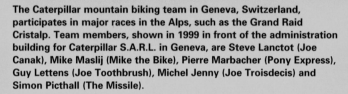

227

Don Fites, chairman from 1990 to 1999, is an avid baseball fan. He's shown as a participant in Chicago Cubs "fantasy" camp in 1991.

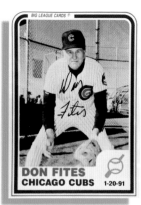

The Caterpillar mountain biking team in Geneva, Switzerland, participates in major races in the Alps, such as the Grand Raid Cristalp. Team members, shown in 1999 in front of the administration building for Caterpillar S.A.R.L. in Geneva, are Steve Lanctot (Joe Canak), Mike Maslij (Mike the Bike), Pierre Marbacher (Pony Express), Guy Lettens (Joe Toothbrush), Michel Jenny (Joe Troisdecis) and Simon Picthall (The Missile).

Many Cat facilities have soccer/football teams.

Starting in 1933, the Dieselettes won Illinois State girls' softball tournaments year after year. Pictured, back row, left to right: Pauline Schlicher Stauch, Joan Nelson, Carol Swettenham Springman, Lorene Ramsey, Coach Chuck McCord, Lou Albrecht, Jan Isonhart Breitbarth, Madeline Dotta and Bev Brown. Front row, left to right: Ona Chaney Winkler, Norma Hardin, Carolyn Thome Hart, Joyce Opper Conway, Esther Graiff Torry and Eleanor Rudolph. They lost only nine games to Illinois teams in 25 years. Photo taken in 1955.

1 9 5 5 - 1 9 6 4

Expansion continued despite a recession-caused downturn in 1958. Sales exceeded one billion dollars for the first time in 1964, with profit at 10.6 percent of sales.

The pattern for non-U.S. operations continued; that is, as we set up manufacturing and marketing operations in a country, our exports to that country increased, resulting in more jobs in the U.S. At the same time, sales and jobs in the host country also grew, and so did its exports.

World Events

1955 - AFL and CIO merge.

First artificial diamonds developed for use in cutting tools and drills.

Disneyland opens in California.

Martin Luther King, Jr., leads Alabama bus boycott, a watershed event in the U.S. Civil Rights Movement.

1956 -Transatlantic cable phone service inaugurated.

Federal Aid Highway Act signed by President Eisenhower.

Automated banking begins in the U.S.

1957 - U.S.S.R. launches Sputnik I and II, first earth satellites.

First entirely phototypeset book published in the United Kingdom.

Rome Treaty signed, launching the Common Market in Europe.

1958 - Alaska becomes 49th state.

First nuclear power plant in the U.S.

Castro's army takes Cuba.

1959 - Hawaii becomes 50th state (New York City studies possibility of becoming 51st state.)

St. Lawrence Seaway opens, connecting Atlantic Ocean with Great Lakes. A one billion dollar construction project.

EFTA (European Free Trade Association) formed.

1955 **1958**

Caterpillar Milestones

1955 - Introduction of D9 Track-Type Tractor.

Production begins in Decatur, Illinois, plant.

A new subsidiary, Caterpillar of Australia, Ltd., is announced. First production of motor graders at Melbourne plant in 1957.

583 Pipelayer goes into production.

Two-for-one stock split.

1956 - Plans announced to build plants in Aurora, Illinois, and Glasgow, Scotland. Also acquired plant near Davenport, Iowa, to make non-current parts.

Acquired The Birtley Company in England.

Caterpillar of Canada, Ltd., announced.

1957 - Morton, Illinois, parts distribution center goes into operation.

Plans announced to build Technical Center in Mossville, Illinois ... a multi-building, campus-like setting.

572 Pipelayer and D353 engine for industrial applications introduced.

6.25" bore engine family introduced.

1958 - Family of marine transmissions introduced.

1959 - Production begins at Mossville, Illinois, engine plant.

Predecessor to Grimbergen distribution center opens in Laken, Belgium.

Cat's first wheel loader, the 944, introduced.

No. 14 Motor Grader introduced.

Three-for-one stock split.

The July 1963 issue of *Fortune* ran a story called **"The Gentle Bulldozers of Peoria."** It started with this sentence: **"Caterpillar Tractor Co.** goes about the business of selling **earthmoving equipment** with a look of **benign, barefoot innocence,** but anyone who tries to outsell it, anywhere in the world, is apt to find out fast that he's in the **big leagues."**

opposite. **Shift change at Grenoble, France, plant in the 1960s. Caterpillar bought an existing facility (background) and converted it to the production of undercarriage components and small machines.**

A No. 12 Motor Grader works on a bypass south of San Mateo, California.

1960 - U.S. scientists develop laser device (light amplification by stimulated emission of radiation).

LAFTA (Latin American Free Trade Association) starts.

U.S. Congress enacts Civil Rights Act.

1961 - Berlin Wall constructed.

Yuri Gagarin orbits the earth.

World population (in millions): China, 660; India, 435; U.S.S.R., 209; U.S., 179; Japan, 95; Pakistan, 94; Brazil, 66; West Germany, 54; Great Britain, 53.

1962 - Cuban Missile Crisis.

General Motors installs first industrial robot.

Mont Blanc Tunnel opens, connecting France and Italy.

1963 - Martin Luther King, Jr.'s, "I Have a Dream" speech.

President Kennedy assassinated.

Friction welding invented.

1964 - First successful lung transplant ... U.S. Surgeon General issues warning on smoking.

U.S. Equal Employment Opportunity Commission established.

Gulf of Tonkin resolution.

First word processor introduced in U.S. by IBM.

1961

1964

1960 - Caterpillar Overseas S.A. formed, with headquarters in Geneva, Switzerland. In 1999, renamed Caterpillar S.A.R.L.

1961 - Production begins at Grenoble, France, plant.

Introduced D398, D379 engines.

1962 - Louis Neumiller retires. Harmon Eberhard named chairman.

First hydraulic scraper; first twin-powered tractor scraper. In total, nine new scraper models introduced.

Subsidiary in South Africa announced.

Caterpillar's first off-highway truck, the 769 at 35-ton capacity, goes into production.

1963 - Joint venture—Tractor Engineers Limited—formed in India with Caterpillar dealer Larsen & Toubro Limited.

Articulated wheel loaders introduced. First models: 988 and 966.

Equal-ownership manufacturing and marketing company with Mitsubishi Heavy Industries, Ltd., of Japan formed.

1964 - Two-for-one stock split.

Harmon S. Eberhard

Becoming a Global Leader

Holt and Best were selling products outside the United States before Caterpillar was formed in 1925. But, says retired Chairman Don Fites, "Export business was still not high priority even in the 1950s. When I first moved overseas in 1956, we didn't even have a vice president over export sales. The bold step of putting a marketing operation on the ground in Europe in 1960 (when Caterpillar Overseas was formed in Geneva, Switzerland) signaled our major thrust into the world marketplace. The joint venture with Mitsubishi in 1963 further cemented our emerging role as a global leader."

A series of international agreements helped stimulate trade. Among them: the General Agreement on Tariffs and Trade (later to become the World Trade Organization), the Rome Treaty of 1957, the Latin American Free Trade Association and the North American Free Trade Agreement.

Caterpillar played a leadership role in support of these initiatives.

Sometimes our strong advocacy of free markets has put us in opposition to American policy, as when we opposed U.S. trade restrictions against the Soviet Union in the early 1980s. The Carter and Reagan administrations sought to punish the Soviets for actions in Poland and Afghanistan by refusing to allow U.S. products to be sold for a major Soviet pipeline. But, as is normally the case with unilateral sanctions, products from another country were purchased and the pipeline was built anyway. The attempt to punish the Soviets was futile; the loser was Caterpillar. Not only did we lose sales to non-U.S. competitors, we gained a reputation as an unreliable supplier. That cost us market share for years to come.

We strongly believe that trade between countries leads to economic and human progress. Thus, trade has been a major company communications theme, especially with policymakers. In 1988, we began advocating "zero tariff" agreements on Cat products. Eleven years later—in January, 1999—Cat customers in more than 20 countries were granted duty-free access to most of the machines we make, which before that time were subject to tariffs that added 6.5 to 11 percent to the cost of an American-made Caterpillar product. That's progress—not as fast as we would like, but progress nonetheless.

above. **Top Caterpillar officers were among those advocating free trade at a National Trade Policy Committee meeting in Washington, 1955. President Eisenhower is second from the left in this White House lawn photo. Louis Neumiller is fourth from the left and William Blackie is on his left.**

The Benefits of Trade

Certainly Caterpillar has reaped great benefit from international trade. We estimate that about 16,000 U.S. jobs can be attributed to our exports, plus about 30,000 supplier jobs. About half our business is outside the U.S., and we expect that to increase to 75 percent in the first decade of the new millennium.

But the benefits to our trading partners are equally great. Good things happen when Caterpillar products are made available to people who need them to improve their standards of living. Trade is a two-way street, benefiting both partners.

"We're greatly concerned about the potential threat of U.S. trade legislation which seeks solutions to the trade deficit through protectionist measures. Let's not repeat the mistakes of the 1930s. The growth in world trade during the past four decades has been truly enormous and has been a principal driver to improve standards of living for both the developed and developing countries alike. Protectionism pursued by any trading partner leads to reciprocity with the end result that everyone loses. Caterpillar will continue to work vigorously to help frame a U.S. policy of free and fair trade because of a sincere belief that it's in the best interests of all trading nations."

Chairman George Schaefer and President Pete Donis in 1987 annual report to stockholders.

below left. **Inocencio Ramos works at Caterpillar's fabrication plant in Monterrey, Mexico. Fabrications are shipped to Sanford, North Carolina, facility for final assembly. The Mexican plant and its jobs benefited from the North American Free Trade Agreement which removed most major trade barriers in North America. This trade agreement not only helped the people of Mexico gain a better standard of living, but created jobs for Caterpillar people in the U.S. because of greater sales to Mexico. Cat sales to Mexico before the trade agreement were $128 million. By 1998, that had jumped to more than $400 million, making Mexico Caterpillar's No. 2 trading partner after Canada.**

above. **This fishing camp in Peru gets power from a Cat generator set. The camp provides people in the area good paying jobs and a brighter future. Peru is a member of Asia-Pacific Economic Cooperation. An APEC agreement liberalized trade in certain key sectors of the economy, including fishing.**

below right. **The Philippines, where rice is a major crop, was a founding member of the Association of South East Asian Nations. By increasing its trading power, this bloc of nations (Brunei Darussalam, Cambodia, Indonesia, Laos, Myanmar, the Philippines, Singapore, Thailand and Vietnam) can move commodities to other countries such as the U.S. Caterpillar, in turn, can sell equipment to build the dams and supply the water needed for farms.**

Interstate Highways

In 1956, the Federal Aid Highway Act authorized the biggest public works project in world history, the U.S. interstate highway system. It started as a 41,000-mile project but expanded to 42,800 miles. Total cost has been about $130 billion. By conservative estimates, the interstate system has returned six dollars in economic productivity for every one dollar it cost to build.

above. *Saturday Evening Post* **ad from 1957.**

left and right. **Interstate highway construction projects like these were a common sight across America in the 1960s and 1970s. These two photos from Caterpillar archives bore no identification, so a number of "oldtimers" were asked about the locations. Their answers: "Anywhere, U.S.A. Four-lane divided highways with cloverleafs and overpasses were being built everywhere, using large numbers of Caterpillar products."**

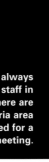

Caterpillar has always maintained a medical staff in its facilities. Shown here are nurses from the Peoria area in about 1964, gathered for a training meeting.

Dr. Harold A. Vonachen

Good Health Is Good Business

An era ended with the retirement of Dr. Harold A. Vonachen in 1963. He had been medical director at Caterpillar since 1927 and was the founder of the "Peoria Plan," a human rehabilitation program for placing physically handicapped people in jobs.

Dr. Vonachen was widely recognized as a leader in industrial medicine. In 1943, he received the Knudsen Award, industrial medicine's highest award, for developing the "Peoria Plan," believed to be the first of its kind in the United States. In 1954, in Washington, D.C., he received the Physician's Award of the President's Committee on Employment of the Physically Handicapped.

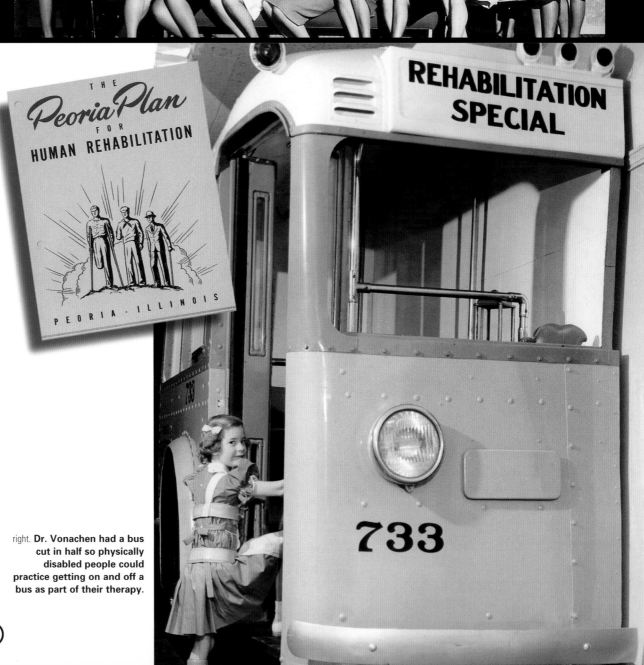

THE Peoria Plan FOR HUMAN REHABILITATION

PEORIA · ILLINOIS

REHABILITATION SPECIAL

733

right. **Dr. Vonachen had a bus cut in half so physically disabled people could practice getting on and off a bus as part of their therapy.**

The Caterpillar Employee Health Initiative

The company's award-winning Healthy Balance
program, introduced in 1997, helps employees and
their families track their health behaviors.

After only a couple of years with the program
in place, Caterpillar people are changing
their behaviors:

• hundreds have stopped smoking,

• more are exercising, and

• thousands are working hard to lose weight.

We believe the best is yet to come.

Early analysis shows more than $40 million in
health care costs can be avoided every year if
only a small percentage of employees change
their unhealthy habits.

It's the truth at Caterpillar. Good health
is good business.

**In a Caterpillar-sponsored
race in Peoria, youngsters
had their chance, too,
to compete. It's one of
the efforts to improve
health of employees
and their families.**

The Healthy Balance program keeps good health in front of
employees with newsletters, books, brochures, videotapes and
activities. *Healthy Balance News* (above and right), an in-house
quarterly newsletter, features success stories and personal
strategies to encourage healthy choices.

1 9 6 5 - 1 9 7 4

Cat sales were strong around the world. The product line was broad enough so that a business decline in one market or geographic region was seemingly balanced by an increase in another. When the United States slid into the 1974-75 recession, Caterpillar sales held up outside the U.S. and the company continued to prosper.

By 1974, we were producing 70 models of machines in 12 product families. Just 10 years before, there had been only 33 Caterpillar models in just seven product families.

Cat planned to build a worldwide headquarters next to the Mossville, Illinois, plant, but changed course and built on two downtown blocks in Peoria. The new building, where about 2,000 people work, opened in 1967.

1965 - Vietnam conflict officially begins.

Medicare and Medicaid established.

BASIC (beginner's all-purpose symbolic instruction code), first computer language designed for use by general public.

1966 - Miranda warnings initiated in the U.S.

Miniskirts come into fashion.

Dr. Michael E. DeBakey implants plastic arteries, leading to an artificial heart.

1967 - Six-day war between Israel and Arab nations.

Dr. Christiaan N. Barnard performs world's first human heart transplant operation.

1968 - Martin Luther King, Jr., and Robert F. Kennedy assassinated.

62 nations sign Nuclear Non-Proliferation Treaty.

Aswan Dam, Egypt, completed.

Automated check cashing pioneered in Great Britain.

1969 - Neil Armstrong and Edwin "Buzz" Aldrin, Jr., are first to walk on the moon.

World population reaches 3.5 billion.

Concorde supersonic aircraft makes first test flight.

1965

1968

1965 - 1676 truck engine introduced.

Grimbergen facility opens in Belgium.

Cat acquires Towmotor Corporation.

First production at Sagamihara, new Caterpillar Mitsubishi, Ltd., plant in Japan.

1966 - Sales in U.S.S.R. resume after three-decade hiatus.

Cat enters into joint venture with Johnson Mfg. to produce elevating scrapers.

William Blackie elected chairman.

1967 - World headquarters building opens in downtown Peoria.

Production begins at Caterpillar Belgium plant at Gosselies.

Caterpillar Retirees Club formed.

Mapleton, Illinois, foundry opens.

Corporate symbol introduced.

1968 - New parts facility in Singapore.

1969 - 1100 engine family introduced; used in Ford medium on-highway trucks.

John Wayne controls a Caterpillar D7 Tractor, one of the main tools used to fight oilwell fires in the 1968 film *Hellfighters*.

CAT D 7

Caterpillar advertising addressed issues of the day.

"They should get diesels off the road."

It's a bitter irony that at a time when Americans enjoy unprecedented prosperity, we seem to be running out of everything from gasoline to clean air.

Most people concede that internal combustion engines are a major cause of air pollution. They also know that the sheer number of them has a lot to do with our fuel shortage.

What may surprise you is that diesel engines have been and can continue helping us solve both problems.

For one thing, diesel engines pollute far less than gasoline engines even without special emissions attachments. What's more, a diesel powered vehicle can travel much farther on a gallon of fuel than a similar gasoline powered machine. Also, diesel fuel is cheaper.

Yes, diesel engines cost a little more to make. When improperly maintained they smoke under load. And some people complain of odor and noise. But those objections are being overcome. The environmental benefits diesels offer are too important to pass up.

Diesel engines are not a cure-all for the fuel shortage and dirty air. But it's good to know that where useful work is needed they do it well and with minimum harmful side effects.

For more information write: Diesel, Dept. 308IN. Caterpillar Tractor Co., Peoria, Illinois 61602.

"If you knew more about diesels, you might think different."

There are no simple solutions. Only intelligent choices.

CATERPILLAR

Caterpillar, Cat and CB are Trademarks of Caterpillar Tractor Co.

1965 through 1974

1970 - Four Vietnam conflict protesters at Kent State University killed.

Fiber optic technology developed.

Floppy disks introduced.

U.S. Clean Air Act becomes law.

1971 - China admitted to the UN.

Intel Co. introduces microprocessor.

First pocket calculator.

26th amendment to U.S. constitution allows 18-year-olds to vote.

1972 - President Nixon visits China after two decades of U.S.-China estrangement.

Watergate controversy begins.

Eleven members of Israeli team and five terrorists killed at Munich Olympics.

1973 - OPEC imposes oil embargo.

MRI (magnetic resonance imager) developed in Great Britain.

Bar coding goes into use in grocery stores.

1974 - President Nixon resigns.

Holographic electron microscope developed.

World population 3.78 billion.

1971

1974

1970 - Sales outside U.S. exceed sales inside U.S. for first time.

1971 - Technical Center at Mossville, Illinois, completed.

1972 - Introduction of 225 Hydraulic Excavator.

William H. Franklin elected chairman.

1973 - Six models of articulated G-Series motor graders introduced.

Caterpillar office opens in Moscow.

1974 - Gray iron foundry at Vernon, France, acquired.

Parts distribution center opens in Memphis, Tennessee.

Production of 3406 heavy-duty diesel truck engine begins in Building BB at Mossville, Illinois, plant, the most modern engine manufacturing plant in the world.

First edition of Caterpillar *Code of Worldwide Business Conduct*.

Original 1974 Code book (right) and edition current in 1999 (left).

Caterpillar Code of Worldwide Business Conduct and Operating Principles

Since the Code was introduced in 1974, every Caterpillar chairman has reaffirmed that no document issued by Caterpillar is more important than this one.

The edition current in 1999 emphasizes that one of the company's most valuable assets is a reputation for integrity:

• *We intend to hold to a single high standard of integrity everywhere. We will keep our word. We won't promise more than we can reasonably expect to deliver; nor will we make commitments we don't intend to keep.*

• *In our advertising and other public communications, we will avoid not only untruths, but also exaggeration and overstatement.*

• *Caterpillar employees shall not engage in activities that produce, or reasonably appear to produce, conflict between personal interests of an employee and interests of the company.*

• *We seek long-lasting relationships—based on integrity—with all whose activities touch upon our own.*

• *The ethical performance of the enterprise is the sum of the ethical performance of the men and women who work here. Thus, we are all expected to adhere to high standards of personal integrity.*

The Code provides details on issues from sharing technology to disclosure of information, from competitive conduct to observance of local laws.

The closing page has these words:

"As a company that manufactures and distributes on a global scale, Caterpillar recognizes it competes in a world composed of different races, religions, cultures, customs, political philosophies, languages, economic resources, geography. We respect these differences. Human pluralism is a strength, not a weakness; no nation has a monopoly on wisdom."

Norman Jones received a "doctor of engines" degree from co-workers after he completed renovation of Old Betsy.

"In 1973, I had the job of restoring Old Betsy, Cat's first diesel engine. With no instructions, I began my work. I handled this piece of history with the greatest care. I made all gaskets. All rods and crankshaft had to be shimmed. Pistons were 6 1/8 inches across the top, 15 inches long, with seven rings per piston. When I started Old Betsy after 40 years, she began to thump, thump. Then she came alive. She passed the 1975 emissions test.

"I timed Old Betsy by heat degrees. Each cylinder had a petcock. By opening this, you determined the heat degrees. Dr. C. G. A. Rosen, retired head of research, flew in from California. He was 83 years old. He opened each petcock, sniffed at the heat, came back to me and said, 'Norm, you've got her close.' I said, 'Art, she is within three heat degrees of each other.'"

Norman V. Jones, retired

"Old Betsy"

Old Betsy as it was presented to the Smithsonian Institution in Washington, D.C., on November 29, 1973. Later it was repainted to match the original 1931 gray color.

1 9 7 5 - 1 9 8 4

Until 1981, all signs suggested a continuing upward trend. The decade of the '70s ended with employment at an all-time high and sales at $7.61 billion. The company was in an expansive mood. We hadn't shown a loss since the Great Depression in 1932.

Signals of a weakening global economy started appearing in 1981. Then, in March, 1982, we fell off a cliff. Sales plunged—not just for us, but for the entire industry. The "order board," the ongoing record of dealer orders, suddenly went blank. It was estimated that the industry had 40 percent over-capacity.

We did what we had to do. Executives took a 10 percent pay cut, and all management employees took cuts up to 10 percent. There were massive layoffs as we curtailed production and reduced capacity. In the midst of this, the United Auto Workers Union went on a seven-month strike. When the strike ended, there was no need for overtime to replenish machine inventory, as was the case in most previous labor disputes. Instead, there were additional layoffs as orders continued to decline. In three years, we lost a billion dollars—roughly a million dollars a day. As someone said, it was discouraging to go to work, work as hard as you could, and go home knowing that the company lost another million dollars despite your efforts.

Caterpillar Milestones / **World Events**

1975 - Work begins on Alaskan oil pipeline.

Oil discovered in North Sea.

Personal computers introduced.

Sony introduces the VCR.

1976 - Landing vehicles from Viking I and II set down on Mars.

Israeli commandos rescue 103 hostages at Entebbe airport.

U.S. Air Force Academy admits 155 women, ending the all-male tradition at U.S. military academies.

1977 - Worldwide oil crisis.

Microsoft founded by Bill Gates and Paul Allen.

Space shuttle "Enterprise" makes its first manned flight.

1978 - Pope John Paul II becomes first non-Italian pope since 1523.

U.S. and People's Republic of China announce establishment of full diplomatic relations.

World population reaches 4.4 billion.

1979 - Cellular phone introduced in Tokyo.

Ayatollah Ruhollah Khomeini takes over in Iran…Shah forced into exile.

Mother Teresa awarded Nobel Peace Prize.

Margaret Thatcher becomes first female prime minister in United Kingdom.

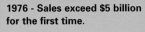

1975 - William L. Naumann elected chairman.

1976 - Sales exceed $5 billion for the first time.

Piracicaba plant opens in Brazil.

Three-for-two stock split.

1977 - Introduction of D10 Track-Type Tractor.

Pontiac, Illinois, plant opens, manufacturing fuel system components.

Lee L. Morgan elected chairman.

1978 - Second foundry opened in Mapleton, Illinois, to increase capacity for engine blocks and heads.

1979 - Construction under way at Lafayette, Indiana, for engine plant to produce large diesel engines.

Our industry had been hit simultaneously by a variety of negative events: a sudden cancellation of major projects in oil-producing countries as the price of oil plummeted; oil-importing countries unable to proceed with infrastructure development because they were using all their funds to pay off past debt for high-priced energy; and a recession in developed countries. On top of that, the undervalued yen gave Japanese manufacturers a competitive edge.

On many transactions, Caterpillar dealers faced a price disadvantage of 40-50 percent or more.

It was a difficult time, but we maintained new product plans and, most importantly, stayed focused on the long term. We avoided those actions that might have improved the bottom line in the short term but could have hurt future competitiveness. Lee Morgan, chairman during the turmoil of the early '80s, said, "It's a remarkable tribute to the strength of our partnership with dealers that, during this time, not one terminated its agreement with Caterpillar to become a dealer for another full-line manufacturer."

1975 through 1984

1980 - Strikes in Poland led by Lech Walesa…Solidarity Party formed.

Eight-year Iran-Iraq war begins.

1981 - MTV introduced.

European Monetary Fund established.

1982 - CD (compact disc) introduced by Sony and Philips.

Supercomputer Cray can perform 100 million arithmetic operations a second.

1983 - Computer advances: Apple offers mouse and icons; IBM introduces first personal computer with hard disk memory device.

1984 - DNA genetic fingerprinting developed.

Computer advances: Laptop/notebook computers appear for first time; CD-ROM introduced; optical disks for data storage introduced.

1981

1984
1984

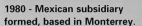

1980 - Mexican subsidiary formed, based in Monterrey.

1981 - Opening of facility in Corinth, Mississippi, to remanufacture engines and components.

Solar Turbines International acquired from International Harvester Company.

Leasing company formed; predecessor of Caterpillar Financial Services Corporation.

The 3500 engine family introduced. Production moves from Mossville, Illinois, to a new plant in Lafayette, Indiana, in 1982.

1982 - 615 Elevating Scraper, 834 Wheel Dozer, 3516 Diesel Engine introduced.

Company suffers loss of $180 million, first loss since 1932. Employment reduced 29 percent.

1983 - Plans announced to close plants in Newcastle, England; Mentor, Ohio; and the original Holt facility in San Leandro, California.

Caterpillar Insurance Company formed.

Joint venture with dealer PT Trakindo begins operations in Indonesia.

U.S. Commercial Division district offices created to better focus field personnel on dealer and customer needs.

1984 - Strategic Planning Conference, an intensive study of corporate strategy, leads to new initiatives in everything from new products to marketing company strengths in financial and logistics areas.

Caterpillar Financial Services Corporation formed.

Caterpillar World Trading Corporation formed.

Solar Turbomach business sold to Sundstrand Corporation.

Plans announced to close Burlington, Iowa, and Edgerton and Milwaukee, Wisconsin, plants.

293 YEARS OF

Chapter 9

Back row: William Blackie, William H. Franklin, William L. Naumann, Lee L. Morgan, chairman 1977-1989. Front row: Harmon S. Eberhard, Louis B. Neumiller. Photo taken September, 1978.

SERVICE

right. **All chairmen have used their office, in Theodore Roosevelt's words, as a "bully pulpit." Lee Morgan, for example, was a leader in advocating exchange rate corrections, especially between the dollar and the yen. His 1982 speech, "The Japanese Challenge in the 1980s," was widely distributed.**

Louis B. Neumiller started as a clerk-stenographer in the Holt facility in Peoria in 1915. He was chairman from 1954 to 1962 and retired from the board in 1969.

Harmon S. Eberhard was 16 years old when he went to work for Holt in San Leandro, California, in 1916. Chairman from 1962 to 1966, he retired from the board in 1973.

William Blackie came to Caterpillar from Price Waterhouse in 1939. He served as chairman from 1966 to 1972 and remained on the board until 1979.

William H. Franklin started at Caterpillar in 1941 as assistant comptroller. Chairman from 1972 to 1975, he served on the board until his retirement in 1982.

William L. Naumann was a machine apprentice starting in 1929, served as chairman 1975 to 1977, and retired from the board in 1984.

Lee L. Morgan came through marketing ranks, starting in 1946. He was chairman from 1977 to 1985 and retired from the board in 1992.

"The kind of people we seek might be described as those having the capacity to learn—to become wise through study, work, observation and experience. The ultimate objective should be wisdom as well as job proficiency. We want people who, as a natural code of personal conduct, like to pursue excellence in all they do. And we'd like them to pursue that excellence preferably on the basis of self-imposed standards. And we want people who are capable of and willing to work at their own self-development, not those who would sit back with an attitude which says, 'If you want me to be a better person, develop me.' We don't believe in depriving people of the opportunity to be the architects of their own future. We want people who will ask questions as they progress through the company. We would rather have people who can discern the questions than those who think they know the answers. It is from questions that we develop new ideas, make progress and grow. We want people who have the work habit—not those to whom work is an imposition. To me, industriousness has in it a sense of morality—on the other hand, idleness is a betrayal of human capacity. We wish to have people who are active and aggressive without being hostile about it. We want them to be mentally and emotionally alert and have the ability to be contemplative—without failing to be diligently active. We certainly wish to have the thinkers, even the philosophers, but they are not going to serve much purpose if their existence on the payroll ends with mere philosophical contemplation. Wisdom must be translated into action. The success of an enterprise is based on the work and ability of its people."

William Blackie, chairman 1966-1972

WORLD TRADING CORPORATION

Alternative Solutions

Caterpillar World Trading Corporation was founded in 1984. It performs a unique function in helping customers buy Caterpillar machines and engines.

Here's how it works.

A machine customer could make higher profits if he had a better machine but he doesn't have the assets to buy it or he is a competitive machine user. Cat World Trading agrees to provide the machine in exchange for a commodity. The Caterpillar trading group then sells the commodity, and return from the sale pays for the machine.

The plan was set up to help customers in countries with foreign exchange shortages. By the end of the century, however, 60 percent of the business was in the U.S. Countertrade has proven to be profitable for both Caterpillar and customers.

MCM, a demolition company in Michigan, got this 345B Excavator in exchange for scrap steel.

EXPANSION IN SOUTHEAST ASIA

A 1983 joint venture agreement with PT Trakindo, Cat dealer in Indonesia, led to expanded business opportunities in this populous country—fourth in population in the world. A new facility in Jakarta allowed us to continue exporting to Indonesia.

In 1997, there was a special ceremony to celebrate the arrival of 51 Cat 789B Off-Highway Trucks for Kaltim Prima Coal, one of the largest, most sophisticated coal mines in the world. The mining company also has a fleet of D10s and D11s and a variety of other Caterpillar products.

There are no simple solutions. Only intelligent choices.

Caterpillar's U.S. advertising in this period focused on issues facing the industries we serve and acknowledged that there were no simple solutions, only intelligent choices. Each ad presented opposing views: "Highway spending is highest in history—Roads are in terrible shape." "We've got to save our beautiful forests—We've got to have more wood." "Gravel pits and quarries are a noisy and dusty nuisance—Sand and gravel are vital to the way we live." "Highways bury good farm land—Highways make farms more productive."

right. **This ad from March, 1975, appeared in *Time*, *Business Week* and *National Geographic*. Then, as now, depletion of non-renewable resources was an issue—and recycling of metals was then, and now, an "intelligent choice."**

opposite. **This 1980 ad hit on another aspect of resource development: mining and its impact on the environment. The closing paragraphs are as appropriate now as they were then.**

"They can't keep making millions of cans forever."

"With recycling we'll have plenty of metal."

Will we run out of metal? Or can we keep on recycling over and over? Both are possibilities, only possibilities.

Certainly the world mineral supplies are limited. More critical, however, is the increasing cost of extracting the ores and reclaiming the land from which they come. U. S. mineral reserves are declining in quality and accessibility. We are heavily dependent now on imports. We can never be entirely self-sufficient.

Recycling can effect costs and probably postpone shortages. But even if everything were recycled, we'd still need great volumes of new metal ore each year.

How much will it cost to meet our needs from lower grade ores? No one knows for sure.

To find out, we should take inventory now. We should explore both private and public lands to learn just what mineral resources we have. Then we can estimate cost of responsible development; meeting strict standards for environmental quality in both mining and processing.

We should encourage such responsible exploration and development worldwide. And we must help keep world trade channels open so vital minerals are available to all countries.

Caterpillar has a stake in this because we manufacture machines used in ore production. And we need a reliable supply of metal to provide 59,000 U.S. jobs. We share every citizen's desire to continue to enjoy the benefits of an economy that simply could not exist without minerals.

There are no simple solutions. Only intelligent choices.

CATERPILLAR

Caterpillar, Cat and CB are Trademarks of Caterpillar Tractor Co.

"Mining is ugly, destroys nature's beauty."

"Mining brings us important minerals."

One looks at mining and sees destruction. Another examines our lifestyle and counts the mineral needs. Can the two be reconciled?

It's true. Miners dig up the land. Surface mining can bury fresh green lands under mounds of sterile subsoil. Many mills produce barren tailings. Chemical leaching can pollute streams. Drive off wildlife. Transform beauty into ugliness. It's easy to see how some despair and call for laws to protect our fields and forests.

At the same time minerals produced from the land are intimately involved in our lives. The Dept. of Interior reports extraordinary mineral dependence—about 40,000 pounds per American per year: Iron, aluminum, coal, copper. And lesser known things: cadmium for paint color, phosphate in fertilizer, boron to make steel tougher and yttrium for TV sets. With demands like that, many argue forcefully for full resource utilization.

To mine or not to mine. Mine disturbance can be controlled. State and Federal coal reclamation laws require return of surface mined lands to near original contour with topsoil replaced. And it can often be done at acceptable cost. Even at that, relatively little land is disturbed by mining. Less than 0.3% of our total land area has brought us all the domestically produced minerals used since 1776. A third of that land has either been reclaimed or reverted to natural state.

Caterpillar makes machines to mine and transport minerals and to reclaim land. We believe Americans should encourage development of our nation's resources. And that development must be carried on within a framework of environmental responsibility.

There are no simple solutions. Only intelligent choices.

CATERPILLAR

Caterpillar, Cat and CB are Trademarks of Caterpillar Tractor Co.

Product advertising spread throughout the world in all major languages including Arabic and French.

Even in remote parts of the world like Christmas Island, Caterpillar products were well known and widely portrayed, as on these postage stamps.

1985-1994

Sales more than doubled in the 10 years, from $6.8 billion in 1985 to $14.3 billion in 1994. Profit went from $198 million to $955 million. But it wasn't a steady increase. We again experienced losses in 1991 ($404 million) and 1992 ($218 million before the effects of accounting changes.) On January 1, 1992, Caterpillar, along with many other large American companies, adopted new accounting standards dealing with post-retirement benefits. This change meant that an additional $2.2 billion had to be reported as a loss.

By the mid-'90s, we began to reap the benefits of years of planned change. The new decentralized organization was beginning to show results. Factory modernization was producing significant cost savings. New ventures that came out of the Strategic Planning Conference were paying off. New products were enthusiastically accepted by customers.

The company's name was changed from Caterpillar Tractor Co. to Caterpillar Inc. in 1986. The new name better reflects broadening product lines.

George Schaefer, chairman 1985-1990, wrote this in *Business Strategy International* magazine in 1990: "This entire phase of strategic change—forming the planning committee, working our way through the process, crafting the mission and vision, and reshaping the organization—has taken about two-and-a-half years. It is our belief that the strategic changes we're making to our product line and manufacturing facilities will allow us to achieve and sustain a long-term competitive advantage."

World Events

1985 - Computer innovations include Microsoft Windows.
Mikhail Gorbachev introduces Glasnost in Soviet Union.
Medical advances include use of lasers to clean clogged arteries.

1986 - Soviet Union launches Mir space station.
Halley's Comet is at its height of visibility.
Digital audio tape technology developed in Japan.

Caterpillar Milestones

1985

1985 - George A. Schaefer elected chairman of the board.
Caterpillar Service Technology Group started.
3600 engine family goes into production.
Air-to-air after-cooled (ATAAC) version of 3406B diesel engine announced.
First Cat backhoe loader built at Leicester, England.
Production of integrated toolcarriers begins.
785 Off-Highway Truck introduced.
Cat acquires DJB Engineering Limited, manufacturer of off-highway articulated dump trucks.
Paving products branding agreement with CMI Corporation starts.
Canada joins USCD and the North American Commercial Division is formed.

1986 - Caterpillar reincorporated as a Delaware corporation. Name changed from Caterpillar Tractor Co. to Caterpillar Inc.
789 Off-Highway Truck introduced.
Advanced Filtration Systems, Inc. formed in Champaign, Illinois, to manufacture filters. Joint venture with Donaldson Company, Inc.
Mentor, Ohio, plant closes.
Caterpillar and Mitsubishi Heavy Industries agree to expand joint venture agreement to include excavators, with design center located in Japan. New company called Shin Caterpillar Mitsubishi.
Caterpillar and The General Electric Company P.L.C. of England announce automated laser-guided lift truck vehicle.

We've helped build across international boundaries before, but never underneath one.

For centuries, the English Channel has remained the most famous, if not most impervious, boundary in the world. Now the long-awaited undersea rail link between Great Britain and France – the Channel Tunnel – is open for business.

For this, one of the most daunting engineering projects of the century, it's no surprise that Caterpillar equipment was used to help move 9 million cubic yards of earth and build access roads and entry points on both sides of the channel.

Wherever the world's builders and planners are at work, you'll find Caterpillar equipment and people.

Of course, we were just as busy above sea level last year, shipping $11.2 billion worth of Caterpillar equipment around the world. But that's only natural.

As the global leader in earthmoving equipment, we're bound to cross a few international borders.

In 1993, we launched a new advertising campaign in *The Wall Street Journal, Forbes, Fortune, The Economist* and *Financial Times.* Some of the ads also appeared as television spots in the U.S., Europe and Latin America.

left. **In this 1994 ad, we tell the story of Caterpillar's involvement in helping build the Channel Tunnel (Chunnel) between Great Britain and France.**

1987 - Black Monday in October...worst U.S. stock market crash since 1929.

Fiber cable laid across Atlantic Ocean.

Work begins on tunnel connecting England and France. The Channel Tunnel was chosen as top construction achievement of the 20th century at CONEXPO/CON-AGG '99.

1988 - UN-mediated cease-fire ends Iran-Iraq conflict.

1989 - Berlin Wall comes down.

In Paris, 149 nations sign ban on use of bacteriological weapons.

1987

1987 - $1.8 billion factory modernization program launched...completed in 1993.

Plans announced to close plants in Davenport, Iowa; Dallas, Oregon; and Glasgow, Scotland.

Caterpillar Logistics Services, Inc., formed.

Challenger 65 Agricultural Tractor reaches market with patented Mobil-trac System.

H and N series of track-type tractors launched.

Navistar International Corp. selects Caterpillar as fuel system component supplier.

General Motors selects Cat 3116 engine as the only diesel option in a new line of medium-duty trucks.

1988 - New Caterpillar trademark introduced... a symbol of change for the future.

Caterpillar Paving Products, Inc., formed, Minneapolis, Minnesota.

Caterpillar Materials Routiers formed, Rantigny, France.

3176 engine introduced. Features electronic fuel injection.

1989

Arizona Proving Ground moves from Phoenix to Tucson.

Reorganization

"It used to be a high compliment to say, 'Those people really know their business.' The real competitive edge comes when your customer can say, 'Those people really know my business.'"
Glen Barton, chairman

In 1990, Caterpillar reorganized. We wanted to respond more quickly to customer needs. That meant we had to move into "high velocity" with new product introductions, with programs to predict future machine and engine servicing needs, with information flow to help customers own and operate their machines more profitably, with business structures that would continue to attract the best new employees from college campuses.

We dismantled the functional hierarchy and established a mix of product and geographic business units, with some centralized support units that could sell their services to the profit centers. Those business units dedicated to products were set up to be more focused, with fewer products targeted to specific market segments to make them more nimble, more responsive to customers.

Barton added: "We believe that our reorganization and the changes it has brought to our way of interacting within the company and with our suppliers, and the focus it has brought to all of us serving on the Caterpillar team, have made us a better company for our shareholders, for our employees and—above all—for our customers."

1990 - Hubble space telescope launched.
East Germany holds first democratic elections.
World population 5.3 billion.

1991 - Soviet Union dissolved. Warsaw Pact formally ended. Leningrad changes name back to St. Petersburg.
Persian Gulf War.
Slovenia and Croatia declare independence.

1990

1990 - Caterpillar reorganizes into profit centers and service centers to better focus on customer needs and the bottom line.
Donald V. Fites elected chairman of the board.
Cat's largest wheel loader, the 994, introduced.
Acquisition of Balderson, a manufacturer of special attachments.

1991 - Plans announced to relocate Caterpillar Financial Services from Peoria to Nashville, Tennessee.
New facility announced in Boonville, Missouri, to produce rubber components.
Caterpillar added to Dow Jones Industrial Average Index, replacing Navistar.
Closing of Brampton, Ontario, facility announced. New facility in Clayton, North Carolina, becomes headquarters for Building Construction Products Division.
Acquisition of Barber-Greene, leading paving equipment manufacturer.

Mission Statement, 1990

"We will provide customers worldwide with differentiated products and services of recognized superior value—pursue businesses in which we can be a leader based on one or more of our strengths—create and maintain a productive work environment in which employee satisfaction is attained with high levels of personal growth and achievement, while conforming to our *Code of Worldwide Business Conduct*—and achieve growth and provide above-average returns for stockholders resulting from both management of ongoing businesses and a studied awareness and development of new opportunities."

1992 - Hurricane Andrew lashes Florida.

Bill Clinton elected president.

1993 - U.S. House of Representatives and Senate approve North American Free Trade Agreement (NAFTA).

Japan's Liberal Democratic Party loses power for first time in 38 years.

37 countries agree to stop dumping nuclear waste into the oceans.

President Clinton signs Family Leave bill into law.

1994 - In first universal suffrage elections in South Africa, Nelson Mandela elected president.

President Clinton signs bill implementing Uruguay provisions of the General Agreement on Tariffs and Trade.

Construction of Three Gorges Dam in China begins.

1992

1992 - Caterpillar China formed.

Energy Power Systems in Australia formed to sell and promote new Cat engines in Australia.

European Excavator Design Center formed in Germany to engineer, produce and market wheeled hydraulic excavators.

Caterpillar Hungary Component Manufacturing formed to manufacture and sell welded steel fabrications.

The 300 family of hydraulic excavators introduced.

First Cat quarry trucks, 771C and 775D, introduced.

First Cat mining shovel, 5130, introduced.

1993 - New plant announced for manufacture of small diesel engines in Greenville, South Carolina.

Grenoble, France, plant produces its first 312A small hydraulic excavator.

New plant at Leland, North Carolina, begins production of small transmissions.

Anchor Coupling, Inc., of Menominee, Michigan, becomes wholly owned subsidiary. Makes hydraulic hose couplings and hose assemblies.

5230 Mining Shovel introduced.

1994

1994 - Exports of U.S.-produced equipment up to $4.51 billion; Cat contribution to U.S. balance of trade reaches $1.37 billion.

Company forms two joint ventures in Russia—one to produce construction machinery components, the other to produce medium- and heavy-duty on-highway diesel truck engines.

First dealership established in Vietnam.

Mectrack in Bazzano, Italy, acquired; manufactures undercarriage components for track products.

Rockwood, Tennessee, facility opened to produce powder metal components.

Large Challenger agricultural tractor production moved from Aurora to DeKalb, Illinois.

Challenger 35 and 45 row-crop tractors introduced.

Two-for-one stock split.

Changing the Culture

The industry-wide downturn of the 1980s—painful as it was—did Caterpillar a favor: it was a wake-up call. It caused us to take a hard look at the company to find ways to remain profitable even in an economic downturn. We had to respond to changing customer needs more rapidly, introduce new products more quickly, adjust production and inventory levels faster. We had to become a high velocity company.

Plant modernization and corporate reorganization were major steps forward. We formalized a high velocity New Product Introduction program. And we changed the compensation system, providing greater rewards for greater results.

Above all, there had to be buy-in by Caterpillar people. Could they adapt to a higher speed, more customer-focused work environment? Could they at the same time retain the time-honored values of the company? Values like ethical operations, dedication to quality, teamwork with customers, dealers and suppliers? Could they propel Caterpillar into a new century of growth?

People have to give that effort; it can't be ordered… it can't be demanded. So Caterpillar set out purposefully to create an environment that could bring out the best in people. That meant a physical environment and a work atmosphere that attract the best and brightest people. It meant moving more decisions downward. It meant assurance of meaningful work for new employees. It meant moving people into new jobs more rapidly. It meant quality education and training for all employees on a regular basis, especially in the fast-moving world of electronic communications. It meant a culture in which empowered people could be adequately rewarded for top effort and results.

We're in a process of continuous cultural change in a fast-paced world. Caterpillar people will ensure our continued leadership in the 21st century.

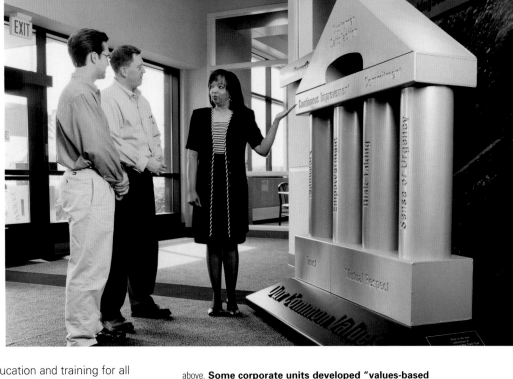

above. **Some corporate units developed "values-based programs" specific to their business. The first such program is the Common Values effort of the Track-Type Tractors Division. Thea Robinson, human resources manager for the division, explains common values to visitors, using a three-dimensional model in the East Peoria headquarters of the Track-Type Tractors Division.**

right. **With a reorganized and rapidly expanding company, we needed a way to make sure our "personality" was well defined and consistently communicated. After intensive study, we developed a list of attributes as shown on the next page.** *Communicating Caterpillar: One Voice* **was introduced throughout the company.**

Attributes • Caterpillar products are **down-to-earth,** straightforward, **gritty** and **rugged.** The Cat name is **enduring.** To meet our customers' expectations, our products have to be **strong,** **powerful** and **reliable.** We are **genuine** and **accessible** and act as an **honest partner** in our relations with dealers, customers and each other—and we're **responsive** and **global** enough to meet our customers' changing needs. We're **serious, thorough** and **professional** about our business, **active** and highly **industrious, dedicated** to helping our customers succeed. Our **commanding** engines and machines are of the highest quality, and that is what makes us **competitive** and our industry's **leader.**

© 1994 CATERPILLAR

Eight months after the Gulf War, we declared a cease-fire of our own.

While the oil fields of Kuwait burned, Caterpillar equipment worked to put out the disastrous fires.

Our equipment is used all over the world. And not just when disaster strikes. Last year, for example, we shipped $11 billion worth of our products to work sites from Alaska to Zimbabwe—including $1.6 billion to countries in Europe.

Our products and support services helped our customers construct irrigation canals and superhighways, mine valuable resources and dig foundations for homes and schools.

Our diesel engines powered trucks, ships, trains, hospitals and, in remote areas like Lillehammer, Norway, provided the power needed at the 1994 Winter Olympics.

At Caterpillar, it's not just what we make. It's what we make possible.

CATERPILLAR

They won't destroy it to create a farm when they realize it is one.

When poor farmers in the Amazon need land to feed their families, they turn to a practice anthropologists call "slash and burn." And, unfortunately, that's just what they're doing to the last great rain forest on earth.

Enter the Tropical Forest Foundation— a unique collaboration of environmental groups and companies like Caterpillar—with a plan to farm the rain forest without destroying it.

The crop is hardwood and a series of pilot projects in Brazil are already showing local people how to harvest timber in a way that makes the jungle a renewable resource.

As a company that operates around the world, we've seen how poverty and hunger can threaten the environment. And that's why we're so pleased about our little tree farm in Brazil that helps the land and, even more importantly, helps the people who live on it.

CATERPILLAR

Entrance to the Caterpillar parts facility in Johannesburg. The distribution center stocks 100,000 line items with 200,000 square feet (18 580 square meters) under roof and an additional 100,000 square feet (9290 square meters) of yard storage.

Caterpillar in South Africa

South African Ian Leach, manager of Caterpillar's parts facility in Johannesburg, wrote this account of the company's role in helping influence the end of apartheid.

"Over the years, international pressure mounted against the South African government's policy of apartheid and, by the late 1970s, American companies in South Africa were strongly urged to disinvest—meaning to sell their business or close the door and cease operations.

"Caterpillar was no exception and the heat was on. We had to make a critical decision. We could stay in South Africa, stand up for our beliefs in equality and push to abolish apartheid; or we could get out of the country, escape the battles and leave our employees jobless and our customers without service. The pressure to disinvest was tremendous and many companies including Caterpillar had to face the decision of losing sales in the United States or abandoning their South African operations.

"Cat's board of directors elected to resist disinvestment and become involved with anti-apartheid efforts. Apartheid conflicted with Caterpillar's *Code of Conduct,* so Cat Africa didn't abide by apartheid rules in the facility.

"By the late 1980s, South Africa was burning, literally. The government declared a 'State of Emergency' and the American Chamber of Commerce in Johannesburg responded by running a 'state of urgency' ad in several national newspapers. The ad, which publicly appealed to the national government to disband apartheid and release all political prisoners, listed Caterpillar as a supporter. We were applauded by the international business community and the U.S. government, but South Africa's government and sectors of the business community had dim views of the group of foreigners who were imposing their domestic views on South Africa.

"I was president of the American Chamber of Commerce at the time. We penned a letter to American companies urging them to defy South Africa's 'Group Areas Act' and to help move blacks into so-called 'white suburbs.' For that, and other civil disobedience, we got ourselves into hot water. The attorney general summoned us to his office and said he believed we were interfering in the domestic affairs of South Africa and that he had enough evidence to charge us with treason.

"But we pushed on. We met personally with the state president and offered some unsolicited but sound advice: move forward with eliminating apartheid and introduce economic change or more companies would withdraw from South Africa and the country would suffer severe economic hardship. He'd obviously received this kind of pressure from many other sources and he knew the only option was to move forward.

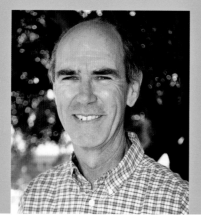

South African Ian Leach is manager of the parts facility. In November, 1999, he was made an honorary life member of the American Chamber of Commerce in South Africa for serving on its board from 1977 to 1998.

Retired Chairman Don Fites and his wife Sylvia with Nelson Mandela, who was president of the Republic of South Africa when the photo was taken in 1994.

"South Africa's government was facing so much pressure both domestically and internationally that on February 2, 1990, the president announced the unbanning of the African National Congress, the release of all political prisoners including Nelson Mandela—who'd been jailed for 27 years—and the commencement of multi-party democratic negotiations.

"In 1994, South Africa held its first democratic election. A miracle had taken place. South Africa is now diligently rebuilding its economic, health care and education systems under the democratically elected government. There's much more emphasis on human development and less on defense and policing. In addition, our country now boasts one of the finest constitutions in the world, which states that discrimination of any kind is strictly prohibited and will not be tolerated.

"American companies, including Caterpillar, that resisted disinvestment during apartheid rule played a crucial role in bringing South Africa to where it is today—a nation of equality and unity. Caterpillar employees should be proud to work for a company that upholds its beliefs. During the apartheid era, Caterpillar received much publicity, both positive and negative, but we fought the battles and, in turn, protected a business interest that continues to flourish today. We have since invested in more than doubling the size of the Johannesburg Distribution Centre and have established a Caterpillar-owned manufacturing plant that specializes in large fabrications."

Retired Chairman Don Fites made the following remarks before the Executives Club of Chicago on April 22, 1999:

"On his first night in the U.S. as President of South Africa, I had the pleasure of introducing Nelson Mandela at a dinner in New York. Seated next to each other for the entire evening, we had plenty of opportunity to discuss South Africa, where I had lived and worked for Caterpillar for five years.

"After a while, I worked up the courage to ask him if he was going to hold it against Caterpillar because we did not leave South Africa in response to sanctions designed to halt apartheid. His response was enlightening—he said, in fact, he was glad we hadn't pulled out. His reasoning was that, first and foremost, American companies had set a very positive example for others to follow in South Africa. And he also noted that companies such as Caterpillar provided employment—and that employment is what South Africa needed most of all."

Led by Crew Chief Tommy Baldwin, Jr., the Caterpillar pit crew changes four tires and fills the car with fuel in less than 16 seconds.

Andy Houston and The Cat Rental Stores race team were contenders all of the 1999 season, completing 99.2 percent of all laps run during the 25-race schedule.

Ward Burton won Caterpillar's first Winston Cup pole position at Michigan Speedway on August 20, 1999, with a new track record of 188.843 miles per hour on the two-mile track.

Driver Harri Luostarinen and the Caterpillar Truck Racing Developments team won the FIA European Supertruck Cup championship in 1997 and were runners-up in 1998.

Cat Racing

Caterpillar started sponsorship in the NASCAR Winston Cup Series in 1992. We teamed with Bill Davis Racing and driver Ward Burton in 1999 to become one of the premier teams in the sport. The Winston Cup Series is NASCAR's top level of competition, with 34 events across the U.S.

Also in 1999, The Cat Rental Stores became the primary sponsor of the Addington Racing NASCAR Craftsman Truck Series team.

In Australia, Cat started sponsoring a Ford team in the Super V8 Series in 1999.

In Europe, Caterpillar has a major presence in the FIA European Supertruck Racing Cup Series, racing a full-sized truck cab powered by the Cat C-12 engine. In 1997, the team won the series championship, using a single engine for the entire season.

The Supertruck racing program has been a big success with our product development people. The standard production C-12 engine produces 410 horsepower (305.8 kilowatts). But fuel system and turbo modifications push the power output to 1,400 horsepower (1044.4 kilowatts) for the racing truck. Engineers have made improvements to areas that showed distress under this extreme application and have corrected problems in production engines before they became apparent in normal usage. The result is a better, more reliable C-12.

1 9 9 5 - 1 9 9 9

Explosive Growth

In this five-year period, Caterpillar added 88 facilities worldwide, 17 joint ventures, and acquired 20 other companies. We introduced 244 new or improved products, from the giant 797 Off-Highway Truck to the new line of compact equipment. Research and engineering expenses climbed from $532 million in 1995 (3.3 percent of sales and revenues) to $838 million in 1998 (4 percent of sales and revenues) as we continued to develop and improve products for the next century.

Profit surpassed a billion dollars for the first time in 1995. In 1997, Caterpillar announced a two-for-one stock split. Annual sales and revenues went over the $20 billion mark in 1998 and, that same year, U.S. exports exceeded $6 billion.

In March, 1998, Caterpillar and the United Auto Workers Union signed a six-year contract ending a widely publicized labor dispute. Caterpillar said in a statement that the "new agreement preserves the company's right to manage key issues and is fair to

employees, providing them with an excellent compensation and benefits package."

We end the century as the world leader in construction and mining equipment, diesel and natural gas engines and industrial gas engines, with a growing family of diverse service organizations including financial and logistics services. We're proud to make progress possible for people around the globe.

Caterpillar Milestones World **Events**

1995 - U.S. and Vietnam establish full economic ties.
Israeli Prime Minister Yitzhak Rabin is assassinated.
Dow Jones Industrial Average closes the year at 5117.
World leaders convene in New York to commemorate 50th anniversary of the United Nations.

1995

1995 - 49 new or improved products introduced.

Mining and Construction Equipment Division created.

Caterpillar announces purchase of 49% stake in generator set manufacturer FG Wilson, Larne, Northern Ireland, from Emerson Electric Company.

E-series articulated trucks introduced.

Caterpillar Elphinstone Pty. Ltd., formed in Australia to manufacture underground mining equipment.

Caterpillar Energy Co., S.A., formed in Guatemala to manufacture engine power systems.

Caterpillar Power Systems, Inc., formed in Tokyo to market engines in Japan.

Hydropro S.r.l. acquired in Jesi, Ancona, Italy, to manufacture hydraulic cylinders.

Caterpillar Redistribution Services, Inc., formed in Dallas, Texas, to purchase and sell used construction equipment.

Financial World **magazine names Don Fites CEO of the Year.**

Cat announces purchase of off-highway transmission business of Dana Corp. located in Wolverhampton, England.

New facility announced for Booneville, Mississippi, to remanufacture components. New facility in Jefferson, Georgia, will make components for Cat fuel systems.

Chief Executive **magazine names Caterpillar board as one of the five best in the U.S.**

Independently owned dealership opens in southwest region of China.

Caterpillar Xuzhou formed to manufacture hydraulic excavators in China.

right. **The 100,000th backhoe loader rolled off the line in Leicester, England, in 1999. A backhoe demonstration and a display of the first Leicester-produced backhoe (1985) were among the events. The Leicester facility is in the background.**

1996 - Boris Yeltsin re-elected Russian president.

Benjamin Netanyahu new Israeli prime minister.

Astronaut Shannon Lucid spends 188 days in space.

1997 - China regains sovereignty over Hong Kong.

Labor Party ends 18 years of Conservative Party rule in Great Britain. Tony Blair is new prime minister.

Chinese President Jiang Zemin meets with President Clinton, tours U.S.

1996

1996 - New subsidiary, Caterpillar Agricultural Products, Inc., formed to design, manufacture and market Cat agricultural products.

24H Motor Grader, the world's largest, introduced.

Caterpillar and Fabryka Maszyn Lubelske of Poland announce establishment of joint venture to produce heavy fabrications.

Dyersburg, Tennessee, facility starts to manufacture parts for transmissions.

Caterpillar acquires Vibra-Ram Wack GmbH, a leading manufacturer of scrap and demolition work tool attachments in Zweibrücken, Germany.

Caterpillar and Trimble announce agreement to develop global positioning system technology for machine control.

Acquisition of MaK Maschinenbau GmbH, a world leader in large diesel engines.

First Mobil-trac-equipped asphalt paver, the AP-1055B, introduced.

1997

1997 - New track shoe manufacturing facility starts up in Skinningrove, England.

Caterpillar and Claas announce plans to form joint venture in agricultural equipment. LEXION combine introduced.

Shanxi International Castings Co., Ltd., joint venture foundry, formed in China.

New facilities in Morganton, North Carolina; Danville, Kentucky; Sumter, South Carolina; LaGrange, Georgia; Oxford, Mississippi; and West Plains, Missouri.

Plans announced to build articulated truck plant in Waco, Texas.

Cat purchases Hewitt Equipment's attachment business.

Caterpillar acquires Skögsjan AB, Swedish manufacturer of forestry machines.

Caterpillar to purchase minority interest in Mincom Pty., supplier of mine management and application software.

Fortune **magazine names Caterpillar one of the most admired companies in the world.**

Cat purchases intellectual property rights for large wheel dozers from Tiger Engineering in Australia.

Cat, ITOCHU and SNT form AsiaTrak, new company to manufacture undercarriage in China.

Cat and Isuzu Motors develop new high-pressure fuel-injection system to be used in Isuzu light-duty diesel engines.

Two-for-one stock split.

left. **The Deployable Universal Combat Earthmover (DEUCE) was developed for the U.S. Army. It uses Mobil-trac technology and can travel at speeds up to 33 miles per hour.**

1998 - President Clinton impeached but stays in office.

Hong Kong International Airport Chek Lap Kok opens. Named one of the top 10 construction achievements of the 20th century by attendees at CONEXPO-CON/AGG '99.

Scientists for the first time isolate and cultivate human embryonic stem cells.

"When you see the product being made or actually watch a parts order being filled, you learn what we mean by quality."

John Slyman, Corporate Visitor Services

Worldwide, about 70,000 customers toured Caterpillar facilities in 1998.

1998

1998 - 797 Mining Truck, the world's largest, unveiled.

Cat purchases Material Handling Crane Systems, Inc., which designs and manufactures components for hydraulic excavators used in the scrap and material handling industry.

Track-Type Tractors Division moves headquarters back to East Peoria, Illinois, (from downtown Peoria) and preserves facade of original Cat headquarters. The old building had been demolished in 1997.

Caterpillar acquires Wrightech, earthmoving equipment manufacturer, and Wright Equipment Company, manufacturer of dragline buckets for mines, both in South Africa.

Transmission Business Unit and Cat Belgium announce they are combining forces to build new transmission facility in Arras, France.

Alliance formed with A.S.V., Inc., a manufacturer of low ground pressure, light construction vehicles.

Cat acquires Veratech Holdings B.V. of the Netherlands, leading bucket and work tool specialist, which includes an extensive line of scrap and demolition tools.

Cat South Africa doubles its size to become a full-service distribution center, serving the southern portion of Africa.

New line of compact machines and nearly 60 work tools unveiled at Bauma, the world's largest construction equipment show, in Munich, Germany.

Steel casting joint venture formed between Cat and Citation Corp. to manufacture ground engaging tools.

Cat and Claas announce plans to build LEXION combine manufacturing facility in Omaha, Nebraska.

Caterpillar acquires assets of Perkins Engines Company.

Fuel Systems opens manufacturing facility in Thomasville, Georgia.

Cat and Finland-based Tamrock Corp. announce joint venture to make hydraulic hammers.

Caterpillar and York International Corp. form a strategic alliance in the temperature-control equipment rental business.

New 250,000-square-foot (23 225-square-meter) facility for Caterpillar Tosno announced, to fabricate components and eventually assemble earthmoving equipment near St. Petersburg, Russia.

far left. **In 1998, Solar Turbines won the prestigious Malcolm Baldrige National Quality Award in the manufacturing category.**

left. **Brazilian President Fernando Henrique Cardoso (left) congratulates Chris Schena, president of Caterpillar Brasil Ltda., after presenting the Prêmio Nacional de Qualidade award at a ceremony in Brasília in 1999. It's the top quality award for a manufacturer in Brazil.**

right. **This new 11-story building in Nashville, Tennessee, is world headquarters for Caterpillar Financial Services.**

above. **In 1999, Bradley University named its new communications facility in Peoria the Caterpillar Global Communications Center.**

1999 - Global hot spots include Kosovo and East Timor.

China and the U.S. sign trade agreement opening way for China to become member of World Trade Organization.

Dow Jones close at 11497.

World population: six billion people.

1999

1999 - Donald V. Fites retires as chairman; Glen A. Barton elected as new chairman.

Track-type tractor named one of *Popular Mechanics'* top 100 inventions of the millennium.

100,000th backhoe loader rolls off the line in Leicester, England.

Lubrizol Corporation and Caterpillar co-developing environmentally beneficial, low-emission diesel fuel.

Seal ring foundry for Taccoa, Georgia, announced.

Vice President Jim Baldwin receives 1999 Illinois River Valley Conservation Award from The Nature Conservancy.

Caterpillar announces 100 percent ownership of generator set manufacturer FG Wilson located in Larne, Northern Ireland, through the purchase of Emerson Electric Company's 51 percent stake.

Cat becomes world's largest producer of diesel engines.

First transmission shipped by Caterpillar Transmission France (Arras) in March.

New 110,000-square-foot (10 219-square-meter) facility in Nuevo Laredo, Mexico, officially inaugurated. Facility remanufactures fuel-injection products.

Glen Barton

left. **The Three Gorges Dam on the Yangtze River will be the world's largest, providing power and flood control to benefit millions of people. It's scheduled for completion in 2009 at a $24-billion estimated cost. More than 300 Cat machines are working on the site.**

Caterpillar in China

Caterpillar products have been associated with China's growth and development for many decades. Today, our commitment has never been stronger. In the 1995-1999 time period, we have invested in joint venture manufacturing facilities to make hydraulic excavators, construction machinery components, diesel engines, undercarriage parts and castings.

Caterpillar China Limited, headquartered in Hong Kong, has offices in Beijing and Shanghai, with manufacturing plants, product support facilities, training centers and Caterpillar dealers located throughout China.

above. **Carnegie Fang (foreground) and Lee Li work on the hydraulic excavator assembly line of Caterpillar Xuzhou Limited.**

above. **Delivery of 20 777C trucks signed by Dick Kahler, president of Caterpillar China Limited, and Zheng Chang, manager of Three Gorges Equipment Company.**

Solar Turbines International Company maintains a sales representative office in Beijing and MaK Motoren GmbH & Co. KG has a sales staff in Shanghai. FG Wilson Incorporated has a China distribution center in Hong Kong.

Caterpillar Xuzhou Limited in Xuzhou City is a joint venture established in 1995 with Xuzhou Construction Machinery Group. AsiaTrak (Tianjin) Limited, located in Tianjin, is a joint venture formed in 1997 with Japan-based Itochu Corporation and SNT Corporation. Shanxi International Casting Company Limited produces engine castings. It's a joint venture with Asian

Strategic Investments Corporation and CITIC Machinery Manufacturing Inc., formed in 1997.

China is the site of some of the world's largest earthmoving projects, including the recently completed Hong Kong Airport and the Three Gorges Dam.

"Shanxi International Casting Company Limited is a testament to Caterpillar's intent and commitment to China. My assignment here has taught me many valuable lessons. I have learned that 'things' don't matter as much as 'feelings.' I feel honored to have worked and struggled with the team that has committed to build this company and appreciative of the opportunity to build a part of the future."

Ron Martin, general manager of Shanxi International Casting Company Limited

Chinese Premier Zhu Rongji inspected a Caterpillar LEXION Combine on his visit to the United States in April, 1999. He saw a demonstration of the machine on the Pritzker farm near Libertyville, Illinois. On the same visit, he had a private meeting with Caterpillar Chairman Glen Barton.

Caterpillar in the Commonwealth of Independent States

In 1998, we dedicated our new marketing headquarters in Moscow, 25 years after the first Moscow office opened in 1973. The new headquarters, employing 150 people, symbolizes our dedication to continued business cooperation in the Commonwealth of Independent States (most of the former Soviet Union republics).

Recent uncertain economic conditions throughout the region are troubling, but we have taken prudent steps to manage operations during this difficult period. We are confident that the long-range opportunities more than outweigh the problems of current instability. We continue to move ahead aggressively with our strategy to be a locally committed partner whose people, products and services make a vital contribution to building the economies of the CIS.

The region's oil fields represent 10 percent of the world's proven reserves and its gas fields represent 40 percent of the world's reserves. Caterpillar products are instrumental in oil and gas projects, mining and infrastructure development…and the region represents enormous potential in forestry, agriculture, building construction and engine power generation.

left. **Caterpillar CIS marketing headquarters in central Moscow. We occupy the top three floors with our world-class commercial and technical support center.**

right. **Ground was broken for Caterpillar Tosno on May 15, 1999. It has 243,000 square feet (22 500 square meters) of manufacturing space on a 59.28-acre site.**

lower right. **A jazz band played at the open house for Caterpillar's new headquarters building in Moscow. The open house commemorated the 25th anniversary of Caterpillar's first Moscow office which opened in 1973.**

Manufacturing

Our manufacturing center is Caterpillar Tosno in St. Petersburg. We currently employ 570 people there, making components and fabrications that are exported to Caterpillar assembly plants in France, Belgium, Sweden, the United Kingdom and Germany. Eventually the facility will employ nearly 800 people and manufacture several models of mid-sized machines.

Distribution

We are building a distribution system unparalleled in the CIS. Since October, 1998, we have appointed these new Caterpillar dealers: Zeppelin for the Moscow-St. Petersburg area and Ukraine; Barlows International for the Kuzbass region; Mirovaya Technica for the Saratov territory of South West Russia; Borusan Makina for Kazakhstan; Bergerat Monnoyeur for the Urals Central Russia region; NC Machinery for the North Russian Far East; and Wagner for South Siberia.

Applied Technology

It has been said that there were more technological breakthroughs in the last decade of the 20th century than in all the preceding decades. Caterpillar experience bears that out. It has also been said there will be more changes in the first decade of the new century than in the entire 20th century. We believe that will be true, too.

Today's laptop computer, as just one example, is 50 times more powerful than a $15-million mainframe 20 years ago. During that time, the global information network of computers, telephones and televisions has increased its information-carrying capacity not a hundred times, not a thousand times, but a million times. The coming decade will see even more startling advances.

In our industry, we're looking at new ways to use technology, like electronically controlled hydraulic power, also known as electrohydraulics, that will let us provide even more precise control of machine implements such as buckets, blades and booms.

Laser technology will dramatically impact manufacturing. Today, lasers are widely used for cutting and welding. Tomorrow, lasers will revolutionize drilling.

New materials are also continually finding their way into our products. For example, structural ceramics are showing great promise in preliminary field tests. And ceramics are also finding their way into manufacturing. Ceramic cutting tools and drill bits allow for much more rapid machining times, thus increasing productivity.

Ceramic thin film technology will likely be found throughout Caterpillar machines and engines over the next decade. These films are on the order of a micron thick (about 1/100th the thickness of a human hair) and are deposited on steel components one atom at a time, giving the process engineer the ability to tailor the properties of the coating with great accuracy, thus increasing the life of components.

A thermal spray gun mixes gases and oxygen to create a high-density material that is deposited onto components one atom at a time. These coatings are used to improve wear resistance and durability in demanding applications.

Computer simulation is already a valuable tool. We use it to re-examine the engine combustion process and to find improvements in metallurgy; we use virtual reality to design machines, engines and components more efficiently and far more quickly.

Sophisticated sensors on machines and engines will monitor performance and feed information back to the dealer. This will enable a machine or engine to signal when a part or system is not performing well so technicians can be on site to fix the problem before the customer even knows there is one.

Meeting Customers' Expectations

Changes made to our products are not driven by a love for technology. Rather, the technology is used because it produces either lower owning and operating costs for the customer…or it meets society's requirements for lower environmental impact…or both. As an example, dealers and customers have told us that our engine electronic control systems must be easy to use and easy to integrate. So we're working on an open architecture system that has these features along with self-diagnostics that will provide a common look and feel across all Cat products, whether they be power generators, gas compressors, industrial chillers, pumping stations or marine applications. Technology will be applied with the customer in mind so that problems can be readily diagnosed and repairs made quickly and easily.

The Global Approach to Technology

Technology development is a global affair, and we have a global technology network that includes thousands of employees around the world. The network also includes research partnerships with more than 30 universities, including master research agreements with Carnegie-Mellon University in Pennsylvania, Purdue University in Indiana and the University of Illinois.

We're working with the University of Illinois on engine combustion, flow visualization and virtual prototyping simulation, and with Purdue on engineering analysis, electronic engine controls and electrohydraulic components.

We're involved with a number of projects specifically related to engines, from fuel spray characteristics at the University of Manchester Institute of Science and Technology in the United Kingdom to thermosciences at the Universities of Hamburg and Aachen in Germany, from work on stratified combustion in gas engines at the Imperial College, University of London, to belt and chain analysis at the Institute of Aerodynamics and Hydrodynamics in Moscow. This technology network not only pursues the best technologies to meet current customer needs but is constantly on the lookout for promising new technologies that could address future needs.

Individually, these and other areas of technology impact the development and manufacture of new products. When combined, these technologies dramatically affect our future product possibilities.

The Responsibility of Diesel Leadership

In 1999, Caterpillar became the world's largest producer of diesel engines.

We're proud of that. But we also know, from long experience, that leadership carries with it responsibility.

When the undervalued Japanese yen threatened U.S. manufacturers in the 1980s, we led American business in seeking exchange rate corrections. We considered that our responsibility as an industry leader.

When trade barriers threatened, we led business efforts in support of initiatives such as the Latin American Free Trade Agreement; and we currently are leading USA*ENGAGE, a coalition opposing unilateral trade sanctions.

As we move into the 21st century, we believe we have two huge responsibilities in terms of our diesel engine leadership role:

We must lead in the defense of the diesel engine as a beneficial and necessary tool for humankind.

We must lead the industry in seeking ways to reduce emissions, even beyond requirements, for the benefit of future generations.

In some quarters, the diesel engine is under attack. But people are hearing only one side of the story. We will do our best to help them hear the whole story. Today's diesel engine represents a quantum leap in technology…expressed in terms of 70 percent reduction in NOx emissions and 90 percent reduction in particulates. Diesels produce one-third less carbon dioxide than gasoline engines. And diesel engine emissions will be reduced an additional 50 to 90 percent over the next decade. The bottom line: today's diesels are one of the cleanest power sources available.

We have to explain that diesel engines convert a gallon of fuel to one-third more useful work than gasoline engines, providing a needed boost to energy conservation and reduction in greenhouse gases.

There's also the often-overlooked economic impact of diesel-powered products. In every respect, they are the backbone power source for mining, building and construction, agriculture, aggregates, forest products, fishing and material handling industries.

In the U.S., diesel-powered barges move 40 percent of the nation's primary iron and steel products. Diesel-powered railroads carry nearly 40 percent of inner-city freight, 70 percent of new automotive vehicles, 64 percent of coal which generates 40 percent of America's electricity and 40 percent of grain and farm products. Diesel trucks ship 55 percent of all goods. In fact, they're the only method of delivering products to 77 percent of America's communities.

As to the second responsibility, we take seriously our leadership role in providing the cleanest possible environment for future generations. We will lead in technology to develop new ways to reduce emissions.

Leadership means responsibility. We will carry out our responsibility.

right. **This ad appeared in 1999 publications.**

270

The Federal Reserve isn't the only driving force behind the economy.

Other drivers also move the world's markets. Truck drivers, for example. And the driving force behind the world's economy is not just rates and ratios—it's diesel engines, too.

The truth is, there is hardly anything that turns up on your table (or your desk) that doesn't somewhere, sometime, ride behind a diesel-powered rig.

And that's the same around the world.

One reason is that diesels are, by nature, economical. They cost less to run, run longer and need less repair. Another reason is that today's diesels are clean. While diesel-powered trucks travel more than 428 billion miles a year, they're responsible for just 2% of the carbon

monoxide in the air. And since the 1980s, there's been a 70% reduction in NOx and a 90% cut in particulates. In the meantime, fuel consumption just keeps getting better.

What does Caterpillar have to do with diesel engines? We make them. For trucks, boats, locomotives and our own machines as well. And for

electric generators of all sizes and shapes. In fact, we're the largest diesel-engine maker in the world.

Central bankers move financial markets. Diesel-powered trucks move the goods.

CATERPILLAR

Into the 21st Century

For 75 years, we have sought to meet or exceed expectations of our customers. We've built a reputation for quality and integrity, and we've earned the global leadership position in our industry. We're proud of that.

We're also proud of the reputation we've built in our attempts to safeguard the environment wherever we do business. Our commitment to preserving and protecting the environment is driven by a fundamental belief: We want to ensure that future generations enjoy the same, or better, quality of life that previous generations have enjoyed. To us, it means making an active commitment to address environmental matters.

Our manufacturing facilities will continue to look for ways to reduce waste, prevent pollution and promote recycling.

Our products will continue to incorporate environmental considerations in their design and use.

Our product support efforts will be aimed at keeping product useful beyond today's expected life cycle as we conserve the earth's resources.

We are committed to projects that encourage the proper use of our products and the contributions they can make toward replenishing and renewing the earth's resources, such as mining reclamation, forest management and conservation farming techniques.

As a company committed to improvement in everything we do, we know there are opportunities to do better. Today and in the future, corporations will be expected to provide an even better accounting of how their processes affect the environment and what they're doing to improve their performance.

We don't have all the answers, but we do know the right questions to ask. With our legacy of good corporate citizenship and focus on "raising the bar," we'll look for ways to further demonstrate the global leadership by which the world has come to know us.

This reforested area in the Southeast is part of more than seven million acres owned by International Paper in the United States. Replanting with "super trees" provides a new harvest of trees in 12 to 15 years. By using such "sustainable management" techniques, foresters protect wildlife habitat, enhance water quality and ensure there are trees for future generations.

1925

Caterpillar
1931

Caterpillar
1932

Caterpillar
1939

Caterpillar
1941

CATERPILLAR
1957

CATERPILLAR
1967

CATERPILLAR

1989

Compiled by the Antique Caterpillar Machinery Owners Club

Financial Summary—1925–1999

Sales & Revenues (in millions)	Profit (in millions)	Average Employment	Year
13.8	3.3	2,537	1925
20.7	4.3	2,931	1926
26.9	5.7	3,511	1927
35.1	8.7	4,897	1928
51.8	12.4	6,875	1929
45.4	9.1	6,282	1930
24.1	1.6	3,737	1931
13.3	<1.6>	3,247	1932
14.4	0.4	3,501	1933
23.8	3.8	5,586	1934
36.4	6.2	7,488	1935
54.1	10.2	11,168	1936
63.2	10.6	12,234	1937
48.2	3.2	9,432	1938
58.4	6.0	10,671	1939
73.1	7.8	11,781	1940
102.0	7.7	15,292	1941
142.2	7.0	16,488	1942
171.4	7.6	18,252	1943
242.2	7.3	20,455	1944
230.6	6.5	18,609	1945
128.4	6.1	19,755	1946
189.1	13.5	20,925	1947
218.0	17.5	21,638	1948
254.9	17.2	22,795	1949
337.3	29.2	24,746	1950
394.3	15.8	28,633	1951
480.8	22.7	31,678	1952
437.8	20.6	29,643	1953
406.7	25.9	25,783	1954
533.0	36.0	31,400	1955
685.9	55.5	37,909	1956
649.9	40.0	39,491	1957
585.2	32.2	31,060	1958
742.3	46.5	42,120	1959
716.0	42.6	40,638	1960
734.3	55.8	35,810	1961
827.0	61.9	36,364	1962
966.1	77.3	38,527	1963
1,216.6	129.1	46,204	1964
1,405.3	158.5	50,800	1965
1,524.0	150.1	55,107	1966
1,472.5	106.4	56,635	1967
1,707.1	121.6	59,848	1968
2,001.6	142.5	63,939	1969
2,127.8	143.8	66,062	1970
2,175.2	128.3	62,528	1971
2,602.2	206.4	62,134	1972
3,182.4	246.8	71,028	1973
4,082.1	229.2	76,993	1974
4,963.7	398.7	79,393	1975
5,042.3	383.2	77,717	1976
5,848.9	445.1	78,565	1977
7,222.0	566.0	84,004	1978
7,618.0	492.0	89,266	1979
8,603.0	565.0	86,350	1980
9,160.0	579.0	83,455	1981
6,472.0	<180.0>	73,249	1982
5,429.0	<345.0>	58,402	1983
6,597.0	<428.0>	61,189	1984
6,760.0	198.0	55,815	1985
7,380.0	76.0	54,024	1986
8,294.0	350.0	53,770	1987
10,435.0	616.0	57,954	1988
11,126.0	497.0	60,784	1989
11,436.0	210.0	59,662	1990
10,182.0	<404.0>	55,950	1991
10,194.0	<2,435.0>	52,340	1992
11,615.0	652.0	50,443	1993
14,328.0	955.0	52,778	1994
16,072.0	1,136.0	54,263	1995
16,522.0	1,361.0	54,968	1996
18,925.0	1,665.0	58,366	1997
20,977.0	1,513.0	64,441	1998
19,702.0	946.0	66,225	1999

left to right. **Glen Barton, Gerald Flaherty, Gerald Shaheen, Richard Thompson and James Owens.**

Officers January 2000

Chairman of the Board and Chief Executive Officer

Glen A. Barton

Group Presidents

Gerald S. Flaherty
James W. Owens
Gerald L. Shaheen
Richard L. Thompson

Vice Presidents

R. Rennie Atterbury III
James W. Baldwin*
Sidney C. Banwart
Vito H. Baumgartner
Michael J. Baunton
James S. Beard
Richard A. Benson
James E. Despain
Michael A. Flexsenhar
Thomas A. Gales**
Donald M. Ings
S.L. (Stu) Levenick
Duane H. Livingston
Robert R. Macier
David A. McKie
F. Lynn McPheeters
Daniel M. Murphy
Douglas R. Oberhelman
Gerald Palmer
Robert C. Petterson
John E. Pfeffer
Siegfried R. Ramseyer
Alan J. Rassi
Gary A. Stroup
Sherril K. West
Donald G. Western
Steven H. Wunning

*Will retire effective April 2000
**Effective April 2000

A Short History of Caterpillar Patents

Caterpillar people have been awarded thousands of patents worldwide. Following are some selected U.S. patents. Many of them represent a family of patents related to a product or component and aren't necessarily the most definitive patent.

Some of these patents were issued to a single individual, some to multiple inventors. Often more than one patent was issued to cover a number of features within a single component. A team of patent professionals chose these patents because they represent major product improvements in either durability, reliability, operating cost, ease of operation, environmental impact, productivity or ease of maintenance.

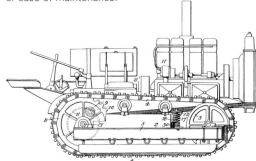

Track-type Tractors

Prior to the formation of Caterpillar Tractor Co., Holt and Best worked independently to develop a power-driven crawler machine. The early steam-driven wheel machines (U.S. Patent Number 436,931) were replaced by internal-combustion-engine-driven crawler tractors (No. 874,008) in order to increase power, reduce size and increase tractive effort.

During the 20s and 30s, improvements were made to the components of the frame (No. 1,661,649), final drive (No. 1,792,682) and transmission (No. 2,079,903). These changes improved suspension and traction of the machine, serviceability of the final drive and ease of transmission shifting.

In the 40s, a welded case and frame assembly (No. 2,363,052) reduced weight and improved strength. The sealed track assembly (No. 2,376,864) increased the life of track components and an improved hydraulic clutch/brake steering arrangement (No. 2,379,628) provided steering control with reduced effort.

In the 50s, the countershaft transmission (No. 2,825,232) distributed bearing loads within the transmission and increased bearing life.

In the 60s, a Duo Cone seal (No. 3,073,689) having face-to-face biased metal rings revolutionized sealing and drastically improved seal and associated component life. A split master link (No. 3,427,079) permitted ease in assembly and disassembly of track. Introduction of hydraulic transmission controls (No. 3,429,328) facilitated ease of gear selection.

In the 70s, a pitch control (No. 3,503,456) was added to the ripper assembly to improve ripping effectiveness. Continued improvements in ground engaging tools, such as the high strength penetration tip (No. 3,959,901),

improved ground penetrability, wear resistance and tool life. The 70s continued to produce innovations including the elevated sprocket (No. 3,828,873) and the segmented sprocket (No. 3,960,412).

With the 80s came the modular sub-assembly (No. 4,276,952) which enhanced drive train assembly and serviceability. This decade also gave birth to differential steer (No. 4,434,680) which provided continuous power to both tracks during steering and thereby improved tractive effort.

In the 90s, an electronic control console (No. 5,244,066) included an arm rest with fingertip electronic controls.

Motor Graders

During the 30s, Caterpillar's motor grader was engine-powered and mechanically driven, and the blade was mechanically controlled (No. 2,034,141).

In the 70s, Caterpillar introduced an adjustable control console (No. 3,737,003) which permitted the operator to position the steering wheel and control levers to an optimum position and thereby reduce operator fatigue. A hydraulically controlled blade (No. 3,739,861) provided accurate implement positioning and low effort control. Blade float (No. 4,034815) let the blade follow the contour of the surface. An articulated motor grader (Design Patent No. 235,113) in the 70s provided improved steerability and permitted a reduced turning radius.

During the 80s a countershaft transmission (No. 4,627,302) offered compactness and facilitated ease of assembly of the components.

Development of a front wheel drive assist (No. 4,341,280) in the 90s improved the operator's control and extended grading capabilities. An electronic control (No. 5,622,226) which reduces bounce of the blade and improves the quality of the graded surface was developed in the 90s.

Loaders

The design of a straight frame wheel loader (Design Patent No. 189,024) began in the 50s and added a new machine to Caterpillar's product line.

Improvements to the wheel loader in the 60s included a device (No. 3,122,247) which automatically positioned the bucket to a predetermined position to improve cycle time.

An articulated wheel loader (Design Patent No. 230,622) was introduced in the 70s. Steering was accomplished by

articulating a front frame and a rear frame about a center pivot. The articulated wheel loader reduced the steering radius, improved position-ability and reduced load cycle time. A rear-engine, hydrostatically driven track-type loader (Design Patent No. 251,845) provided continuous power to both tracks, even during steering.

In the 80s, a replaceable bucket corner tooth assembly (No. 4,182,057) substantially increased the life of the loader bucket.

In the 90s, electronic control systems (No. 5,323,667) for the engine and transmission coordinated engine and transmission operation to improve operator ride/comfort and increase component life.

Excavators

Hydraulic excavators require high-pressure hydraulic systems and led Caterpillar to develop components capable of operating at these higher pressures. In the 60s, a high-pressure, wire-reinforced hose (No. 3,357,456) was one such component.

A variable displacement, pressure compensated pump (No. 3,738,779) was developed in the 70s to provide high pressure only when needed. Another high-pressure hydraulic system development was for positive control of the load-supporting hydraulic implement cylinders (No. 3,805,678) and accuracy of implement position.

In the 70s, a box beam-constructed excavator boom (No. 3,902,295) offered light weight, high strength and additional payload capability.

In the 80s, an improved stick structure (No. 4,428,173) was developed. The structure included improvements in the position and types of welded joints, reducing stress within the joints and thus providing increased structural life.

In the late 90s, a hydraulic flow priority system (No. 5,490,384) was developed to ensure priority flow to desired hydraulic functions.

Also in the late 90s, a quick-disconnect coupling (No. 5,634,736) increased versatility of the machine by enabling easier changing of attachments.

Scrapers

Scrapers in the 40s and 50s used cables to raise and lower the bowl and to move the ejector. Latching mechanisms (No. 2,573,765) held the members in a stationary position during loading.

In the 50s, hydraulic cylinders provided articulated steering (No. 2,614,644) between the tractor portion and the scraper portion enabling more precise steering control.

In the 60s, improvements were made to the elevating mechanism (No. 3,210,868) of the self-loading scraper to enhance loading capabilities. The push/pull scraper and hydraulic controls (No. 3,339,659) provided quicker loading without the need for a separate pusher. A cushion hitch (No. 3,311,389) was added to the scraper in the 60s to improve ride and reduce operator fatigue.

Trucks

Development of a mechanically driven off-highway truck (Design Patent No. 188,314) in the 60s provided Caterpillar with a line of equipment to move large amounts of material a longer distance in a shorter time.

In the 60s, a gas over oil strut (No. 3,300,202) was designed for the front suspension of the truck. It provided higher load carrying characteristics and maintained the desired ride characteristics.

In the 70s, a modular truck body (No. 3,923, 337) provided the ability to transport large truck bodies in segments and weld the segments together at the work site.

Also in the 70s, an oil disc brake arrangement (No. 3,927,737) with high heat dissipation characteristics improved braking capacity.

In the 80s, an apparatus was provided to control the slip (No. 4,349,233) between two driving wheels. This apparatus brakes the slipping wheel and transfers power to the non-slipping wheel.

A payload monitor arrangement (No. 4,635,739) was designed in the 80s to inform the operator of the weight of the load in the truck.

In the 90s, a computerized monitoring system (No. 5,374,917) was designed to monitor and display information for the operator relating to the operation of various system parameters.

Agricultural Tractors

Caterpillar introduced a frictionally driven belted machine (No. 4,681,177) in the 80s. The continuous rubber belt (Design Patent No. 309,314) permitted the machine to be driven on public roads to and from the work site.

In order to eliminate the problem of belt stretching and to maintain the belt on the drive wheel, a special wire reinforced belt arrangement (No. 4,721,498) was designed in the 80s. This arrangement included the combination of wires laid straight with layers of wires laid at different angles.

In the 90s, a row crop agricultural machine (No. 5,018,591) was added. This machine permits adjusting the gauge between the opposed belts so that it can be used to till various crops. This arrangement also added a larger drive wheel which provides additional surface contact with the belt and adds to the tractive force, thus reducing the tendency of slip between the belt and the drive wheel.

Forestry Products

In the 70s, Caterpillar introduced a combined loader-skidder (No. 3,508,676) that could both load and skid logs.

Also in the 70s, a tree harvesting head (No. 3,669,161) included a mechanism to cut the tree and a drive mechanism to move the tree though the harvesting head to remove the limbs.

In the 90s, Caterpillar purchased a company that produced forestry products. One such product is a harvesting head (No. 5,219,010) that is used to cut the tree, remove the limbs and cut the log to the desired length. Another such product is a forwarder machine (No. 5,366,337) that picks up the delimbed logs at the harvesting location, loads them on a bed of the forwarder machine and transports them.

Pipelayers

In the 50s, Caterpillar introduced the pipelayer machine (No. 2,712,873) which was basically a modified track-type tractor with a cable-controlled boom assembly mounted on the side of the machine.

To offset the weight of the pipe hanging from one side, it was necessary to provide a counterweight mechanism (No. 2,891681).

In the 70s, hydraulic cable controls replaced mechanical cable controls and in the 80s an improved hydraulic cable control (No. 4,278,155) was developed to brake the winch by controlling a fluid driven motor. This control arrangement provided more precise control of the brake during both release and application of the brake.

Engines

In the 30s, diesel engines with fuel injection systems replaced gas engines. An improved fuel transfer mechanism (No. 2,145,533) was introduced to more efficiently supply fuel to the diesels.

In the 50s, with the increased power output of the diesel engine, it was necessary to provide a more efficient lubrication system (No. 2,550,967). A fuel injection system (No. 2,603,159) improved the supply of fuel to the engine by venting entrained air or gas from the system.

In the 70s, improved manufacturing methods enabled the development of an improved torsional vibration damper (No. 3,512,612). The damper used a viscous fluid housed between weights to more effectively control engine vibrations.

In the late 70s, an articulated piston (No. 4,056,044) using a metal crown and an aluminum skirt interconnected by a wrist pin was designed and later introduced into the engine to increase engine horsepower while maintaining the existing envelope of the engine configuration.

In the 80s, Caterpillar entered the gas turbine market through the purchase of Solar Turbines Incorporated. The recuperator, which enhanced thermal efficiency of the gas turbine engine, was further improved by the introduction of a thermally balanced restraint system (No. 4,697,633).

Also in the 80s, an ebullient cooled turbocharger (Reissue Patent No. 30,333) increased turbocharger life by improving cooling effectiveness within the bearing area. The automotive industry in turn licensed this technology and used it in several turbocharged automobiles.

The 80s also saw improvements in fuel injection systems. One such improvement was a unit fuel injection pump (No. 4,327,694) which provided increased fuel injection pressures at each cylinder. Thus, the unit injector resulted in reduced leaks while providing reduced emissions, improved mixing and overall increased engine performance.

Electronic controls (No. 4,368,705) were added to the engines in the 80s to improve engine efficiency. For example, operating parameters of the engine were merged with injection timing, enabling Environmental Protection Agency emission limits to be met.

In the 90s, a hydraulically actuated, electronically controlled unit fuel injector system (No. 5,191,867) further improved engine operating efficiencies. The system provided an apparatus that detected the pressure of the hydraulic actuating fluid and corrected the pressure with an electronic closed loop system to more accurately control fuel injection timing and fuel quantity.

In the 90s, the control of emissions for the gas turbine engine was enhanced through the use of a low emission combustion system (No. 5,896,741). The air/fuel ratio was more precisely controlled by reducing the flow of compressed air into the combustor, thus reducing emissions.

Patents for the Future

Diagnostic and prognostic systems will play an important role in future Caterpillar equipment. A current example of one such system is an apparatus and method for providing historical data of machine operating parameters (No. 5,463,567). During operation, the system compiles machine performance data of predefined system parameters and compares the historical data to the current performance data. This information can then be used to diagnose current failures, predict future failures and evaluate machine and/or operator performance.

A satellite based navigation system (No. 5,359,521) has been developed for determining the position of one or many machines. This system permits the accurate location of the machine(s) at a work site. A mobile machine material system (No. 5,850,341) includes storing a real time position, in three dimensional space, of the machine as it works the site and compares the worked site to a three-dimension model of the desired site. Thus, a dynamic site data base is used to update the site as material is worked and directs the machinery in altering the site to a desired state.

CATERPILLAR® 75 YEARS

In April, 1925, C. L. Best Tractor Co. and The Holt Manufacturing Company merged to form Caterpillar Tractor Co., a California corporation. In 1986, the company was reincorporated as a Delaware corporation and named Caterpillar Inc.

Caterpillar people—employees and dealers—design, manufacture, market, finance and provide support for Cat machines and engines. And those Cat products help make progress possible around the world.

Produced by

Corporate Public Affairs
Caterpillar Inc.
100 N.E. Adams, Peoria, Illinois 61629
www.CAT.com

Editor: Gilbert C. Nolde

Nolde retired as manager of Public Communications for Caterpillar in 1992 after a 37-year career with the company.

Special thanks to the many employees, retirees, dealers and suppliers who provided information and in countless ways assisted in making this book possible.

Design

Simantel Group, Peoria, Illinois

Publishing

Forbes Custom Publishing, New York, New York

Prepress

Scanning and film-based color proofs prepared by Professional Graphics Inc., Peoria, Illinois.

Printing and Binding

Regent Publishing Services, Hong Kong

Dust jacket: two blacks plus PMS 877 metallic silver and match PMS Cat Yellow with UV coating

Endpapers: black and match PMS Cat Yellow

Text: 4-color process and match PMS Cat Yellow throughout with spot gloss varnish

Standard edition: black canvas cloth on 3 mm board

Deluxe edition: black cow hide with metallic PMS 877 and match PMS Cat Yellow foil stamp

page	Photo Credits
8-9	Courtesy of CILCO
5, 22	Randy Leffingwell
86, 87	Chris Shinn
ii, iv, v, 20 46, 231, 251	Gary Walters
272-273	Jack Kenner
117	Courtesy of Eric Orleman collection
	Primary photography from the Caterpillar archives
	Special thanks to Jim Karl, retired Caterpillar photographer
	Special thanks to all the photographers who have contributed to this book through product photography over the years
	Special thanks for use of memorabilia: Bernie Daily Gary Maier Mike Taylor Vernon Wright

COMPETITIVO
Zugänglich
515
ENDURING
経験
Our Stori
DOWN-TO-EARTH
DEDICA

es
D5CXL
DOS
Values
Genuíno
PROUD TO MAKE THE BEST
EQUIPMENT ON EARTH
СИЛА
3600
STR
ACC